New General Mathematics Revision

D1477360

J B Channon MA
formerly Assistant Master at Rugby School

A McLeish Smith BA
formerly Second Master at Lawrence Sheriff School, Rugby

H C Head MA
Assistant Master at Rugby School

Longman

LONGMAN GROUP LIMITED
London

Associated companies, branches and representatives throughout the world

© Longman Group Ltd, 1976

First published 1976
Third impression 1978

ISBN 0 582 33201X

Printed in Great Britain by Hazell Watson & Viney Ltd, Aylesbury.

Longman Group Limited

Preface

This book is intended for those who have already covered an O Level syllabus, and either need a fresh selection of examples, or as adults need a quick revision course. For this reason the explanations have been kept to a minimum, and the authors have relied more on worked examples to illustrate likely difficulties.

It was felt that at this stage the order is relatively unimportant. Therefore for any particular topic the elementary and the more difficult parts are put together in a single chapter, thus making the book simpler to use.

The examples in the final sets are taken from past O Level papers, and the authors are grateful to the examining bodies for their permission to use them (acknowledgements on page iv).

J.B.C.
A.McL.S.
H.C.H.

Rugby 1976

Acknowledgements

We are grateful to the following Examining Boards for permission to reproduce questions from past Examination Papers in Mathematics:

University of Cambridge Local Examinations Syndicate; Joint Matriculation Board; University of London School Examinations Department; Oxford and Cambridge Schools Examination Board; Oxford Delagacy of Local Examinations; Southern Universities' Joint Board; Welsh Joint Education Committee and the Midlands Mathematical Experiment.

Contents

Contents

Contents

Tables

Length

10 millimetres (mm) = 1 centimetre (cm)

10 cm = 1 decimetre (dm)

10 dm = 1 metre (m) = 1 000 mm

10 m = 1 decametre (dam)

10 dam = 1 hectometre (hm)

10 hm = 1 kilometre (km) = 1 000 m

The decimetre, decametre and hectometre are very rarely used

Area

100 sq mm (mm^2) = 1 sq cm (cm^2)

100 sq cm = 1 sq dm (dm^2)

and so on

1 sq dam (dam^2) = 1 are (a) = $100 \ m^2$

100 ares = 1 sq hm (hm^2) = 1 hectare (ha) = $10 \ 000 \ m^2$

100 ha = 1 sq km (km^2)

The hectare is the only unit in which the prefix hecto is in common use

Volume

1 000 cu mm (mm^3) = 1 cu cm (cm^3)

1 000 cu cm = 1 cu dm (dm^3)

and so on

Capacity

10 millilitres (ml) = 1 centilitre (cl)

10 cl = 1 decilitre (dl)

10 dl = 1 litre (l) = 1 000 ml

1 litre = $1 \ dm^3$ = $1 \ 000 \ cm^3$

Mass

10 milligrams (mg) = 1 centigram (cg)

10 cg = 1 decigram (dg)

10 dg = 1 gram (g) = 1 000 mg

10 g = 1 decagram (dag)

10 dag = 1 hectogram (hg)

10 hg = 1 kilogram (kg) = 1 000 g

1 000 kg = 1 tonne (t)

The centigram, decigram, decagram and hectogram are very rarely used

Chapter 1

Number systems. Binary numbers

Base 10 (denary)	$623 = 6 \times 10^2 + 2 \times 10 + 3$
Base 8 (octal)	$713 = 7 \times 8^2 + 1 \times 8 + 3$
Base 6	$3\,214 = 3 \times 6^3 + 2 \times 6^2 + 1 \times 6 + 4$
Base 2 (binary)	$10\,110 = 1 \times 2^4 + 0 \times 2^3$
	$\qquad\qquad + 1 \times 2^2 + 1 \times 2 + 0$

Example 1 *Convert 123 in denary to octal.*

$$
\begin{array}{r}
8)\;\;123 \\ \hline
8)\quad\;\; 15 + 3 \quad \text{i.e. } 15 \times 8 + 3 \times 1 \\ \hline
8)\qquad 1 + 7 \quad \text{i.e. } 1 \times 8^2 + 7 \times 8 \\ \hline
\qquad 0 + 1 \quad \text{i.e. } 0 \times 8^3 + 1 \times 8^2
\end{array}
$$

Ans.   173

Example 2 *Convert 173 in octal to denary.*

$$
\begin{array}{lll}
1 & 7 & \qquad 3 \\
8 & & \\ \hline
8 + 7 = & 15 & \\
& \underline{8} & \\
& \overline{120} + 3 = & 123
\end{array}
$$

Example 3 $A = 243$ *and* $B = 15$ *are both base 6 numbers. Calculate* $A + B,\ A - B,\ A \times B$ *and* $A \div B$.

$$
\begin{array}{r}
243 \\
+\ 15 \\ \hline
302
\end{array}
$$

Working from the right,
$3 + 5 = 8$, which is $1 \times 6 + 2$.
Write 2, and carry 1 to the next column.
$4 + 1 + 1 = 6$, which is $1 \times 6 + 0$.
Write 0, and carry 1 to the next column.
$2 + 1 = 3$.

$$
\begin{array}{r}
243 \\
- \ 15 \\
\hline
224
\end{array}
\qquad
\begin{array}{l}
1 \times 6 + 3 - 5 = 4 \\
3 - 1 = 2
\end{array}
$$

$$
\begin{array}{r}
243 \\
\times \ 15 \\
\hline
243 \\
2143 \\
\hline
5013
\end{array}
\qquad
\begin{array}{l}
5 \times 3 = 15 = 2 \times 6 + 3. \\
\text{Write 3, and carry 2.} \\
5 \times 4 + 2 = 22 = 3 \times 6 + 4. \\
\text{Write 4, and carry 3.} \\
5 \times 2 + 3 = 13 = 2 \times 6 + 1. \\
\text{Etc.}
\end{array}
$$

$$
\begin{array}{r}
13 \\
15) \ \overline{243} \\
15 \\
\hline
53 \\
53 \\
\hline
\end{array}
$$

Exercise 1a

Convert the following denary numbers to octal:

1. 13   **2.** 32   **3.** 117   **4.** 891   **5.** 1 871

Convert the following numbers with base 5 to denary:

6. 13   **7.** 43   **8.** 233   **9.** 1 423   **10.** 2 314

Nos. 11–14 are in octal.

11. $57 + 743$ **12.** $162 - 75$

13. $1\,322 \times 13$ **14.** $1\,176 \div 26$

Nos. 15–20 are base 6.

15. $1\,231 + 543 + 35$ **16.** $453 - 105$

17. 534×24 **18.** $2\,404 \div 32$

19. $13\,541 + 2\,554$ **20.** $1\,453 \times 135$

Example 4. *Convert 86 in denary to binary.*

2) 86
2) 43 + 0
2) 21 + 1
2) 10 + 1
2) 5 + 0
2) 2 + 1
2) 1 + 0

Ans. 1 010 110

Example 5 *Convert 1 011 in binary to denary.*

1   0   1   1

$\frac{2}{2}$ + 0 = 2

$\quad\quad \frac{2}{4}$ + 1 = 5

$\quad\quad\quad \frac{2}{10}$ + 1 = 11

Exercise 1b

Convert the following denary numbers to binary:
  1. 6   **2.** 11   **3.** 21   **4.** 37   **5.** 49
  6. 61   **7.** 87   **8.** 103   **9.** 201   **10.** 270

Convert the following binary numbers to denary:
11. 11   **12.** 101   **13.** 1 001   **14.** 1 010
15. 11 001   **16.** 11 011   **17.** 1 100   **18.** 10 111
19. 1 000   **20.** 1 111 111

Example 6 *Add*   1 010 101
                          110 111
                     ―――――――――
                       10 001 100

Subtraction by adding the complement

Example 7   *Subtract* 11 101 *from* 1 101 011.

1 101 011	Keeping the same number of digits in both numbers,
1 100 010	11 101 is written 0 011 101. The complement of this
+̶ 1̶ 001 101	number is obtained by writing 0 for 1 and 1 for 0,
1	i.e. 1 100 010. After addition, the leading 1 is removed
1 001 110	and 1 is added.

Exercise 1c

Add the following binary numbers:

1. 110 + 10   **2.** 1 101 + 111
3. 1 100 + 101   **4.** 1 110 + 1 010
5. 11 010 + 1 011   **6.** 100 110 + 11 011
7. 110 110 + 110 001   **8.** 1 010 110 + 101 110

Evaluate the following binary subtractions using the complement:

9. 101 − 11   **10.** 1 100 − 110
11. 1 101 − 1 010   **12.** 10 100 − 1 010
13. 10 110 − 1 110   **14.** 11 011 − 101
15. 101 101 − 10 101   **16.** 1 010 110 − 110 101

Example 8   *Multiply* 110 110 *by* 11.

```
   110 110
        11
  1 101 10
   110 110
10 100 010      Ans.
```

Example 9   *Divide* 1 001 110 *by* 110.

```
          1 101
110)  1 001 110
       110
       ‾‾‾
       111
       110
       ‾‾‾
       110
       110
       ‾‾‾      Ans. 1 101
```

Exercise 1d

Evaluate the following binary multiplications:

1. 1 101 × 10   **2.** 1 011 × 11
3. 1 110 × 101   **4.** 11 011 × 110
5. 10 110 × 1 010   **6.** 11 011 × 1 100
7. 110 110 × 1 001   **8.** 101 010 × 110

Evaluate the following binary divisions:

9. 11 011 ÷ 11   **10.** 110 010 ÷ 101
11. 1 000 010 ÷ 110   **12.** 110 110 ÷ 1 001
13. 110 111 ÷ 1 011   **14.** 1 000 001 ÷ 1 101
15. 101 101 ÷ 1 111   **16.** 10 000 101 ÷ 10 011

Chapter 2

Sets

Union and intersection

The union ($\cup$) of two sets is a third set which includes all the elements of the first two. For example

$$\{1, 2, 3\} \cup \{2, 3, 4\} = \{1, 2, 3, 4\}.$$

The intersection ($\cap$) of two sets is a third set which includes only those elements which occur in both the first two. For example

$$\{1, 2, 3\} \cap \{2, 3, 4\} = \{2, 3\}.$$

If $A = \{1, 2, 3\}$ and $B = \{2, 3, 4\}$ the union and intersection can be represented by Venn diagrams:

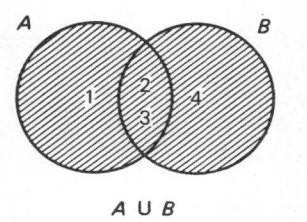

$A \cup B$ $A \cap B$

Fig. 1

Complements

When a set is divided into a number of subsets this set is called the **entity** or **universal** set. In a Venn diagram the entity, $\mathscr{E}$, is usually shown as a rectangle as in Fig. 2.

If A is a subset of $\mathscr{E}$ then the complement of A, written A', is a set consisting of all the elements of $\mathscr{E}$ which are not members of A. For instance if $\mathscr{E} = \{1, 2, 3, 4, 5, 6\}$ and $A = \{2, 5\}$ then

$$A' = \{1, 3, 4, 6\}.$$

The shaded area in Fig. 2 represents A' and in Fig. 3 $(A \cup B)'$.

6

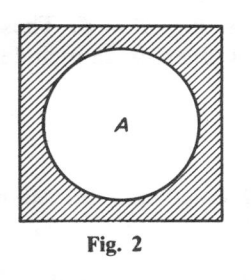

Fig. 2

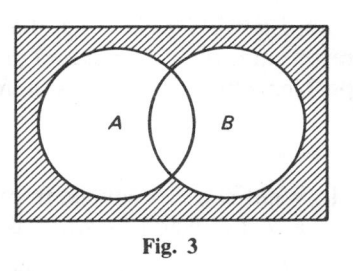

Fig. 3

Example 1 *All policemen have big feet; all detectives are policemen; all children have small feet. If these statements were true what could be deduced from them?*

Let $\mathscr{E}$ = the set of all humans,
P = the set of all policemen,
B = the set of all people with big feet,
D = the set of all detectives,
C = the set of all children.

Then P is a subset of B, written $P \subset B$, $D \subset P$ and $C \subset B'$.

$\therefore D \subset P \subset B \therefore D \subset B.$

All detectives have big feet.

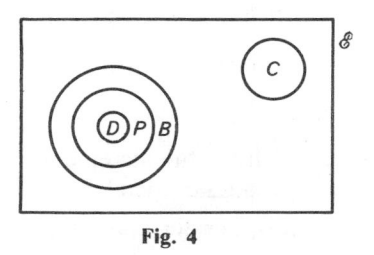

Fig. 4

From the diagram it can be seen that no detectives are children and no policemen are children.

If $C \subset B'$ then $B \subset C'$.

$\therefore$ all people with big feet are not children.

7

In Fig. 4, $P \cap B' = \emptyset$, the **empty** set, and $B \cup P' = \mathscr{E}$. These results are true if $P \subset B$ and imply that $P \subset B$. Exercise 2a includes problems based on these statements.

Exercise 2a

1. What can be deduced from the following statements: (a) oak is a sort of wood (b) wood is inflammable?

2. What can be deduced from the statements (a) all kings are monarchs (b) all monarchs are heads of state?

3. What can be deduced from the following statements: (a) all rhombuses are parallelograms (b) all parallelograms are quadrilaterals?

4. What can be deduced from the following statements: (a) all people over 18 are allowed to vote in elections (b) all men in the armed forces are over 18?

5. From the statements coal is black and ink is black can it be deduced that ink is coal or coal is ink?

6. What, if anything, can be deduced from the following statements: (a) a pencil-case contains a ruler (b) a pencil-case contains a rubber (c) a satchel contains a pencil-case?

7. If $\mathscr{E} = \{1, 2, 3, 4, 5, 6, 7, 8, 9, 10, 11, 12\}$,

   $A = \{1, 3, 9, 11\}, \qquad B = \{2, 3, 9, 10\}$

   write down the sets A', B', $A' \cap B'$, $(A \cup B)'$, $(A \cap B)'$, $A' \cup B'$.

8. What can be deduced from the statements: (a) all boys study mathematics (b) no girl studies metalwork?

9. What can be deduced from the statements: (a) all barristers are lawyers (b) no judge has not been a barrister?

10. What can be deduced from the statements: (a) all qualified teachers have been to university or college of education (b) all qualified teachers without degrees have been to college of education?

11. What can be deduced from the statements: (a) wood is inflammable (b) tables are made of wood (c) things which are inflammable are dangerous?

12. What, if anything, can be deduced from the statements: (a) sliderules can be used to multiply (b) desk calculators can be used to multiply (c) machines which can be used to multiply can be called computers?

Example 2   *In a form,* 16 *boys study chemistry,* 20 *study Latin and* 11 *study geography. Of these subjects* 7 *study chemistry only,* 8 *study Latin only,* 6 *study chemistry and Latin only and* 4 *study Latin and geography only.*

 (i) *How many study all three subjects?*
(ii) *How many boys are there in the form if it is assumed that all boys study at least one of these subjects?*

In the Venn diagram (Fig. 5) C is the chemistry set (16 members), L is the Latin set (20 members), G is the geography set (11 members). The 7 who study chemistry only are represented by the part of the area C which does not lie within G or L. Hence in the figure, 7 is written on this area. Similarly, using the other information given in the question, 8, 6 and 4 are written on the appropriate areas.

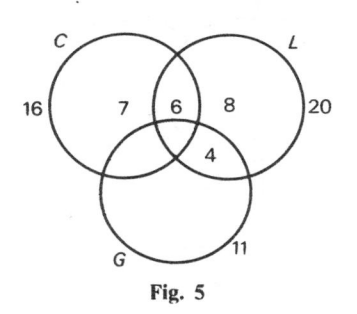

Fig. 5

(i) Those who study all three subjects are represented by the dotted area since this area lies within C, L and G. Hence the number studying all three subjects $= 20 - 6 - 8 - 4 = 2$.

9

(ii) The number studying chemistry and geography
only $= 16 - 7 - 6 - 2$
    $= 1$

The number studying geography only $= 11 - 4 - 2 - 1 = 4$
$\therefore$ the total number of boys in the form
    $= 7 + 6 + 8 + 1 + 2 + 4 + 4 = 32.$

In Example 3, which follows, the language of sets is used. Note that the number in set A is written $n\{A\}$.

Example 3 *In a group of 12 students, 8 are wearing pullovers, 7 are wearing jackets and 6 are wearing scarves. Four are wearing pullovers and jackets, 3 jackets and scarves and 5 pullovers and scarves. Each student is wearing at least one of these garments. How many are wearing all three?*

Let P be the set of those wearing pullovers, J those wearing jackets and S those wearing scarves.

The statement that each student is wearing at least one garment implies that $P \cup J \cup S = \mathscr{E}$. In Fig. 6 the three circles show the numbers of students wearing the three garments. The centre section $P \cap J \cap S$ shows the number wearing all three, which is marked x.

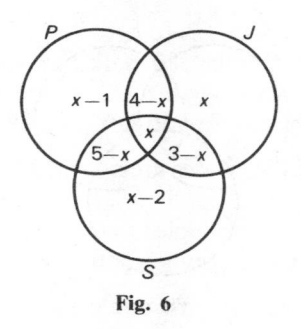

Fig. 6

Four students wear pullovers and jackets.
$\therefore n\{P \cap J\} = 4.$
$\therefore 4 - x$ is written in the appropriate space.

Similarly $n\{J \cap S\} = 3$ and $n\{P \cap S\} = 5$, so that $3 - x$ and $5 - x$ are written in the correct spaces.

As $n\{P\} = 8$, the number wearing pullovers only i.e. $n\{(S \cup J)'\}$ is $8 - (4 - x) - x - (5 - x) = 8 - 4 + x - x - 5 + x = x - 1$.

Similarly $n\{(P \cup S)'\} = x$ and $n\{(P \cup J)'\} = x - 2$.

As there are 12 students, $n\{P \cup J \cup S\} = 12$.

$$\therefore \ (x - 1) + (4 - x) + x + (5 - x) + x + (3 - x) + (x - 2) = 12$$

$$\therefore \ x + 9 = 12$$

$$\therefore \ x = \ 3$$

$\therefore$ 3 students are wearing all three garments.

Note that '4 are wearing pullovers and jackets' includes those who are wearing all three garments.

Exercise 2b

Nos. 1–3 are based on a diagram like Fig. 3.

1. Out of 60 people interviewed in the street 40 are women and 25 are over 40. If 10 of the men are over 40 how many of the women are under 40?

2. In a school of 600 pupils, 380 walk to school and 80 are in the sixth form. If 20 of the sixth form do not walk to school, how many of the non-sixth form do not walk to school?

3. In a street 40% of the houses are owner-occupied and 55% of the houses are semi-detached. If 8% of the houses are nonsemi-detached and owner-occupied, what percentage of the semi-detached houses are not owner-occupied?

4. All of 40 houses have at least one method of heating: solid fuel, gas and electricity. Ten have gas only, 15 have electricity only and 5 have solid fuel only. If 4 have all three methods of heating and equal numbers have two methods, how many altogether have gas?

5. An employment agency has 90 girls seeking secretarial jobs. Sixty-five have certificates in typing, 42 have certificates in shorthand and 33 have certificates in book-keeping. If 15 have all three certificates, 29 have certificates in typing and shorthand, 17 have certificates in shorthand and book-keeping and 26 have certificates in typing and book-keeping, how many have no certificate?

6. A form of 34 boys were asked whether they had electric trains, radio controlled aeroplanes and/or electric cars. Seventeen had trains, 13 had cars, 16 had planes, 5 had trains and cars, 6 had trains and planes and 5 had cars and planes. If equal numbers had all three and none, how many had none?

7. At a flower show 66 people entered exhibits. 13 showed roses only, 12 showed dahlias only and 8 showed chrysanthemums only. 5 showed roses and dahlias only, 9 showed dahlias and chrysanthemums only and 7 showed roses and chrysanthemums only. If the number who showed all three species is half of those who did not show any of these three, how many showed roses?

8. In a canteen, bacon, eggs and sausages are offered for lunch. 107 people chose at least one of these three; 59 chose bacon, 69 chose eggs, 27 chose both bacon and eggs, 22 sausage and bacon and 25 eggs and sausage; 8 chose all three. How many chose (i) bacon only, (ii) egg only, (iii) sausage only?

Chapter 3

Simple interest

If the symbol P is used for the principal, T for the number of years, R for the rate per cent, and I for the interest,

then $I = \dfrac{PTR}{100}$, $\qquad P = \dfrac{100I}{TR}$, $\qquad T = \dfrac{100I}{PR}$, $\qquad R = \dfrac{100I}{PT}$.

Example 1 *Find, correct to the nearest penny, the simple interest on £324·68 for 8 years at $4\frac{1}{2}\%$ per annum.*

$$\text{Interest} = \frac{£324\!\cdot\!68 \times 8 \times 4\frac{1}{2}}{100}$$

$$= £3\!\cdot\!246\,8 \times 36$$

$$= £116\!\cdot\!884\,8$$

$$= £116\!\cdot\!88 \text{ to the nearest penny.}$$

Example 2 *Find the rate per cent per annum at which £142 will earn £59·61 in 12 years.*

$$\text{Rate} = \frac{100 \times 59\!\cdot\!61}{142 \times 12}\,\%$$

$$= \frac{5\,961}{1\,704}\,\%$$

$$= 3\!\cdot\!498\ldots\%$$

$$\therefore \text{ rate} = 3\tfrac{1}{2}\%.$$

When the period of the loan involves **days**, ignore the first day and count the last.

Example 3   *A man borrows £219 on 19 July, and on 22 September he repays it, with interest at 9%. Find the total sum that he pays to clear the debt.*

$$\begin{aligned}
\text{Days in July} \quad & 12 \\
\text{August} \quad & 31 \\
\text{September} \quad & 22
\end{aligned}$$

$$\therefore \text{ period of loan} = \overline{65} \text{ days} = \frac{65}{365}\text{yr} = \frac{13}{73}\text{yr}$$

$$\begin{aligned}
\therefore \text{ interest} &= £\frac{219 \times \frac{13}{73} \times 9}{100} \\
&= £\frac{219 \times 13 \times 9}{73 \times 100} \\
&= £\frac{3 \times 13 \times 9}{100} \\
&= £3\cdot51
\end{aligned}$$

∴ he pays £222·51 altogether.

This sum of the principal and the interest is called the **amount**.

When the amount is given, with the time and rate, the principal is found by proportion.

Example 4   *Find the principal that would amount to £223·55 in 1 yr 8 mth at 9% per annum.*

The interest on £100 would be £9 × $1\frac{2}{3}$ = £15

∴ £115 is the amount of £100

$$\therefore \text{ £}223\cdot55 \text{ is the amount of £}100 \times \frac{223\cdot55}{115}$$

$$\begin{aligned}
&= £\frac{22\,355}{115} \\
&= £\frac{4\,471}{23} \\
&= £194\cdot391\ldots
\end{aligned}$$

∴ the principal is £194·39 to the nearest penny.

Exercise 3

Give answers to the nearest penny where necessary.

1. Find the simple interest on £126·42 for 6 years at $3\frac{1}{2}\%$ per annum.

2. Find the time in which £168·40 will earn £29·47 at 5% per annum.

3. Find the time in which £213·65 will amount to £299·11 at 5% per annum.

4. If £206·40 increases by £30·96 in 6 years, find the rate per cent per annum.

5. Find the principal which earns £115·38 in 8 years at $4\frac{1}{2}\%$ per annum.

6. Find the simple interest on £72·80 from 21 June to 14 November at $12\frac{1}{2}\%$ per annum.

7. Find the principal which amounts to £142·83 in 5 years at 3% per annum.

8. If £272·45 is invested for 10 years at $3\frac{3}{4}\%$ per annum, find the simple interest which it earns.

9. Find the rate per cent at which £213·82 will earn £74·84 in 7 years.

10. A man wishes to have £650 available for a cash payment in 4 years' time. Find how much he must invest now at 5% per annum to make this possible.

11. Find the time in which £108·33 will amount to £123·50 at 8% per annum.

12. Find the rate per cent per annum at which £380 earns £128·25 in 7 years 6 months.

13. Find the simple interest on £832·50 for 292 days at 9% per annum.

14. Find the sum which earns £7·19 interest if invested in a Building Society at $7\frac{1}{2}\%$ on 6 April and withdrawn on 11 November of the same year.

15. A man has £2 370 invested in a Building Society which pays interest at the rate of 6% per annum, and £1 850 in a Bank yielding 5%. Find correct to 2 decimal places the rate per cent per annum which he is receiving on the two investments together.

Chapter 4

Vectors. Displacements

Example 1 *Find the co-ordinates of the vertices of the triangle* DEF *which is the result of displacing* ABC *where* A *is* (1, 2), B *is* (3, 5) *and* C *is* (2, 7) *and* $\overrightarrow{AD}$ *is represented by the vector* (3, 1).

D is (1, 2) + (3, 1) = (4, 3)
E is (3, 5) + (3, 1) = (6, 6)
F is (2, 7) + (3, 1) = (5, 8)

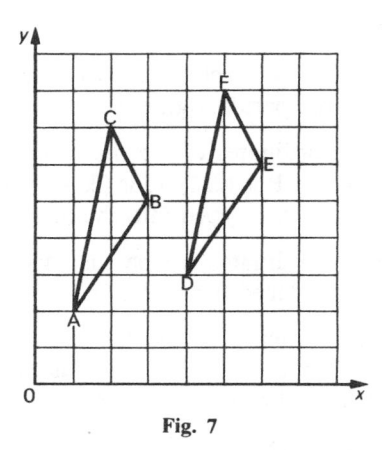

Fig. 7

Exercise 4

1. Find the co-ordinates of the vertices of the triangle which is the displacement of △OAB where O is (0, 0), A is (3, 4) and B is (1, 6), given that O is displaced to (2, 1).

2. What are the co-ordinates of the vertices of the triangle which is the displacement of △OAB of no. 1 through $\overrightarrow{OB}$?

17

3. What are the co-ordinates of the displacement of the square ABCD where A is (2, 3), B is (4, 3), C is (4, 5) and D is (2, 5), given that the origin is mapped into (3, 4)?

4. What are the co-ordinates of the displacement of the square ABCD of no. 3 when it is displaced through (5, 2)?

5. What are the co-ordinates of the displacement of the rectangle DEFG where D is (4, 0), E is (0, 3), F is (6, 11) and G is (10, 8) when it is displaced through (2, 4)?

6. What are the co-ordinates of the displacement of the rectangle DEFG of no. 5 when it is displaced through (−3, 2)?

7. What are the co-ordinates of the displacement of the parallelogram HIJK where H is (−2, 3), I is (−3, −1), J is (1, 2) and K is (2, 6) when it is displaced through (4, −3)?

8. What displacement will return the displacement of HIJK in no. 7 to the original parallelogram?

9. What are the co-ordinates of the displacement of the quadrilateral PQRS where P is (2, 1), Q is (3, −1), R is (−1, −2) and S is (−2, 4) when P is mapped into the origin?

10. What are the co-ordinates of the displacement of PQRS of no. 9 when it is displaced through $\overrightarrow{PQ}$?

11. What are the co-ordinates of the displacement of the rhombus TUVW where T is (2, 1), U is (3, 3), V is (2, 5) and W is (1, 3) when it is displaced through (−2, −3)?

12. What are the co-ordinates of the displacement of the rhombus TUVW of no. 11 when it is displaced through $\overrightarrow{UW}$?

Chapter 5

Statistics

Mean

The **mean** or arithmetic mean is equal to the sum of all the numbers in a set divided by the number of them.

Median

If a set of numbers is arranged in order of size, going either up or down, the middle term is called the **median.** If there is an even number of terms the median is taken as the mean of the two middle terms.

Mode

The number of times any particular number occurs in a set is called its **frequency** (f) and the number which occurs most often (that is which has the greatest frequency) is called the **mode.**

Example 1   *Find the mean, median and mode of the following set of numbers*: 12, 16, 8, 11, 12, 8, 2, 8, 1, 14.

The sum of the numbers $= 92$

The number of numbers $= 10$

$\therefore$ the mean $= \dfrac{\Sigma x}{n} = \dfrac{92}{10} = 9 \cdot 2$

Arranging the numbers in ascending order

1, 2, 8, 8, 8, 11, 12, 12, 14, 16

The median is $\dfrac{8 + 11}{2} = 9.5$

The mode is 8.

Example 2 *The heights (x cm) of the boys in a class are in the following ranges, all measurements being to the nearest centimetre.*

x	150–154	155–159	160–164	165–169	170–174	175–179
f	2	5	11	8	7	1

Find the average height.

To find the mean it is assumed that each height is the mid-value of the range given. A **working mean** is chosen and the deviations from the working mean used as follows.

Let working mean be 162.

Class interval	Class centre	Frequency (f)	Deviation (d)	$f \times d$
150–154	152	2	−10	−20
155–159	157	5	−5	−25
160–164	162	11		
165–169	167	8	+ 5	+40
170–174	172	7	+10	+70
175–179	177	1	+15	+15
				−45 + 125

Total deviation $= \Sigma fd = 80$

Total number $= \Sigma f = 34$

∴ mean deviation $= \frac{80}{34} = 2\frac{6}{17}$

∴ mean height $= 162 + 2\frac{6}{17} \simeq 164.4$ cm.

The modal class is 160–164.

If the median also is required, this would be the mark between boys numbered 17 and 18 in the ordered range and this would come somewhere in the 160–164 class. A more accurate estimate can be obtained by constructing a **cumulative-frequency** table and then drawing an **ogive** (Fig. 8).

Class	Frequency	Cumulative frequency
150–154	2	2
155–159	5	2 + 5 = 7
160–164	11	7 + 11 = 18
165–169	8	18 + 8 = 26
170–174	7	26 + 7 = 33
175–179	1	33 + 1 = 34

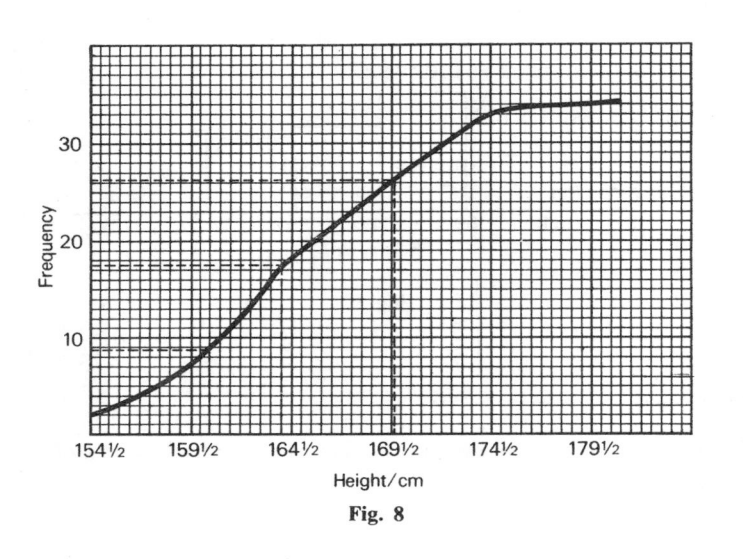

Fig. 8

As the heights are quoted to the nearest cm the true ranges are $149\frac{1}{2}$–$154\frac{1}{2}$ etc. and the points on the ogive are plotted at the top of each range.

Reading from $17\frac{1}{2}$ on the frequency axis the median is 164 cm.

21

Quartiles

The lower quartile is one-quarter of the way up the distribution and the upper quartile three-quarters of the way up, the median being half way between them. These quartiles are respectively $8\frac{3}{4}$ and $26\frac{1}{4}$ on the frequency axis which correspond to 160·5 and 169·7 on the height axis. The interquartile range is therefore 160·5 cm to 169·7 cm.

Histogram

The data of Example 2 can be represented by a bar chart called a histogram, shown in Fig. 9.

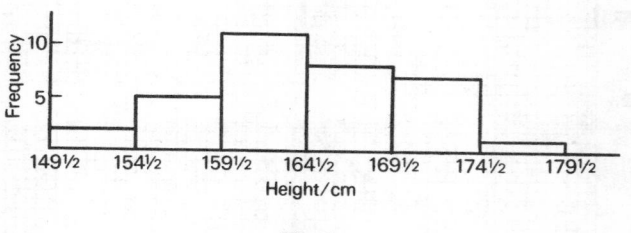

Fig. 9

Exercise 5

Calculate the mean, mode and median of the following sets of numbers.

1. 2, 4, 4, 6, 7

2. 3, 5, 5, 7, 7, 7, 9, 9

3. 11, 9, 6, 4, 3, 12, 1, 6, 5

4. 110, 120, 113, 116, 119, 127, 117, 118, 118, 113

Draw histograms and ogives for the following distributions and read off the median and the interquartile range for each. State also the modal class and calculate the mean.

5.

Class	1–5	6–10	11–15	16–20	21–25
Frequency	1	7	11	6	5

6.

Class	1–10	11–20	21–30	31–40	41–50	51–60
Frequency	2	7	13	21	16	1

7.

Class	6–12	13–19	20–26	27–33	34–40	41–47
Frequency	3	6	12	15	13	6

8. A survey of the households in a street was made into the number of people living in each house with the following result:

Number of residents	1	2	3	4	5	6
Frequency	4	18	10	17	6	5

Calculate the mean, mode and median. Draw the histogram.

9. The ages of the students in an evening class are as follows:

Age group	under 20	20–29	30–39	40–49	50–59	60 or over
Frequency	4	7	3	1	3	2

Calculate the mean and state the modal class. Draw the ogive and find the median and interquartile range. (Assume that the under 20 group is centred on 15 and the 60 or over group on 65.)

10. The percentage marks for 80 candidates in an examination are grouped as follows:

Percentage	0–9	10–19	20–29	30–39	40–49
Frequency	1	3	7	10	17

Percentage	50–59	60–69	70–79	80–89	90–99
Frequency	20	12	5	3	2

Find the mean mark. Draw a cumulative frequency diagram and find the median and interquartile range. If 70% of the candidates pass, what is the pass mark?

11. The masses (in kg to the nearest kg) of 40 men are as follows:

59 54 51 56 59 61 60 61 59 58
62 61 63 64 58 57 56 60 62 60
61 65 58 57 54 52 62 67 69 49
56 58 60 60 62 58 51 57 70 63

Taking class intervals 45–49, 50–54, ... draw up a table of frequencies and find the median and interquartile range from an ogive. Calculate the mean by considering each class as being concentrated at the mid-value.

12. The masses (in kg to the nearest kg) of a set of 40 women are as follows:

45 48 51 46 43 50 53 59 60 41
46 49 50 47 56 49 51 52 53 50
41 51 47 42 58 50 50 51 48 47
50 49 53 57 52 43 48 50 49 40

Taking class intervals 40–44, 45–49, ... draw up a table of frequencies. Find the mean mass, the median and interquartile range.

Chapter 6

Factors

Example 1   *Factorise* $(x - a)(3x + 2a) - (x - a)^2$.

The two parts of the expression have the factor $(x - a)$ in common.

$$\therefore \; (x - a)(3x + 2a) - (x - a)^2 = (x - a)\{(3x + 2a) - (x - a)\}$$
$$= (x - a)(3x + 2a - x + a)$$
$$= (x - a)(2x + 3a)$$

Example 2   *By factorising, simplify* $63 \times 29 + 37 \times 29$.

$$63 \times 29 + 37 \times 29 = 29(63 + 37)$$
$$= 29 \times 100$$
$$= 2\,900.$$

Example 3   *Factorise* $am + 3bn - an - 3bm$.

The terms am and an have a in common.
The terms $3bm$ and $3bn$ have $3b$ in common.
Grouping pairs in this way,

$$am + 3bn - an - 3bm = am - an - 3bm + 3bn$$
$$= a(m - n) - 3b(m - n)$$
$$= (m - n)(a - 3b)$$

If all the terms contain a common factor, it should be taken out *first* as in Example 4.

Example 4   *Factorise* $3chm + 6dhm - 9ckm - 18dkm$.

$$3chm + 6dhm - 9ckm - 18dkm = 3m[ch + 2dh - 3ck - 6dk]$$
$$= 3m[h(c + 2d) - 3k(c + 2d)]$$
$$= 3m(c + 2d)(h - 3k)$$

Example 5 *Factorise* $3x^2 - 13x - 10$.

The first term is $3x^2$, which is the product of $3x$ and x.
  Hence $3x^2 - 13x - 10 = (3x \dots)(x \dots)$.
  The last term is -10, which is the product of 10 and 1, or 5 and 2, with *unlike* signs.
  This produces as possible factors:

$(3x + 10)(x - 1)$ $(3x + 5)(x - 2)$

$(3x - 10)(x + 1)$ $(3x - 5)(x + 2)$

$(3x + 1)(x - 10)$ $(3x + 2)(x - 5)$

$(3x - 1)(x + 10)$ $(3x - 2)(x + 5)$

  These all give $3x^2$ as the first term, and -10 as the last term. The only one which gives $-13x$ as the middle term is

$(3x + 2)(x - 5)$.

Hence $3x^2 - 13x - 10 = (3x + 2)(x - 5)$.

  With practice it will be found unnecessary to write down all the possibilities.

Example 6 *Factorise* $3x^2 - 13xy - 10y^2$.

This example is closely related to Example 5 as the coefficients are the same, and it is easily seen that

$3x^2 - 13xy - 10y^2 = (3x + 2y)(x - 5y)$.

Example 7 *Factorise* $3x^2y^2 - 13xy - 10$.

This example has the same coefficients as those in Example 5, and

$3x^2y^2 - 13xy - 10 = (3xy + 2)(xy - 5)$.

Example 8 *Factorise* $6 - 15x + 9x^2$.

The factor 3, which is common to all terms, is taken out first.

$6 - 15x + 9x^2 = 3(2 - 5x + 3x^2)$

For producing the 2 and the $3x^2$ the possibilities are

$(1 + x)(2 + 3x)$ $(1 + 3x)(2 + x)$

$(1 - x)(2 - 3x)$ $(1 - 3x)(2 - x)$

and of these, the third one gives $-5x$ for the middle term.

$$\therefore\ 6 - 15x + 9x^2 = 3(2 - 5x + 3x^2)$$
$$= 3(1 - x)(2 - 3x)$$

$$(a + b)^2 = a^2 + 2ab + b^2$$
$$(a - b)^2 = a^2 - 2ab + b^2$$
$$a^2 - b^2 = (a + b)(a - b)$$
$$a^2 + b^2 \text{ has no factors}$$

Example 9   *Factorise* $d^2 - 10dm + 25m^2$.

d^2 is the square of d.
$25m^2$ is the square of $5m$.
$10dm$ is twice the product of d and $5m$.

$$\therefore\ d^2 - 10dm + 25m^2 = (d - 5m)^2.$$

Example 10   *Factorise* $16a^2 - 25b^2$.

$$16a^2 - 25b^2 = (4a)^2 - (5b)^2$$
$$= (4a + 5b)(4a - 5b)$$

Example 11   *Factorise* $3m^2 - 48$.

$$3m^2 - 48 = 3(m^2 - 16)$$
$$= 3(m^2 - 4^2)$$
$$= 3(m - 4)(m + 4)$$

Example 12   *Factorise* $9a^2 - 4(c - 2d)^2$.

$9a^2$ is the square of $3a$.

$4(c - 2d)^2$ is the square of $2(c - 2d)$.

$\therefore\ 9a^2 - 4(c - 2d)^2 = [3a + 2(c - 2d)][3a - 2(c - 2d)]$

$$= (3a + 2c - 4d)(3a - 2c + 4d)$$

Exercise 6a

By factorising, simplify

1. $18 \times 57 + 18 \times 43$ 2. $23 \times 119 - 23 \times 19$
3. $243 \times 4 + 243 \times 6$ 4. $28 \times 752 + 28 \times 248$
5. $63 \times 47 - 43 \times 47$ 6. $61 \times 127 - 77 \times 61$

Write down the expansions of

7. $(3a + 1)^2$ 8. $(b - 4)^2$ 9. $(2c - 5d)^2$ 10. $(4m + 3n)^2$

Factorise

11. $(3c - d)(m - n) + (3c - d)(2m - 3n)$
12. $ac + bc + 2ad + 2bd$
13. $x^2 - 16a^2$ 14. $4c^2 - 25d^2$
15. $a^2 - 3a - 10$ 16. $a^2 - 3ab - 10b^2$
17. $a^2b^2 - 3ab - 10$ 18. $5m^2 - 45n^2$
19. $hm - 2km - 2hn + 4kn$
20. $(2a + b)^2 - (2a + b)(a - 3b)$
21. $3m^2 - 10m + 3$ 22. $c^2d^2 - 81$
23. $16x^2 - 9a^2m^2$ 24. $6n^2 + 13n + 6$
25. $4a^2 + 20a + 25$ 26. $9h^2 - 36k^2$
27. $(5a - 3b)(a - 2b) - (4a + b)(a - 2b)$
28. $25a^2b^2c^2 - 9d^2$ 29. $m^2/9 - n^2/4$
30. $3su + tu - 6sv - 2tv$ 31. $9x^2 - 12xy + 4y^2$
32. $12d^2 + 5d - 2$ 33. $x^4 - y^2$
34. $10m^2n^2 - 7mn - 12$ 35. $16 - n^4$
36. $(a + b)^2 - c^2$ 37. $x^2 - (m - n)^2$
38. $(m + 2n)(3a - b) - (a - 3b)(m + 2n)$
39. $2 - h - 15h^2$ 40. $2am - bm + 3bn - 6an$
41. $a^2 - 15ab + 54b^2$ 42. $m^2 - 15mn - 54n^2$
43. $(c - 2d)^2 - 9e^2$ 44. $12x^2 + 35xy + 18y^2$
45. $(h - k)(2h - 3k) + (h - k)^2$

46. $6acx - 8ady + 4acy - 12adx$

47. $6a^2 - 19ax - 36x^2$ **48.** $25a^2 - 4(m + 2n)^2$

49. $25a^2 - 4(a - 2b)^2$ **50.** $9a^2 - (3a - 2b)^2$

Cubic factors

$$a^3 + b^3 = (a + b)(a^2 - ab + b^2)$$
$$a^3 - b^3 = (a - b)(a^2 + ab + b^2)$$

Example 13   *Factorise* $8x^3 - 1$.

$$8x^3 - 1 = (2x)^3 - 1^3$$
$$= [2x - 1][(2x)^2 + (2x) \times 1 + 1^2]$$
$$= (2x - 1)(4x^2 + 2x + 1)$$

Example 14   *Factorise* $64m^3n^6 + 27a^9$.

$$64m^3n^6 + 27a^9 = (4mn^2)^3 + (3a^3)^3$$
$$= [4mn^2 + 3a^3][(4mn^2)^2 - (4mn^2)(3a^3) + (3a^3)^2]$$
$$= (4mn^2 + 3a^3)(16m^2n^4 - 12mn^2a^3 + 9a^6)$$

Example 15   *Factorise* $(5a - 1)^3 - (a + 3)^3$.

$$(5a - 1)^3 - (a + 3)^3$$
$$= [(5a - 1) - (a + 3)][(5a - 1)^2 + (5a - 1)(a + 3) + (a + 3)^2]$$
$$= (5a - 1 - a - 3)$$
$$\times (25a^2 - 10a + 1 + 5a^2 + 14a - 3 + a^2 + 6a + 9)$$
$$= (4a - 4)(31a^2 + 10a + 7)$$
$$= 4(a - 1)(31a^2 + 10a + 7)$$

Exercise 6b

Factorise

1. $a^3 + 8$ **2.** $8 - m^3$ **3.** $1 - 8u^3$ **4.** $27x^3 + 8y^3$
5. $8 - 125x^3$ **6.** $64m^3 + 8$ **7.** $2a^6 + 16$ **8.** $m^6 - n^3$
9. $8a^9 + 27b^9$ **10.** $8a^3b^3c^3 + x^3$

11. $\dfrac{a^3}{m^3} - 1$ **12.** $8 + \dfrac{m^3}{x^3}$

13. $2x^3 - 54a^3b^3$ **14.** $1 - m^6$ **15.** $(x - 3y)^3 + 8y^3$
16. $(m + 2n)^3 - 27n^3$ **17.** $27x^3 - (2x - 3)^3$
18. $(4a + b)^3 + (a - b)^3$ **19.** $(3a - 1)^3 - (a + 2)^3$
20. $(2x + a)^3 + (3x - 2a)^3$

Chapter 7

Percentages

Example 1   *When the length of a spring is increased by* 16% *it becomes* 377 *mm. Find the actual increase.*

116% of the original length = 377 mm
∴ 16% of the original length = 377 × $\frac{16}{116}$ mm
                                = 52 mm

∴ the actual increase is 52 mm.

Notice that there is no need to find the original length.

Example 2   *When a refrigerator is sold for* £93 *the profit is* 24%. *What should the selling price be to secure a profit of* 28%?

124% of cost price = £93
∴ 128% of cost price = £93 × $\frac{128}{124}$
                      = £93 × $\frac{32}{31}$
                      = £96
∴ the selling price should be £96.

Notice that there is no need to find the cost price.

Example 3   *A shop sells* 72% *of its stock of hats, and the number sold is* 418 *more than the number of hats remaining. How many hats were in stock originally?*

72% of the stock is sold.
∴ 28% of the stock is left.
The difference is 44%.

∴   44% of the original stock = 418 hats
∴ 100% of the original stock = 418 × $\frac{100}{44}$ hats
                              = 38 × $\frac{100}{4}$ hats
                              = 950 hats.

Example 4   *A dealer sells a second-hand car to a man and makes a profit of 15%. The man then resells it to a woman for £874, making a loss of 5%. How much did the dealer pay for the car?*

The dealer paid $\frac{100}{115}$ of what the man paid.
The man paid $\frac{100}{95}$ of what the woman paid.
∴ the dealer paid $\frac{100}{115}$ of $\frac{100}{95}$ of what the woman paid
$= \frac{100}{115} \times \frac{100}{95} \times £874$
$= \frac{20}{23} \times \frac{20}{19} \times £874$
$= 20 \times 20 \times £2$
$= £800.$

Exercise 7

1. When the mass of a pile of soil is increased by 16% it becomes 1 102 kg. Find the original mass.

2. Find the number such that 182 is the difference between increasing it by 12% and decreasing it by 16%.

3. A retailer makes a profit of $12\frac{1}{2}\%$ by selling some goods for £9·45. Find his cash profit.

4. When a car is sold for £1 134 the profit is 35%. Find the selling price that would have given a profit of 25%.

5. If the length of a rectangle is increased by 5% and the width decreased by 10%, find the percentage alteration in the area.

6. When a boat is sold for £752 the profit is $17\frac{1}{2}\%$. What would have been the percentage profit if the boat had been sold for £784?

7. A grocer sold 45% of his stock of sugar, and the amount that he sold was 96 kg less than the amount left. How much did he sell?

8. When 24% of the contents of a water-tank are drained away the volume remaining is 323 litres. Find the amount drained away.

9. A Building Society offers interest to its investors at the gross rate of 9·3 %, but retains 30 % of the interest to pay as tax to the Inland Revenue. Find the net rate per cent received by investors.

10. If the Building Society in no. 9 changes its rate of interest so that investors receive a net rate of 6·72 %, find the gross rate which the Society offers.

11. If the radius of a circle is increased by 5 %, find the percentage increase in area.

12. A wholesaler buys goods for £496 and sells to a retailer at a profit of 25 %. The retailer makes a profit of 30 %. Find the retail price.

13 A sells some goods to B and makes a profit of 15 %. B resells to C at a loss of 5 %. If C pays £13·11, how much did A pay for the goods?

14. A man spends 57 % of his money, and the amount that he spends is £2·24 more than he has left. How much money had he originally?

15. If a dealer made a profit of 22½ % by selling a second-hand car for £588, find what his percentage profit would have been if he could have sold it for £612.

16. If a profit of 24 % was made when a bicycle was sold for £34·10, find the selling price that would have given a profit of 28 %.

17. In 1972 the number of new cars sold in Great Britain was 1 637 775, and 401 994 of these were Fords. Express the Ford sales as a percentage of the total sales, correct to 1 decimal place.

18. The number of cars manufactured by British Leyland and sold in Great Britain was 516 440 in 1971 and 542 440 in 1972. Find the percentage increase in sales, correct to three significant figures.

19. A man's income is increased by 15%, and then reduced by 15%. Is his final income greater or less than the original, and by how much per cent?

20. A man bought a house for £12 800. Five years later, when its value had appreciated by $17\frac{1}{2}$%, he decided to sell. If the purchaser paid a deposit of 15%, how much remained to be paid?

21. A man's salary was £2 056 in 1972, and was 15% more in 1973. If he paid $17\frac{1}{2}$% of his salary in income-tax, how much tax did he pay in 1973?

22. A wholesaler sells some furniture to a retailer at a profit of $22\frac{1}{2}$%. The retailer makes a profit of $27\frac{1}{2}$% by selling to a customer for £1 024·59. What did the wholesaler pay for the furniture?

Chapter 8
Logarithms

Indices

Basic Laws

1. $a^x \times a^y = a^{x+y}$
2. $a^x \div a^y = a^{x-y}$
3. $(a^x)^y = a^{xy}$

Basic applications

4. $a^{\frac{1}{n}} = \sqrt[n]{a}$ 5. $a^0 = 1$

6. $a^{-n} = \dfrac{1}{a^n}$ 7. $a^{\frac{x}{y}} = \sqrt[y]{a^x} \text{ or } (\sqrt[y]{a})^x$

Example 1   *Simplify* $25^{\frac{1}{2}}, 27^{\frac{1}{3}}, 27^{-\frac{2}{3}}, 9^{\frac{1}{4}} \times 9^{\frac{1}{4}}, \left(\frac{81}{16}\right)^{-\frac{3}{4}}$

$25^{\frac{1}{2}} = \sqrt{25} = \pm 5$

$27^{\frac{1}{3}} = \sqrt[3]{27} = 3$

$27^{-\frac{2}{3}} = \dfrac{1}{27^{\frac{2}{3}}} = \dfrac{1}{(\sqrt[3]{27})^2} = \dfrac{1}{3^2} = \dfrac{1}{9}$

$9^{\frac{1}{4}} \times 9^{\frac{1}{4}} = 9^{\frac{1}{4}+\frac{1}{4}} = 9^{\frac{1}{2}} = \pm 3$

$\left(\dfrac{81}{16}\right)^{-\frac{3}{4}} = \left(\dfrac{16}{81}\right)^{\frac{3}{4}} = \left(\dfrac{\pm 2}{\pm 3}\right)^3 = \pm\dfrac{8}{27}$

Exercise 8a

Simplify

1. $2a^2 \times 5a$ 2. $(2a)^2 \times 5a$ 3. $2a^2 \times (5a)^3$
4. $2a^{-2} \times 5a$ 5. $(2a)^{-2} \times 5a$ 6. $2a^{-2} \times (5a)^3$

7. 2^{-4} **8.** $8^{\frac{2}{3}}$ **9.** $4^{-\frac{1}{2}}$

10. $\sqrt{1\frac{9}{16}}$ **11.** $(\frac{1}{9})^{-\frac{1}{2}}$ **12.** $2^{\frac{2}{3}} \times 2^{\frac{4}{3}}$

13. $0.09^{\frac{1}{2}}$ **14.** $5^x \times 5^{-x}$ **15.** $\sqrt[3]{4^{1.5}}$

16. $(\frac{27}{48})^{-\frac{3}{2}}$ **17.** $0.216^{-\frac{2}{3}}$ **18.** $\sqrt[3]{8a^{-6}}$

Rewrite the following, using positive indices only, $\left(\text{e.g. } ab^{-2} = \dfrac{a}{b^2}\right)$:

19. x^{-3} **20.** xy^{-1} **21.** $(xy)^{-1}$

22. $a^{-2}b^3$ **23.** $(ab^{-3})^2$ **24.** $3x^{-\frac{1}{2}}$

Solve for x the following equations:

25. $x^{\frac{1}{2}} = 3$ **26.** $x^{\frac{1}{3}} = 2$ **27.** $x^{-2} = 16$

28. $3x^3 = 24$ **29.** $x^{-\frac{2}{3}} = 9$ **30.** $5x = 80x^{-\frac{1}{3}}$

Logarithms   (numbers greater than 1)

Example 2   *Evaluate* $\dfrac{82.47 \times 24.85}{209.3}$

No.	Log.
82.47	1.916 3
24.85	1.395 4
Numerator	3.311 7
209.3	2.320 7
9.795	0.991 0

Check $\dfrac{80 \times 25}{200} = 10$

Ans.   9.795

Example 3 *Evaluate* $\sqrt[3]{\dfrac{4\,087}{59\cdot34}}$

No.	Log.
4 087	3·611 5
59·34	1·773 4
	1·838 1 ÷ 3
4·100	= 0·612 7

Check $\sqrt[3]{\dfrac{4\,000}{60}} = \sqrt[3]{66}\ldots$

$$= 4\cdot\ldots$$

$$(4^3 = 64)$$

Ans.   4·100

Example 4 *Evaluate* $\left(\dfrac{6 + \sqrt[3]{5\cdot674}}{6 - \sqrt[3]{5\cdot674}}\right)^2$

No.	Log.
$\sqrt[3]{5\cdot674}$	0·753 9 ÷ 3
1·783	= 0·2513
6 + 1·783 = 7·783	0·891 2
6 − 1·783 = 4·217	0·625 0
	0·266 2 × 2
3·407	= 0·532 4

Check $\left(\dfrac{6 + 1\cdot5}{6 - 1\cdot5}\right)^2 = \left(\dfrac{7\cdot5}{4\cdot5}\right)^2 = \left(\dfrac{5}{3}\right)^2 = \dfrac{25}{9} \risingdotseq 3$

Ans.   3·407

Example 5 *Evaluate* $\dfrac{\sqrt[3]{207\cdot6} \times 12\cdot84^4}{4\cdot102^5 \times 77\cdot63}$.

No.	Log.	
$\sqrt[3]{207\cdot6}$ $12\cdot84^4$	$2\cdot317\,3 \div 3 = 0\cdot772\,4$ $1\cdot108\,6 \times 4 = 4\cdot434\,4$	
Numerator	$5\cdot206\,8$	$5\cdot206\,8$
$4\cdot102^5$ $77\cdot63$	$0\cdot613\,0 \times 5 = 3\cdot065\,0$ $1\cdot890\,1$	
Denominator	$4\cdot955\,1$	$4\cdot955\,1$
$1\cdot785$		$0\cdot251\,7$

Check $\dfrac{6 \times 160 \times 160}{16 \times 16 \times 4 \times 80} = \dfrac{15}{8} = 1\cdot8\ldots$

Ans. 1·785.

Exercise 8b

Evaluate the following, checking answers wherever it is reasonable to do so:

1. $11\cdot29 \times 6\cdot83 \times 24\cdot76$ 2. $38\cdot97 \times 107\cdot8 \div 81\cdot65$

3. $7\cdot936^2$ 4. $\sqrt[3]{65\cdot84}$ 5. $\sqrt[5]{29\cdot17}$

6. $\sqrt{3\cdot97 \times 15\cdot4}$ 7. $\left(\dfrac{21\cdot56}{2\cdot83}\right)^2$ 8. $\sqrt[4]{3\cdot87^3}$

9. $1\cdot067^{10}$ 10. $4\cdot836^2 \times 2\cdot184^3$ 11. $\sqrt[3]{\dfrac{729\,4}{63\cdot85}}$

12. $\dfrac{38\cdot86 \times 509\cdot2}{76\cdot71}$ 13. $\sqrt{61\cdot73^2 - 38\cdot27^2}$ 14. $4\cdot679^{0\cdot4}$

15. $3\cdot025^3 - \sqrt[4]{759\cdot4}$ 16. $12\cdot34^2 - 9\cdot88 \times 12\cdot34$

17. $\dfrac{298 \cdot 4}{18 \cdot 65 \times 9 \cdot 732}$

18. $\dfrac{118 \cdot 6}{34 \cdot 95} - \dfrac{2\,837}{1\,964}$

19. $\dfrac{2 \cdot 874^3 + 6}{2 \cdot 874^3 - 6}$

20. $\sqrt[5]{\left(\dfrac{95 \cdot 84 \times 317 \cdot 2}{286 \cdot 1 \times 7 \cdot 86}\right)^2}$

21. $\dfrac{846\,000}{25 \cdot 3^3 \times \sqrt{124 \cdot 3}}$

22. $\dfrac{\sqrt[3]{489 \cdot 7^2}}{\sqrt[5]{9\,134}}$

Logarithms (including numbers less than 1)

Example 6 *Evaluate* $0 \cdot 692\,4 \times 0 \cdot 083\,7$

No.	Log.
0·692 4	$\bar{1}$·840 3
0·083 7	$\bar{2}$·922 7
0·057 94	$\bar{2}$·763 0

Check $0 \cdot 7 \times 0 \cdot 08 = 0 \cdot 056$

Ans. 0·057 94.

Example 7 *Evaluate* $0 \cdot 006\,219 \div 0 \cdot 830\,6$

$$\frac{0 \cdot 006\,219}{0 \cdot 830\,6} = \frac{6 \cdot 219}{830 \cdot 6}$$

No.	Log.
6·219	0·793 7
830·6	2·919 4
0·007 487	$\bar{3}$·874 3

Check $\dfrac{6}{800} = 0 \cdot 007\,5$

Ans. 0·007 487.

Exercise 8c

Evaluate the following, checking every answer:

1. $8.921 \times 0.086\ 25$ **2.** $0.054\ 7 \times 0.439\ 9$

3. $95.46 \div 325.7$ **4.** $4.257 \div 76.84$

5. $0.021\ 3 \div 0.086\ 6$ **6.** $0.082\ 4 \div 0.009\ 627$

7. $0.285\ 6 \times 11.27 \times 0.076\ 7$ **8.** $\dfrac{0.886\ 2 \times 0.025\ 7}{0.052\ 16}$

9. $\dfrac{0.764\ 1 \times 0.382\ 5}{0.095\ 6}$ **10.** $\dfrac{0.932\ 8 \times 0.087\ 4}{2.886 \times 0.023\ 9}$

Example 8   *Evaluate* 0.592^3.

No.	Log.
0.592^3	$\overline{1}.772\ 3 \times 3$
$0.207\ 4$	$= \overline{1}.316\ 9$

Check $0.6^3 = 0.216$

Ans. $0.207\ 4$.

Example 9   *Evaluate* $\sqrt[4]{0.007\ 86}$.

No.	Log.
$\sqrt[4]{0.007\ 86}$	$\overline{3}.895\ 4 \div 4$
	$= (\overline{4} + 1.895\ 4) \div 4$
$0.297\ 7$	$= \overline{1}.473\ 8(5)$

Check $0.3^4 = 0.008\ 1$

Ans. $0.297\ 7$.

N.B. In Example 8 it is simpler to check the fourth power of 0.3 than to try to guess the fourth root of 0.008.

Example 10 *Evaluate* $0.068\ 5^2 \div 0.837^3$.

No.	Log.
$0.068\ 5^2$	$\bar{2}.835\ 7 \times 2 = \bar{3}.671\ 4$
0.837^3	$\bar{1}.922\ 7 \times 3 = \bar{1}.768\ 1$
$0.008\ 004$	$\bar{3}.903\ 3$

Check $\dfrac{0.07^2}{0.8^3} = \dfrac{0.004\ 9}{0.512} \simeq \dfrac{0.005}{0.5}$

$$= 0.01$$

Ans. 0.008 004.

Standard form. A number expressed in the form $a \times 10^b$, where a is a number between 1 and 10 and b is a positive or negative integer, is said to be in standard form. The number 'a' is often given to 3 sig. fig.;

e.g.
$$293.8 \simeq 2.94 \times 10^2$$
$$0.002\ 938 \simeq 2.94 \times 10^{-3}$$

N.B. The power of 10 is the characteristic of the logarithm of the number concerned.

Example 11 *Evaluate* $\sqrt[5]{6.78 \times 10^{-8}}$, *giving the answer in standard form to 3 sig. fig.*

No.	Log.
$\sqrt[5]{6.78 \times 10^{-8}}$	$\bar{8}.831\ 2 \div 5$
	$= (\overline{10} + 2.831\ 2) \div 5$
3.683×10^{-2}	$= \bar{2}.566\ 2$

Ans. 3.68×10^{-2}.

Exercise 8d

Evaluate the following, checking answers when it is reasonable to do so. If the question is given in standard form express the answer in the same way, and to the same number of sig. fig..

1. $0.516\ 8^2$ **2.** $0.392\ 7^3$ **3.** $0.883\ 4^4$

4. $\sqrt[3]{0.123\ 4}$ **5.** $\sqrt[3]{0.031\ 2}$ **6.** $\sqrt[5]{0.006\ 92}$

7. $0.984\ 5^{10}$ **8.** $\sqrt[10]{0.053\ 84}$ **9.** $\sqrt[4]{0.023\ 71^3}$

10. $\sqrt[3]{0.203\ 4 \times 0.393\ 5}$ **11.** $\sqrt[4]{1.092 \times 0.008\ 64}$

12. $\left(\dfrac{0.030\ 6}{0.147\ 8}\right)^3$ **13.** $\sqrt[3]{\dfrac{0.173\ 2}{0.023\ 71}}$ **14.** $0.083\ 7^{0.6}$

15. $(2.69 \times 10^4)^3$ **16.** $\sqrt[5]{8.451 \times 10^{-4}}$ **17.** $(6.08 \times 10^{-3})^4$

18. $\dfrac{5.29 \times 10^{-3}}{9.84 \times 10^{-15}}$ **19.** $\sqrt[4]{8.62 \times 10^{-7}}$ **20.** $\dfrac{2.684^3 - 5}{2.684^3 + 5}$

Chapter 9

Pythagoras' theorem

In a right-angled triangle the square on the hypotenuse is equal to the sum of the squares on the other two sides.

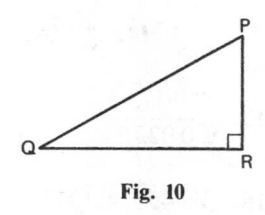

Fig. 10

In the rt.-∠d △ in Fig. 10

$PQ^2 = PR^2 + QR^2$.

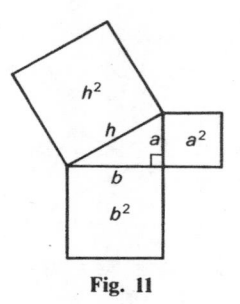

Fig. 11

In Fig. 11, if the lengths of the sides are respectively h, a and b units, then $h^2 = a^2 + b^2$.

Notice also that

$a^2 = h^2 - b^2$ and $b^2 = h^2 - a^2$.

Example 1 *In Fig.* 12, *if* AC = 12 cm, BC = 5 cm, CD = 11 cm, *find* AD.

Let AD = x cm and AB = y cm.
In rt.-$\angle$d $\triangle$ ABC

$$AB^2 = AC^2 - BC^2$$

$$\therefore \ y^2 = 12^2 - 5^2$$
$$= 144 - 25$$
$$= 119.$$

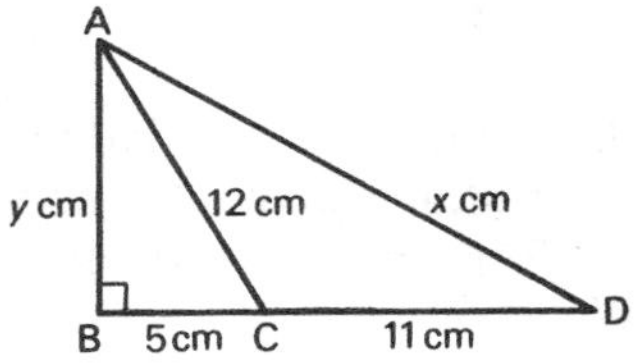

In rt.-$\angle$d $\triangle$ ABD,
$$AD^2 = AB^2 + BD^2$$
$$\therefore \ x^2 = y^2 + 16^2$$
$$= 119 + 256$$
$$= 375$$

$$\therefore \ x = \sqrt{375} \simeq 19\cdot4$$
$$\therefore \ AD = 19\cdot4 \text{ cm correct to 3 sig. fig.}$$

Notice that when y^2 has been found to be 119 there is no need to find y, since it is y^2 that is needed in the subsequent working.

Exercise 9a

In nos. 1–6 find the value of x.

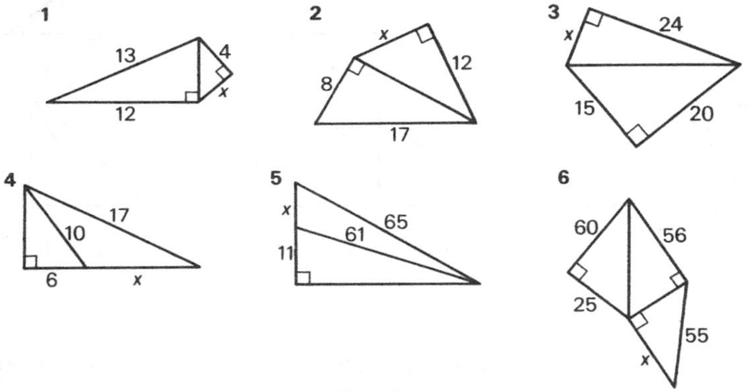

Fig. 13

7. A mast 35 m high is supported by wires attached to its top and to points on the level ground 12 m from its base. Find the length of each wire.

8. A builder has a ladder 17 m long, and he places it against a building so that the upper end is 15 m from the ground. How far from the wall is the foot of the ladder?

9. One side of a right-angled triangle is 24 cm long, and the length of the hypotenuse is 25 cm. Find the length of the third side, and the area of the triangle.

10. Find the perpendicular height of a cone with a slant height of 29 cm and a circular base of radius 21 cm.

11. AD is an altitude of $\triangle$ ABC. If AD = 2·4 cm, BD = 3·2 cm, CD = 1·8 cm, prove that BÂC is a right angle.

In nos. 12–17 find the value of x correct to 3 significant figures.

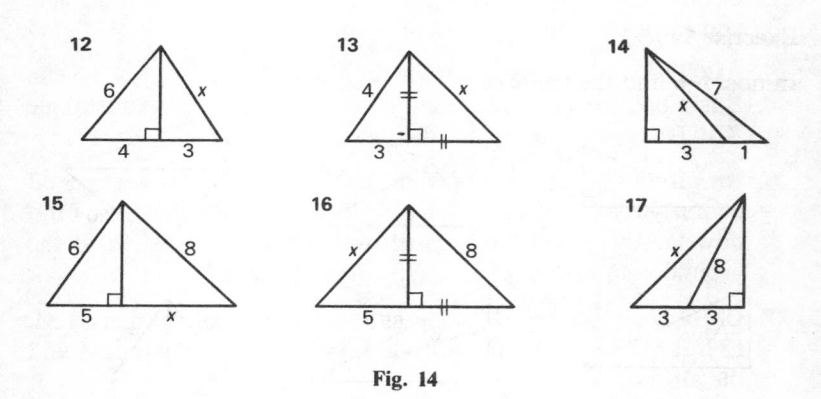

Fig. 14

In nos. 18–28 give answers correct to 3 significant figures where necessary.

18. A mast is supported by wires attached to its top and to points on the level ground 10 m from its base. If each wire is 31 m long, find the height of the mast.

19. A rectangle is 4·3 cm long, and the length of each diagonal is 5·1 cm. Find the width and the area of the rectangle.

20. A lean-to shed is 3 m wide, 2·9 m high at the back, and 2·3 m high at the front. Each side is a trapezium 2 m wide. Find the area of the roof.

21. ABC is a triangle in which $AC = 2$ m, $BC = 3$ m, and $\widehat{C}$ is obtuse. The perpendicular from A to $\overline{BC}$ produced is $\overline{AD}$, where $CD = 1$ m. Calculate AB.

22. ABC is a triangle in which $\widehat{C} = 90°$, $AB = 3·5$ cm, $AC = 2·1$ cm. Calculate the length of the perpendicular from C to $\overline{AB}$.

23. Find the radius of the base of a right circular cone if its perpendicular height and slant height are 12 cm and 16 cm respectively.

24. One side of a right-angled triangle is 56 cm long, and the length of the hypotenuse is 64·5 cm. Find the length of the third side and the area of the triangle.

25. ABCD is a rectangle in which $AB = 2·8$ cm, $AD = 3·3$ cm. E is a point on $\overline{DC}$ produced such that $\triangle$ AED and rectangle ABCD are equal in area. Calculate DE and AE.

26. An aircraft is heading NW at 720 km h^{-1}, but is carried off course by a wind of 40 km h^{-1} blowing from the SW. Find how far the aircraft travels in twenty minutes relative to the ground, and on what bearing (nearest degree).

27. LMN is an isosceles triangle in which the equal sides are $\overline{LM}$, $\overline{LN}$. If $MN = 8$ cm and altitude $LX = 9$ cm, calculate LM and the altitude MY.

28. The diagonals $\overline{PR}$, $\overline{QS}$ of a rectangle meet at O, and $\triangle$ POS is equilateral. X is a point in $\overline{PS}$ such that $XS = 3XP$. If $PS = 4$ cm, calculate QX.

Example 2   *Triangle* PQR *is right-angled at* R, *and* $\overline{\text{PX}}, \overline{\text{QY}}$ *are medians. Prove that* $\text{PX}^2 + \text{QY}^2 = \frac{5}{4}\text{PQ}^2$.

Given $\triangle$PQR in which $\hat{\text{R}} = 90°$, and $\overline{\text{PX}}, \overline{\text{QY}}$ are medians.

To prove $\text{PX}^2 + \text{QY}^2 = \frac{5}{4}\text{PQ}^2$.

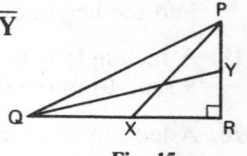

Fig. 15

Proof   Since $\triangle$s PXR, QYR are right-angled at R,

$$
\begin{aligned}
\text{PX}^2 + \text{QY}^2 &= \text{PR}^2 + \text{XR}^2 + \text{QR}^2 + \text{YR}^2 \\
&= \text{PR}^2 + (\tfrac{1}{2}\text{QR})^2 + \text{QR}^2 + (\tfrac{1}{2}\text{PR})^2 \\
&= \text{PR}^2 + \tfrac{1}{4}\text{QR}^2 + \text{QR}^2 + \tfrac{1}{4}\text{PR}^2 \\
&= \tfrac{5}{4}\text{PR}^2 + \tfrac{5}{4}\text{QR}^2 \\
&= \tfrac{5}{4}(\text{PR}^2 + \text{QR}^2) \\
&= \tfrac{5}{4}\text{PQ}^2 \text{ since } \triangle\text{PQR is right-angled at R.}
\end{aligned}
$$

Example 3 $\overline{\text{LD}}$ *is an altitude of* $\triangle$LMN, *in which* LM > LN. *Prove that* $\text{LM}^2 - \text{LN}^2 = \text{MN}(\text{MD} - \text{DN})$.

Given $\triangle$LMN in which $\overline{\text{LD}}$ is an altitude, and LM > LN.

To prove $\text{LM}^2 - \text{LN}^2 = \text{MN}(\text{MD} - \text{DN})$.

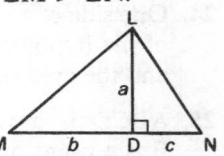

Fig. 16

Proof   Since $\triangle$s LMD, LND are right-angled at D,

$$
\begin{aligned}
\text{LM}^2 - \text{LN}^2 &= (\text{LD}^2 + \text{MD}^2) - (\text{LD}^2 + \text{DN}^2) \\
&= \text{LD}^2 + \text{MD}^2 - \text{LD}^2 - \text{DN}^2 \\
&= \text{MD}^2 - \text{DN}^2 \\
&= (\text{MD} + \text{DN})(\text{MD} - \text{DN}) \\
&= \text{MN}(\text{MD} - \text{DN}).
\end{aligned}
$$

Alternatively

$$
\begin{aligned}
\text{LM}^2 - \text{LN}^2 &= (a^2 + b^2) - (a^2 + c^2) \\
&= b^2 - c^2 \\
&= (b + c)(b - c) \\
&= \text{MN}(\text{MD} - \text{DN}).
\end{aligned}
$$

Exercise 9b

1. $\overline{\text{ADO}}$, $\overline{\text{BCO}}$ are straight lines which meet at right angles. Prove that $AB^2 + CD^2 = AC^2 + BD^2$.

2. In $\triangle PQR$, $QR = \frac{1}{2}PR$ and $\hat{R} = 90°$. Prove that $4PQ^2 = 5PR^2$.

3. ABCD is a rectangle. P, Q, R, S are points on $\overline{\text{AB}}$, $\overline{\text{BC}}$, $\overline{\text{CD}}$, $\overline{\text{DA}}$ respectively such that $AP = 2PB$, $BQ = 2QC$, $CR = 2RD$, $DS = 2SA$. Prove that PQRS is a parallelogram.

4. $\triangle ABC$ is right-angled at A, and $AB = 2AC$. $\triangle BCD$ is right-angled at B, and $BD = BA$. Prove that $CD = 3AC$.

5. ABCD is a rectangle such that $AB = 2AD$, and M is the mid-point of $\overline{\text{DC}}$. A line $\overline{\text{AN}}$ at right angles to $\overline{\text{AM}}$ meets $\overline{\text{CB}}$ produced at N. Prove that $AN = 2AM$.

6. Squares PQRS, QTUV are drawn on the same side of a straight line $\overline{\text{PQT}}$. Prove that $RU^2 + ST^2 = 3(PQ^2 + QT^2)$.

7. Triangles PXQ, PYQ are right-angled at X, Y respectively, and lie on opposite sides of a common base $\overline{\text{PQ}}$. Perpendiculars $\overline{\text{PM}}$, $\overline{\text{QN}}$ are drawn from P, Q to $\overline{\text{XY}}$.
   Prove that $MX^2 + NX^2 = MY^2 + NY^2$.

8. ABCD is a square. The sides $\overline{\text{AB}}$, $\overline{\text{BC}}$, $\overline{\text{CD}}$, $\overline{\text{DA}}$ are produced to W, X, Y, Z respectively so that $BW = CX = DY = AZ = AB$. Prove that WXYZ is a square, and that its area is 5 times the area of the square ABCD.

9. $\triangle ABC$ is right-angled at A, and $AB = AC$. $\overline{\text{BC}}$ is produced to D so that $CD = AC$. Prove that $BC \times BD = AD^2$.

10. $\triangle ABC$ is right-angled at A, and $AB = \frac{1}{2}AC$. If $\overline{\text{AD}}$ is an altitude, prove that $BC = 5BD$.

Chapter 10

Quadratic equations

Example 1 *Solve the equation* $3x^2 + 5x - 28 = 0$.

$$3x^2 + 5x - 28 = 0$$
$$\therefore (x + 4)(3x - 7) = 0$$
$$\therefore \text{ either } x + 4 = 0 \text{ or } 3x - 7 = 0$$
$$\therefore x = -4 \text{ or } 3x = 7$$
$$\therefore x = -4 \text{ or } x = \tfrac{7}{3}$$
$$\therefore x = -4 \text{ or } 2\tfrac{1}{3}$$

Example 2 *Solve the equation* $y^2 - 4y = 0$.

$$y^2 - 4y = 0$$
$$\therefore y(y - 4) = 0$$
$$\therefore \text{ either } y = 0 \text{ or } y - 4 = 0$$
$$\therefore y = 0 \text{ or } 4$$

Example 3 *Find the equation whose roots are 2 and* $-3\tfrac{1}{2}$.

If $x = 2$ or $-3\tfrac{1}{2}$
then either $x - 2 = 0$ or $x + 3\tfrac{1}{2} = 0$
$$\therefore x - 2 = 0 \text{ or } 2x + 7 = 0$$
$$\therefore (x - 2)(2x + 7) = 0$$
$$\therefore 2x^2 + 3x - 14 = 0.$$

Sum and product of roots

In the equation $ax^2 + bx + c = 0$

$$\text{the sum of the roots} = -\frac{b}{a}$$

$$\text{and the product of the roots} = \frac{c}{a}$$

50

Example 4 *Solve the equation $2m^2 - 3m - 27 = 0$ and check by finding the sum and product of the roots.*

$$2m^2 - 3m - 27 = 0$$
$$\therefore\ (m + 3)(2m - 9) = 0$$
$$\therefore\ m + 3 = 0 \text{ or } 2m - 9 = 0$$
$$\therefore\ m = -3 \text{ or } \tfrac{9}{2}$$
i.e. $m = -3$ or $4\tfrac{1}{2}$.

Check Sum of roots $= -3 + 4\tfrac{1}{2} = 1\tfrac{1}{2} = \tfrac{3}{2}$
Product of roots $= -3 \times 4\tfrac{1}{2} = -13\tfrac{1}{2} = -\tfrac{27}{2}$.
These agree with the coefficients in the given equation.

Exercise 10a

Solve the following equations, and check the answers to the first ten by finding the sum and product of the roots.

1. $x^2 - 10x + 21 = 0$ **2.** $m^2 + 3m + 2 = 0$
3. $a^2 + a - 6 = 0$ **4.** $n^2 - 3n - 10 = 0$
5. $x^2 + x - 2 = 0$ **6.** $y^2 + 3y = 0$
7. $2d^2 - 7d + 6 = 0$ **8.** $4e^2 + 11e + 6 = 0$
9. $a^2 - 4 = 0$ **10.** $a^2 - 4a = 0$
11. $2t^2 + 7t + 5 = 0$ **12.** $3u^2 - 10u - 8 = 0$
13. $8w^2 - 18w + 9 = 0$ **14.** $12d^2 - 19d - 18 = 0$
15. $8n^2 + 2n - 21 = 0$

Find the equation whose roots are
16. $2, 5$ **17.** $-3, 4$ **18.** $0, 5$ **19.** $1\tfrac{1}{2}, 2\tfrac{1}{2}$ **20.** $1\tfrac{3}{4}, -2\tfrac{1}{3}$

The following example uses the fact that if $m^2 = 9$, then $m = \pm 3$, since $(+3)^2 = 9$ and $(-3)^2 = 9$.

Example 5 *Solve the equation $(x + 2)^2 = 5$.*

$$(x + 2)^2 = 5$$
$$\therefore\ x + 2 = \pm\sqrt{5}$$
$$\therefore\ x = -2 \pm \sqrt{5}.$$

A result such as this may be expressed approximately in decimals by putting $\pm\sqrt{5}$ as $\pm 2\cdot 24$,

i.e. $x = -2 \pm 2\cdot 24$
$= -2 + 2\cdot 24 \text{ or } -2 - 2\cdot 24$
$= 0\cdot 24 \text{ or } -4\cdot 24.$

Example 6   *What must be added to $a^2 - 7a$ to make it into a perfect square, and of what expression is the result the square?*

The coefficient of a is -7, half of this is $-\frac{7}{2}$, and the square of $-\frac{7}{2}$ is $+\frac{49}{4}$.

$\therefore \frac{49}{4}$ must be added, and then
$$a^2 - 7a + \tfrac{49}{4} = (a - \tfrac{7}{2})^2$$
i.e. $a^2 - 7a + 12\frac{1}{4} = (a - 3\frac{1}{2})^2.$

Check by squaring out the bracket.

Example 7   *Solve the equation $m^2 - 6m + 2 = 0$.*

The L.H.S. does not factorise, and so the equation is first re-arranged to make the L.H.S. a perfect square.

$m^2 - 6m + 2 = 0.$

Subtract 2 from both sides.

$m^2 - 6m = -2.$

Add 9 to both sides.

$m^2 - 6m + 9 = -2 + 9$
$\therefore (m - 3)^2 = 7$
$\therefore m - 3 = \pm\sqrt{7}$
$\therefore m = 3 \pm \sqrt{7}.$

Example 8   *Solve the equation $x^2 + 5x - 3 = 0$.*

The L.H.S. does not factorise.

$x^2 + 5x - 3 = 0$
$\therefore x^2 + 5x = 3$

Add to both sides the square of $\frac{5}{2}$.

$$x^2 + 5x + \left(\frac{5}{2}\right)^2 = 3 + \frac{25}{4}$$

$$= \frac{12 + 25}{4}$$

$$\therefore \left(x + \frac{5}{2}\right)^2 = \frac{37}{4}$$

$$\therefore x + \frac{5}{2} = \pm\sqrt{\frac{37}{4}}$$

$$= \pm\frac{\sqrt{37}}{2}$$

$$\therefore x = -\frac{5}{2} \pm \frac{\sqrt{37}}{2}$$

$$= \frac{-5 \pm \sqrt{37}}{2}$$

If the L.H.S. will factorise it is better to use the method of factorising, instead of completing the square.

Exercise 10b

Solve the following equations. Factorise where possible, but otherwise solve by completing the square. Do *not* put the answer in decimal form.

1. $a^2 - 4a - 12 = 0$
2. $b^2 - 4b - 5 = 0$
3. $c^2 + 4c - 6 = 0$
4. $d^2 - 4d + 2 = 0$
5. $e^2 + 6e + 9 = 0$
6. $m^2 - 8m + 9 = 0$
7. $n^2 + 10n - 1 = 0$
8. $x^2 + 10x - 11 = 0$
9. $u^2 + 3u + 1 = 0$
10. $w^2 - 5w - 3 = 0$
11. $x^2 - x - 2 = 0$
12. $m^2 - m - 3 = 0$
13. $n^2 + 8n + 13 = 0$
14. $a^2 + 7a + 11 = 0$
15. $d^2 - 9d - 2 = 0$

Example 9 *Solve the equation* $2x^2 - 10x + 7 = 0$ (2 *decimal places*).

First make the coefficient of x^2 unity, by dividing both sides by 2.
Then the equation becomes

$x^2 - 5x + 3\frac{1}{2} = 0$
$\therefore \; x^2 - 5x = -3\frac{1}{2}$.

Make the L.H.S. a perfect square by adding to both sides the
square of half the coefficient of x.

Then $\quad x^2 - 5x + \left(\dfrac{5}{2}\right)^2 = -3\frac{1}{2} + \frac{25}{4}$

$\therefore \; \left(x - \dfrac{5}{2}\right)^2 = \dfrac{-14 + 25}{4}$

$= \dfrac{11}{4}$

$\therefore \; x - \dfrac{5}{2} = \pm\sqrt{\dfrac{11}{4}}$

$= \pm\dfrac{\sqrt{11}}{2}$

$\therefore \; x = \dfrac{5}{2} \pm \dfrac{\sqrt{11}}{2}$

$= \dfrac{5 \pm 3\cdot317}{2}$ approx.

$= \dfrac{8\cdot317 \text{ or } 1\cdot683}{2}$

$= 4\cdot16$ or $0\cdot84$ to 2 dec. pl.

It is often easier to introduce decimals earlier in the working,

e.g. $(x - \frac{5}{2})^2 = \frac{11}{4}$
$\therefore \; (x - 2\cdot5)^2 = 2\cdot75$

$$\therefore \ x - 2 \cdot 5 = \pm\sqrt{2 \cdot 75}$$
$$\therefore \ x = 2 \cdot 5 \pm 1 \cdot 66 \text{ to 2 dec. pl.}$$
$$= 4 \cdot 16 \text{ or } 0 \cdot 84 \text{ to 2 dec. pl.}$$

Check From the coefficients in the given equation,
sum of roots should be $+\frac{10}{2}$, i.e. 5
product of roots should be $+\frac{7}{2}$, i.e. $3\frac{1}{2}$
$4 \cdot 16 + 0 \cdot 84 = 5$ and $4 \cdot 16 \times 0 \cdot 84 = 3 \cdot 494 \ldots$.

Imaginary roots

Example 10 *Solve the equation $x^2 - 6x + 13 = 0$.*

$$x^2 - 6x + 13 = 0$$
$$\therefore \ x^2 - 6x = -13$$
$$\therefore \ x^2 - 6x + 9 = -13 + 9$$
$$\therefore \ (x - 3)^2 = -4$$
$$\therefore \ x - 3 = \pm\sqrt{-4}, \text{ which is imaginary.}$$

$\therefore$ the roots are imaginary.

Exercise 10c

Solve the following equations by factorising if possible, but otherwise
by completing the square. If the roots involve decimals, give them
correct to 2 places. Square root tables may be used.

1. $x^2 - 4x + 2 = 0$ 2. $a^2 - 4a - 5 = 0$
3. $m^2 - 4m + 5 = 0$ 4. $d^2 + 6d - 5 = 0$
5. $n^2 + 6n + 5 = 0$ 6. $e^2 + 3e - 2 = 0$
7. $u^2 - u - 1 = 0$ 8. $c^2 - 5c + 5 = 0$
9. $2s^2 - 7s + 5 = 0$ 10. $2w^2 - 8w - 11 = 0$
11. $2x^2 - 8x + 11 = 0$ 12. $2x^2 - 10x - 7 = 0$
13. $2x^2 - 9x - 5 = 0$ 14. $3d^2 = 6d + 4$
15. $2a^2 + 7a = 6$ 16. $2m^2 + 7m + 6 = 0$
17. $3n^2 + 2 = 9n$ 18. $(4x + 1)(x - 2) = (x + 3)(2x + 1)$

19. $\frac{3}{4}x^2 + x - \frac{1}{2} = 0$ 20. $\dfrac{a + 1}{a} = \dfrac{3a + 2}{4}$

Problems leading to quadratic equations

Example 11 *A piece of wire* 40 *cm long is bent to form the perimeter of a right-angled triangle with hypotenuse of length* 17 cm. *Find the lengths of the other two sides.*

The sum of the lengths of the other two sides = (40 − 17) cm
$$= 23 \text{ cm.}$$

Let the length of one of the sides be x cm.
Then the length of the other is $(23 - x)$ cm.
∴ by Pythagoras

$$x^2 + (23 - x)^2 = 17^2$$
$$\therefore \ x^2 + 529 - 46x + x^2 = 289$$
$$\therefore \ 2x^2 - 46x + 529 - 289 = 0$$
$$\therefore \ 2x^2 - 46x + 240 = 0$$
$$\therefore \ x^2 - 23x + 120 = 0$$
$$\therefore \ (x - 8)(x - 15) = 0$$
$$\therefore \ x = 8 \text{ or } 15$$

If the length of one side is 8 cm the length of the other side is
(23 − 8) cm = 15 cm
If the length of one side is 15 cm the length of the other is
(23 − 15) cm = 8 cm
∴ the lengths of the other two sides are 8 cm and 15 cm.

Check $8^2 + 15^2 = 64 + 225 = 289 = 17^2.$

Exercise 10d

1. Find the whole number such that 5 times its square subtracted from 16 times the number leaves 3.

2. Find two consecutive odd numbers such that the sum of their squares is equal to 202.

3. Find three consecutive numbers such that the sum of their squares is equal to 194.

4. A man is now three times as old as his son, and 9 years ago the product of their ages was 120. Find their present ages.

5. Find the whole number such that 3 times its square is 18 more than 25 times the number.

6. A carpet measuring 5 m by 4 m is laid in one corner of a room of area 56 m^2, so that strips of equal width of uncovered floor are left along one side and along one end. Find the width of these strips.

7. The width of a room is equal to the height, the length is 12 m, and the area of the walls is 128 m^2. Find the height.

8. The length of a rectangle is 6 cm more than the width, and the area is 130 cm^2. Find the length, correct to 3 sig. fig..

9. A man buys a certain number of pens for £3·96, and the number of pence that each one costs him is 4 more than the number of pens that he buys. Find the cost of each pen.

10. A stone is thrown upwards, and its height h metres after t seconds is given by the formula $h = 35t - 5t^2$. How long does it take to reach a height of 50 m? Explain the meaning of the double answer.

11. The base of a triangle is 3 cm more than the altitude, and the area is 40 cm^2. Find the length of the base in centimetres, correct to 2 decimal places.

12. A yard is paved with square tiles of a certain size. If the tiles had measured 10 cm less each way, $2\frac{1}{4}$ times as many would have been needed. Find the size of the larger tiles.

13. A room is $9\frac{1}{2}$ m long, the width is $1\frac{1}{2}$ m more than the height, and the area of the walls is 84 m^2. Find the height.

14. A room, 18 m by 14 m, is carpeted so that a border of uncovered floor of uniform width is left all round. If the area of the carpet is 165 m^2, find the width of the border.

15. A square lawn is bounded on three sides by a flower-bed 2 m wide. If the area of the bed is $\frac{7}{8}$ that of the lawn, find the length of a side of the lawn.

16. A length of drain-pipe is made of earthenware 1 cm thick, and the volume of the earthenware is equal to the volume of the space inside the pipe. Find the inside radius of the pipe, correct to 3 sig. fig..

Solution by formula

If the general form of a quadratic equation is taken to be $ax^2 + bx + c = 0$, then the roots are given by the formula

$$x = \frac{-b \pm \sqrt{b^2 - 4ac}}{2a}.$$

Example 12 *Find, correct to 2 decimal places, the roots of the equation* $3x^2 - 7x - 2 = 0$.

Comparing $3x^2 - 7x - 2 = 0$ with $ax^2 + bx + c = 0$,

$a = 3, b = -7, c = -2.$

$$\therefore \ x = \frac{-(-7) \pm \sqrt{(-7)^2 - 4 \times 3 \times (-2)}}{2 \times 3}$$

$$= \frac{7 \pm \sqrt{49 + 24}}{6}$$

$$= \frac{7 \pm \sqrt{73}}{6}$$

$$\simeq \frac{7 \pm 8 \cdot 544}{6}$$

$$= \frac{15 \cdot 544}{6} \text{ or } \frac{-1 \cdot 544}{6}$$

$$\simeq 2 \cdot 59 \text{ or } -0 \cdot 26.$$

Exercise 10e

Use the formula to solve the following equations, giving the roots correct to 2 decimal places where necessary.

1. $x^2 - 4x + 3 = 0$ 2. $x^2 + 2x - 3 = 0$
3. $2x^2 + 5x - 12 = 0$ 4. $2x^2 - x + 3 = 0$
5. $2x^2 + x - 3 = 0$ 6. $x^2 + 5x + 2 = 0$
7. $x^2 - 3x - 1 = 0$ 8. $3x^2 - 5x + 1 = 0$
9. $3x^2 + 2x - 4 = 0$ 10. $2x^2 + 8x + 3 = 0$
11. $2x^2 - 7x - 2 = 0$ 12. $3x^2 + x - 7 = 0$
13. $5x^2 - 8x + 2 = 0$ 14. $4x^2 - 11x + 5 = 0$
15. $5x + 7 = \dfrac{2}{x}$ 16. $3x + 2 = \dfrac{5}{x - 3}$

Graphical solution of quadratics will be found in Chapter 24.

Chapter 11

Areas and volumes of similar figures

The ratio of similar **areas** is the **square** of the ratio of corresponding lengths.

The ratio of similar **volumes** is the **cube** of the ratio of corresponding lengths.

Example 1 *A piece of laminated board one metre long and 80 cm wide costs 48p. What would be the cost of a piece of the same shape and 75 cm long?*

$$\text{Ratio of corresponding lengths} = \frac{75 \text{ cm}}{100 \text{ cm}} = \frac{3}{4}$$

$\therefore$ ratio of corresponding areas $= (\frac{3}{4})^2 = \frac{9}{16}$

$\therefore$ cost of smaller piece $= \frac{9}{16}$ of 48p $= 27$p.

Example 2 *Two similarly shaped cans hold respectively 2 litres and 6·75 litres. If the smaller can is 16 cm in diameter, what is the diameter of the larger?*

$$\text{Ratio of volumes} = \frac{6 \cdot 75 \text{ litres}}{2 \text{ litres}} = \frac{27}{8} = \left(\frac{3}{2}\right)^3$$

$\therefore$ ratio of corresponding lengths $= \frac{3}{2}$

$\therefore$ diameter of larger can $= \frac{3}{2}$ of 16 cm $= 24$ cm.

Exercise 11

1. A maker of cylindrical lampshades offers two sizes, respectively 12 cm and 15 cm in diameter. The smaller requires 400 cm² of material. How much is needed for the larger?

2. A bucket 30 cm deep holds 12½ litres. What is the capacity of a similar bucket 24 cm deep?

3. Circular discs are stamped out of a thick sheet of brass: if the mass of a disc of diameter 6 cm is 120 g, what is the mass of one of diameter 15 cm?

4. What is the diameter of a disc from no. 3 if its mass is 270 g?

5. The mass of 100 spherical shot is 150 g. What would be the mass of 100 shot of twice the diameter?

6. A circular piece of dough on the pastry-board is 2·7 cm thick. It is rolled out until its diameter is one and a half times what it was originally. How thick is it then?

7. If an oil-drum with a capacity of 25 litres is 60 cm deep, what is the depth of a similar drum which holds 1·6 litres?

8. A conical vessel is 10 cm deep. If it is half-filled with liquid, what is the depth of the liquid? (2 sig. fig.)

9. A balloon 6 cm in diameter is blown out until its diameter is 12 cm. What multiple of the old surface is the new one, and how is the thickness of the skin affected?

10. A sculptor about to make a marble statue 120 cm high begins by making a plaster model 36 cm high. The mass of the model is 7·2 kg. If the density of plaster is only one-third that of marble, what will be the mass of the finished statue?

11. A dolls' house is made as an exact model of a real house. The real garage door is of area 6·2 m² and that of the corresponding door in the dolls' house 155 cm². If the dolls' house water-butt holds 55 cm³, what is the capacity of the full size one in litres?

12. A man got a set of plans for a model yacht, intending to build one for his son. Unfortunately the plans called for 2·5 kg of lead for the keel, and he could collect only 1·28 kg, so he decided to scale down the plans in such a way that this amount would be sufficient. If the length of the deck in the plan was 1·5 m, how long was the deck of the smaller model? and if the smaller model's sails were 5 760 cm² in area, how much was needed for the sails of the larger version?

Chapter 12

Flow charts

Example 1 *Write a flow chart to draw a pie chart from a given set of values.*

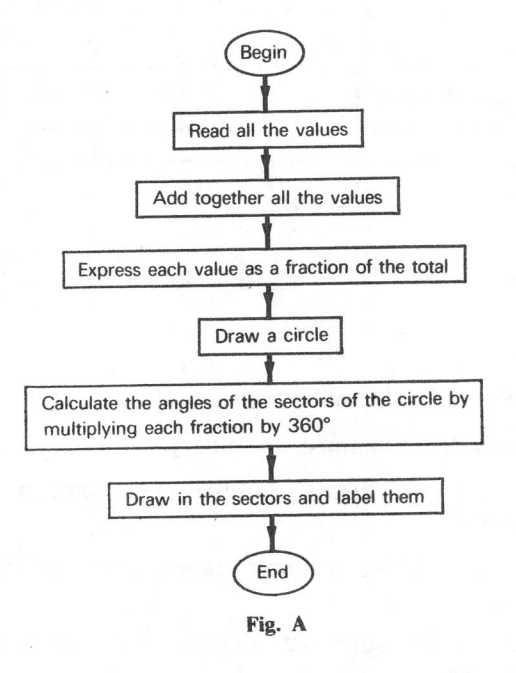

Fig. A

Example 2 *Write a flow chart to read two numbers* A *and* B *and express the smaller as a percentage of the larger.*

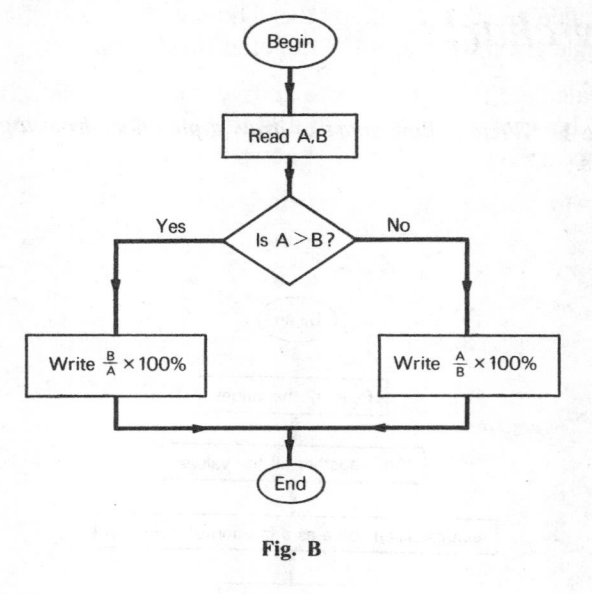

Fig. B

Exercise 12

Write flow charts for the following:

1. To convert denary numbers to binary.

2. To subtract one binary number from another using the complement.

3. To calculate the rate of simple interest given amount, principal and time.

4. To calculate the sum and product of the roots of a given quadratic equation.

5. To read a set of numbers and calculate their mode.

6. To read a set of numbers and calculate their median.

7. To calculate the cost price of an article given its selling price and the percentage profit or loss.

8. To calculate the length of the hypotenuse of a right-angled triangle given the lengths of the other two sides.

9. To calculate the surface area and volume of a solid given the ratio between the height of it and that of a similar solid whose surface area and volume are known.

10. The way you get up in the morning.

Chapter 13

Slide rule

The following flow chart shows how to multiply a by b using a slide rule.

```
                            ┌─────────┐
                            │  Begin  │
                            └─────────┘
                                 │
        ┌────────────────────────────────────────────────┐
        │   Express a and b in standard form             │
        │   as a = a′ × 10ⁿ and b = b′ × 10ᵐ            │
        └────────────────────────────────────────────────┘
                                 │
            ┌────────────────────────────────────────┐
            │   Set 1 on C scale against a′ on D scale │
            └────────────────────────────────────────┘
                                 │
   Yes                ◇ Is b′ on C scale off ◇              No
 ┌───────────────────   the end of D scale?   ───────────────────┐
 │                                                               │
┌──────────────────────┐                        ┌──────────────────────┐
│ Set 10 on C scale    │                        │ Read a′b′ on D scale │
│ against a′ on D scale│                        │ against b′ on C scale│
└──────────────────────┘                        └──────────────────────┘
 │                                                               │
┌──────────────────────────┐                                    │
│ Read a′b′ ÷ 10 on D scale │                                    │
│ against b′ on C scale     │                                    │
└──────────────────────────┘                                    │
 │                                                               │
 └──────────────────┬────────────────────────────────────────────┘
                    │
      ┌──────────────────────────────────┐
      │   Answer is a′b′ × 10ⁿ⁺ᵐ         │
      └──────────────────────────────────┘
                    │
              ┌─────────┐
              │   End   │
              └─────────┘
```

The following flow chart shows how to multiply a by b using a slide rule. Express a and b in standard form as $a = a' \times 10^n$ and $b = b' \times 10^m$. Set 1 on C scale against a' on D scale. Is b' on C scale off the end of D scale? Yes: Set 10 on C scale against a' on D scale. Read $a'b' \div 10$ on D scale against b' on C scale. No: Read $a'b'$ on D scale against b' on C scale. Answer is $a'b' \times 10^{n+m}$.

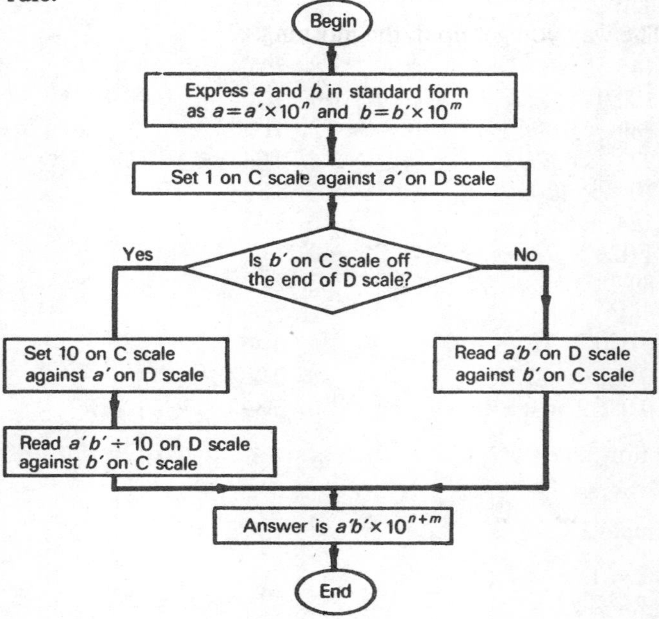

Fig. C

Example 1   *Multiply 52·4 by 0·031 6.*

$$52\cdot4 = 5\cdot24 \times 10^1$$
$$0\cdot031\,6 = 3\cdot16 \times 10^{-2}.$$

1 on C scale against 5·24 on D scale puts 3·16 on C scale off the end of D scale; 10 on C scale against 5·24 on D scale gives 1·656 on D scale against 3·16 on C scale.

$$5.24 \times 3.16 = 1.656 \times 10 = 16.56$$
$$\therefore \quad 52.4 \times 0.031\ 6 = 16.56 \times 10^{1-2}$$
$$= 1.656.$$

Exercise 13a

Use a slide rule to perform the following multiplications:

1. 2.3×3.1	**2.** 3.31×1.82
3. 3.61×4.23	**4.** 5.62×8.31
5. 12.2×2.81	**6.** 35.1×8.98
7. 145×167	**8.** 295×341
9. $1\ 250 \times 0.423$	**10.** $4\ 560 \times 0.026\ 7$
11. $289 \times 0.006\ 17$	**12.** $31\ 200 \times 421$
13. $923 \times 0.069\ 9$	**14.** $0.043\ 6 \times 0.013\ 9$
15. 10.4×12.1	**16.** 8.89×6.79
17. 124×6.83	**18.** 3.43×3.51
19. $1\ 021 \times 20.4$	**20.** 13.6×148
21. 89.2×61.3	**22.** 21.3×32.5
23. 761×0.634	**24.** 256×79.2
25. $2\ 040 \times 31.2$	**26.** $0.468 \times 8\ 230$
27. 0.682×0.731	**28.** $0.057 \times 0.006\ 82$
29. $0.086\ 2 \times 0.538$	**30.** $0.846 \times 0.010\ 11$

The flow chart on page 68 shows how to divide a by b using a slide rule.

Example 2 *Divide* 148 *by* 0.473.

$$148 = 1.48 \times 10^2$$
$$0.473 = 4.73 \times 10^{-1}$$

From slide rule $1.48 \div 4.73 = 0.313$
$$\therefore \quad 148 \div 0.473 = 0.313 \times 10^{2-(-1)}$$
$$= 313.$$

Exercise 13b

Perform the following divisions using a slide rule:

1. $6 \div 4$	**2.** $4 \div 9$
3. $11 \div 13$	**4.** $21 \div 17$
5. $4.8 \div 2.1$	**6.** $3.6 \div 7.1$

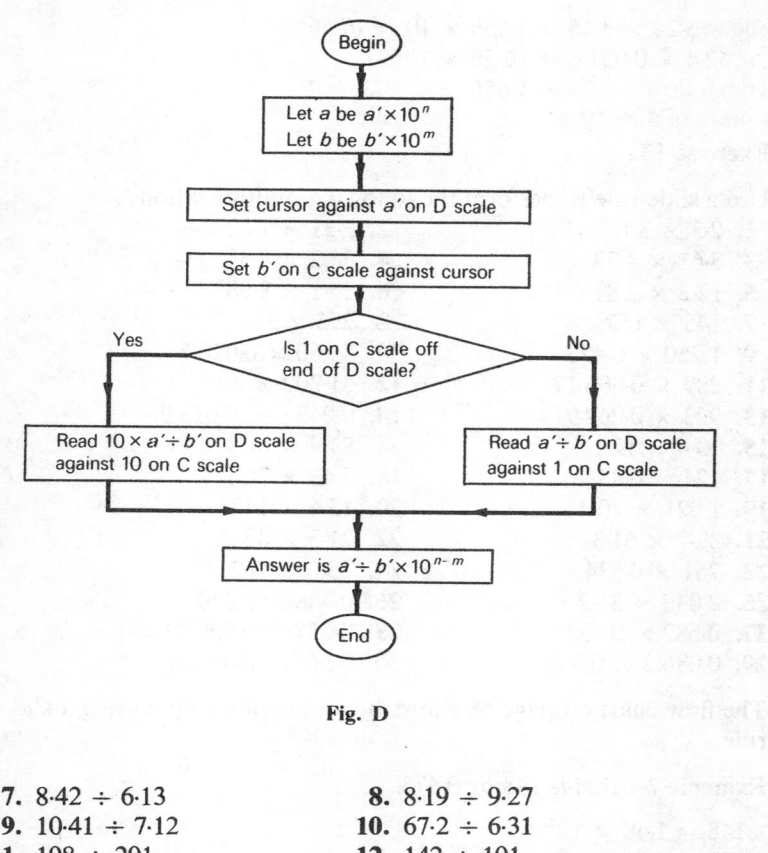

Fig. D

7. $8.42 \div 6.13$	**8.** $8.19 \div 9.27$
9. $10.41 \div 7.12$	**10.** $67.2 \div 6.31$
11. $198 \div 201$	**12.** $142 \div 101$
13. $18.6 \div 791$	**14.** $268 \div 342$
15. $16.2 \div 248$	**16.** $79.8 \div 846$
17. $347 \div 26.2$	**18.** $1\,020 \div 31.3$
19. $41.2 \div 2\,170$	**20.** $169 \div 423$
21. $0.692 \div 0.423$	**22.** $0.521 \div 0.687$
23. $0.423 \div 2.81$	**24.** $0.462 \div 0.089\,1$
25. $0.043\,2 \div 462$	**26.** $0.008\,71 \div 0.768$
27. $0.796 \div 2\,430$	**28.** $4\,620 \div 759$
29. $1\,240 \div 0.004\,62$	**30.** $0.000\,638 \div 0.004\,18.$

Squares

The following flow chart is designed to show how to read the square of a number from a slide rule.

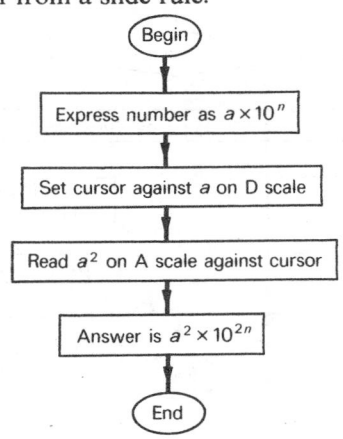

Fig. E

Example 3 *Find the square of* 0·012 7.

$$0·012\,7 = 1·27 \times 10^{-2}$$
From the slide rule $1·27^2 = 1·613$
$$\therefore\ 0·012\,7^2 = 1·27^2 \times 10^{-4}$$
$$= 1·613 \times 10^{-4}$$
$$= 0·000\,161\,3.$$

Exercise 13c

Find the squares of the following numbers:

1. 3·21	**2.** 8·56	**3.** 25·1	**4.** 72·3
5. 0·416	**6.** 0·823	**7.** 421	**8.** 0·046 3
9. 0·016 8	**10.** 1 921	**11.** 7 830	**12.** 0·000 694

Square roots

The following flow chart shows how to find the square root of a number using a slide rule.

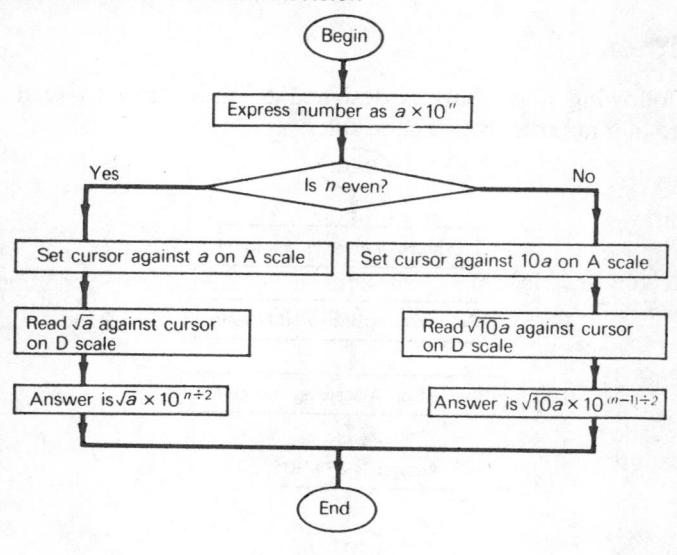

Fig. F

Example 4 *Find the square root of* 6 120.

$6\ 120 = 6.12 \times 10^3 = 61.2 \times 10^2$

From slide rule $\sqrt{61.2} = 7.82$
$$\therefore \sqrt{6\ 120} = 7.82 \times 10^{(3 - 1) \div 2}$$
$$= 7.82 \times 10^1$$
$$= 78.2.$$

Exercise 13d

Find the square roots of the following numbers:

1. 2	**2.** 30	**3.** 6.3
4. 61.2	**5.** 152	**6.** 1 789
7. 58 100	**8.** 629 000	**9.** 0.386
10. 0.033 2	**11.** 0.005 36	**12.** 0.000 002 14

Use a slide rule to evaluate the following:

13. $3\sqrt{2}$	**14.** $\sqrt{7} \div \sqrt{6}$	**15.** $12\sqrt{21}$
16. $\sqrt{42} \times \sqrt{51}$	**17.** $3 \div \sqrt{8}$	**18.** $\sqrt{82} \div \sqrt{27}$
19. $42 \div \sqrt{17}$	**20.** $\sqrt{9.2} \div \sqrt{0.86}.$	

Chapter 14

Trigonometry in a plane

Six ratios

The trigonometrical ratios are defined in terms of the hypotenuse, opposite and adjacent sides of a right-angled triangle as follows:

$$\text{sine } \theta = \frac{\text{opp.}}{\text{hyp.}} \qquad \cosine \theta = \frac{\text{adj.}}{\text{hyp.}} \qquad \text{tangent } \theta = \frac{\text{opp.}}{\text{adj.}}$$

$$\text{cosecant } \theta = \frac{\text{hyp.}}{\text{opp.}} \qquad \text{secant } \theta = \frac{\text{hyp.}}{\text{adj.}} \qquad \text{cotangent } \theta = \frac{\text{adj.}}{\text{opp.}}.$$

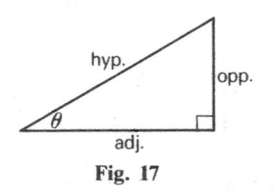

Fig. 17

Example 1 *The hypotenuse of the triangle* ABC *is of length* 10 *cm.* AB̂C = 90° *and* BÂC = 30°. *Find* AB *and* BC.

$$\frac{AB}{10} = \cos 30°$$

∴ AB = 10 cos 30° cm = 10 × 0·866 cm = 8·66 cm

$$\frac{BC}{10} = \sin 30°$$

∴ BC = 10 sin 30° cm = 10 × 0·5 cm = 5 cm.

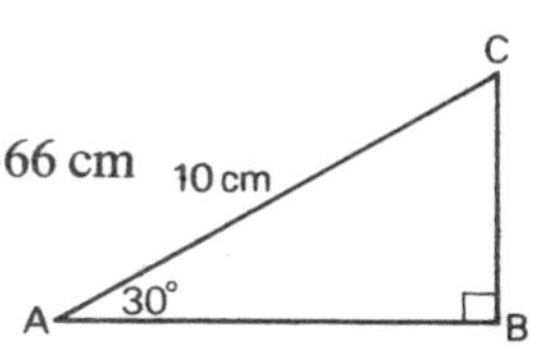

Fig. 18

Example 2 *A wire joins a point on a vertical mast 12 m above ground to a point on the horizontal ground 8 m from the foot of the mast. What is the angle of inclination of the wire to the ground and what is the length of the wire.*

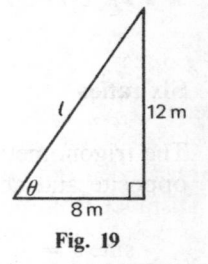

$\tan \theta = \frac{12}{8} = 1 \cdot 5$

$\therefore \theta = 56° 19'$

$\sec \theta = \frac{l}{8}$

$\therefore l = 8 \times \sec 56° 19'$

$\quad = 8 \times 1 \cdot 803\,1$

$\quad = 14 \cdot 424\,8$

Fig. 19

$\therefore$ the angle of inclination is 56° 19' and the length of the wire is 14·4 m.

Note that it is the custom to quote the answer to 3 significant figures when using four-figure tables but that in this case 4 figures would have been possible as the secant is quoted correct to 5 figures, provided that the data is quoted to that accuracy. If it is assumed that the data is quoted only to the nearest metre, then the answer can be quoted only to that accuracy.

Example 3 *From the top of a vertical cliff 100 m high the angle of depression of a buoy out at sea is 10° 14'. Find how far from the foot of the cliff the buoy is and how far from the top of the cliff.*

Note that the angle of depression is the angle between the horizontal and the line joining the buoy and the top of the cliff.

$$\cot 10° 14' = \frac{d}{100}$$

$$\therefore d = 100 \cot 10° 14' = 100 \times 5 \cdot 540\,3$$

$$\simeq 554$$

$$\operatorname{cosec} 10° 14' = \frac{h}{100}$$

$\therefore \ h = \cdot 100 \operatorname{cosec} 10° \ 14' = 100 \times 5 \cdot 629 \ 8$

$\simeq 563.$

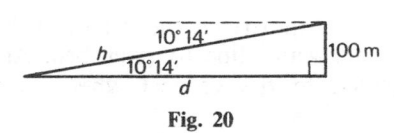

Fig. 20

Distance from buoy to foot of cliff = 554 m
Distance from buoy to top of cliff = 563 m.

Exercise 14

1. An aircraft takes off at an angle of 5° 10′ to the ground. How high is it when it has moved 2 000 m horizontally from take off?

2. When the gradient of a road is described as 1 in 9 it means that it rises 1 m for every 9 m along the road. What is the angle of slope of such a hill?

3. The angle of elevation of the top of a vertical mast from a point on the level ground 240 m away from its foot is $31\frac{1}{2}°$. How high is the mast?

4. The angle of elevation of the top of a cliff from a point on the sea 220 m away from its foot is 23° 20′. The angle of elevation of the top of a lighthouse set on the edge of the cliff from the same point is 26° 48′. What is the height of the lighthouse?

5. A picture is hung from a hook by a cord 90 cm long attached to the picture at two points at the same height and 60 cm apart. What is the inclination to the horizontal of each part of the cord?

6. A tripod consists of three legs each 1·05 m long, the height of the top of the tripod above the ground being 90 cm. What is the inclination to the horizontal of each leg?

7. A man walks 11 km due north from A to B and then 6·5 km due east to C. What is the bearing from A of C and the distance AC?

73

8. The angle of depression of a boat from the bridge of a liner is 2° 24′. If the bridge is 85 m above the water what is the distance from the bridge to the boat?

9. A yacht is anchored in a river, the length of the anchor chain being 22·5 m from water line to river bed. At what angle is the chain inclined to the vertical when the river is 7·5 m deep?

10. A glider is at a height of 250 m when the wire between it and the ground is inclined at 25° to the vertical. What is the length of the wire?

11. A plank rests with one end on the ground and the other end on the back of a lorry 1·2 m above the ground. The plank is inclined at 21° to the ground. How long is the plank?

12. A yacht sails 5 km from A to B on a bearing of 035° and then 6 km from B to C on a bearing of 125°. What is the distance and bearing of C from A?

13. The angle of elevation of the top of a building from a point on the ground 150 m away from the foot of the building is 17°. What is the height of the building?

14. A ladder 4 m long rests against the side of a house such that its foot is 1·6 m from the foot of the house. What is the angle which the ladder makes with the horizontal?

15. A fishing line is inclined at 42° to the water. The tip of the rod is 4·5 m above the water. What is the length of the line from the tip of the rod to the water?

16. The top of a sloping roof is 1·3 m above the bottom and the length of slope is 2·5 m. What is the angle which the roof makes with the horizontal?

17. The angle of elevation of the top of a radio mast, known to be 124 m high, from a certain point at the same level as its foot is 22° 10′. What is the distance between the foot of the mast and the given point?

18. The angle of elevation of the top of a hill 895 m high from a point 205 m high is 10° 12′. What is the distance between the two points?

19. The shallow end of a swimming pool is 1 m deep and the deep end is 3·6 m. If the length is 50 m and the slope constant what angle does the bottom of the pool make with the horizontal?

20. The ridge of a tent is 1·25 m from the ground and the width of the tent is 1·7 m. Find the angle between each side of the tent and the horizontal.

Chapter 15
Everyday arithmetic

Rates

A householder's **rates** are his share of the total amount that has to be paid for all the services provided: a typical rating scheme is set out on page 77.

The **rateable value** of a property is a calculated figure which is used as a basis for the actual rate charged.

Example 1   *The rateable value of a house is £174 and the rates are 67p in the £. What annual rate is payable (nearest penny)?*

On £1 the rate is 67p
∴ on £174 the rate is 174 × 67p = 11 658p
   = £116·58.

Example 2   *The estimated products of a penny rate in (a) a district, (b) a county are respectively £10 684 and £392 755. If the total amounts required by district and county are respectively £128 893 and £23 846 748, what were the actual rates in the pound (nearest penny)?*

(a) Rate for district = 128 893 ÷ 10 684p = 12p,
(b) Rate for county = 23 846 748 ÷ 392 755p = 61p.

Exercise 15a

1. In 1976 Richard Roe owned a house in Tootham of which the rateable value was £139. What rate did he pay (a) to the borough, (b) to the county? (See table.)

Borough of Tootham (Total rateable value £684 617) Budget of expenses for year ending 31 March, 1976			
Purpose	Borough p	County p	Total p
Education	—	52·38	52·38
Public health	2·27	4·52	6·79
Social services	3·14	6·05	9·19
Police	—	7·46	7·46
Fire service	—	2·18	2·18
Highways and bridges	0·65	12·64	13·29
Car parks	0·14	—	0·14
Refuse collection	2·36	—	2·36
Parks and gardens	0·45	—	0·45
Other services	4·35	8·71	13·06
	13·36	93·94	107·30
Deductions	3·34	35·94	39·28
	10·02	58·00	68·02
Sewerage	6·41	—	6·41
Water service	8·57	—	8·57
TOTALS	25·00	58·00	83·00

2. How much did Richard Roe in no. 1 contribute in 1976 towards (a) education, (b) refuse collection, (c) social services, (d) water?

3. What percentage of Tootham's total rate before deductions goes to education?

4. Mr. John Doe of Tootham paid a total rate of £147·74 in 1976. What was the rateable value of his house?

5. If a Tootham householder's rates in 1976 amounted to £156·87, how much of this sum was earmarked for (a) the police, (b) highways and bridges, (c) parks and gardens?

6. What total expenditure did Tootham's Borough Treasurer budget for in 1976?

7. In 1972 the rates throughout the country were reassessed. For example one rateable value of £95 in 1972 became £136 in 1973. If a man paid 78p in the £ in 1972 and the amounts which he actually paid in cash in these years were the same, what was the rate in 1973?

8. It is proposed to build a sports centre in Tootham at a gross cost of £515 000, this cost to be spread over 25 years. What additional annual cost will this project put on to the rates (per £, to the nearest penny)?

Gas and electricity

Gas 1 unit = 100 megajoules
1 m^3 has calorific value of 38 megajoules

$\therefore 1 \text{ m}^3 = \frac{38}{100}$ units = 0·38 units.

Example 3 *In one quarter a householder uses* 123 *cubic metres of natural gas at* 15·2p *per unit: there is also a standing charge of* 44p *per quarter. What is the householder's gas bill for this quarter?*

No. of m^3 used = 123
$\therefore$ no. of units used = 123 × 0·38
$\therefore$ cost = 123 × 0·38 × 15·2p
= 710·4p
charge = 44p
_____
$\therefore$ total cost = 754·4p
$\simeq$ £7·54.

Electricity

Example 4 *The reading on an electricity meter changes from* 43 328 *to* 43 912 *in one quarter. What is the cost of electricity for the quarter if the first* 75 *units are rated at* 3·81p *and the remainder at* 1·42p?

No of units used = 43 912 − 43 328
$$= 584$$
75 units at 3·81p cost 75 × 3·81p =   285·75p
509 units at 1·42p cost 509 × 1·42p =   722·78p
_____

Total cost = 1 008·53p
≃ £10·09.

Exercise 15b

1. What is the quarterly gas bill for a consumer who uses 89 units of gas at 14·8p per unit, the standing charge being £2·03?

2. What is the cost of 438 units of electricity if the first 82 units are rated at 3·74p per unit and the rest at 0·93p?

3. If the consumer in no. 2 can halve his consumption of electricity, what will his bill be then?

4. A householder uses 96 units of gas at 15·2p per unit and has to pay an additional 'primary charge' of £4·80 per quarter. What is his quarterly bill for gas?

5. One electricity board sells its power to consumers on the 'domestic tariff' in three blocks, the units in block 1 being rated at 3·380p, in block 2 at 1·128p and in block 3 at 0·892p. For one customer the allocations in blocks 1 and 2 are respectively 78 and 68 units, block 3 accounting for the remainder. If his consumption is 617 units what is his total bill?

6. Another customer in the same area as the one in no. 5 uses 823 units: what is his bill?

7. In one quarter a householder's meter indicates a consumption of 234 cubic metres of gas. What will be his gas bill if the rate is 14·7p per unit and the standing charge is £3·62?

8. A householder's electricity meter changes from 21 756 to 22 429 in one quarter. If the first 72 units are rated at 3·78p per unit and the remainder at 0·95p, what is his bill for electricity in this quarter?

Income tax

The basic rates of income tax are apt to vary from year to year, but a typical scheme is shown in the table below, which sets out the rates chargeable on taxable income (i.e. what is left after all deductions have been made):

Basic rate—33 % on first £4 500 of taxable income
Higher rates—38 % on next   500 ,,   ,,   ,,
           43 % ,,   ,, 1 000 ,,   ,,   ,,
           48 % ,,   ,, 1 000 ,,   ,,   ,,
           53 % ,,   ,, 1 000 ,,   ,,   ,,
           58 % ,,   ,, 2 000 ,,   ,,   ,,
           63 % ,,   ,, 2 000 ,,   ,,   ,,
           68 % ,,   ,, 3 000 ,,   ,,   ,,
           73 % ,,   ,, 5 000 ,,   ,,   ,,
           83 % on the remainder.

Allowed as deductions:

  (i) £625 for a single person (or on a wife's earned income),
 (ii) £865 for a man and wife (if wife is not earning),
(iii) £240 for each child under 11,
    £275 ,,   ,,   ,, between 11 and 16,
    £305 ,,   ,,   ,, over 16 receiving full-time education.

If part of a taxpayer's income is derived from investments this part is also liable to a **surcharge** of 10 % on the amount between £1 001 and £2 000, and of 15 % on the amount by which it exceeds £2 000.

Example 5 *A married man with two children aged* 10 *and* 15 *is paid* £2 500 *a year. How much tax does he pay?*

	£	£
Gross income		2 500
Allowances (ii) man and wife	865	
(iii) children	515	
	1 380	1 380
Taxable income		1 120

Tax = 33 % of £1 120 = £369·60.

Example 6 *A widower gets a salary of* £12 100 *a year: he has two children between* 11 *and* 16 *and also two at university. He has an investment income of* £2 800 *and is allowed to deduct* £1 685 *as 'expenses allowance'. How much tax does he pay altogether?*

		£	£
Earned income			12 100
Investment income			2 800
Gross income			14 900
Allowances (i) single man		625	
(ii) 2 schoolchildren		550	
(iii) 2 at university		610	
(iv) expenses		1 685	
		3 470	3 470
Taxable income			11 430

		£
Tax—33 % of £4 500		1 485
38 % „ 500		190
43 % „ 1 000		430
48 % „ 1 000		480
53 % „ 1 000		530

81

58% of	2 000	1 160
63% „	1 430	900·90
	11 430	5 175·90
Surcharge—10% „	1 000	100
15% „	800	120

Total tax   5 395·90.

Exercise 15c

Calculate the amount of income tax due in the following cases.
1. A bachelor earning £2 500 a year.
2. A bachelor paid £25 000 a year.
3. A married man with no children earning £1 900 a year.
4. A widow, with children aged 10 and 13, who gets £1 250 a year.
5. A widower with a salary of £5 800 who has two children at university.
6. A married man with an income of £2 740 a year who has children aged 9 and 13.
7. A married man earning £3 850 a year if he has twin boys aged 10 and a daughter of 15.
8. A married man with children aged 13 and 15 still at school and another, aged 19, at the Technical College. His salary is £6 200 a year and he gets an additional allowance of £562 for Life Insurance premiums paid.
9. A married company director with no children whose salary is £12 500 a year and who has also an investment income of £3 546, if he can claim an expense allowance of £1 468.
10. A married man with children of 15, 17 and 18, the two oldest being students, receives a salary of £44 000 and his income from investments is £4 618. His allowance for expenses is £3 724. What tax does he pay and what percentage is this of his gross income?

Chapter 16

Long multiplication and division

Example 1 *Multiply $m^3 - 2mn^2 - 3n^3$ by $4m - 3n$.*

In the first expression a term containing m^2n might have been expected between m^3 and $-2mn^2$. This means that the expression might have been written as $m^3 + 0m^2n - 2mn^2 - 3n^3$. In practice a gap is left where this term would have appeared. **Separate columns** are kept for like terms.

$$
\begin{array}{l}
m^3 \qquad\quad\ -\ 2mn^2\ -\ 3n^3 \\
4m\ -\ 3n \\
\hline
4m^4 \qquad\quad -\ 8m^2n^2\ -\ 12mn^3 \\
\qquad -\ 3m^3n \qquad\qquad\ +\ 6mn^3\ +\ 9n^4 \\
\hline
4m^4\ -\ 3m^3n\ -\ 8m^2n^2\ -\ 6mn^3\ +\ 9n^4 \\
\hline
\end{array}
$$

Example 2 *Divide $6x^4 + 28x - 17x^3 - 17$ by $2x - 3$.*

The expressions are first arranged so that the terms in each are in the same order of powers (both descending or both ascending), and gaps are left for missing terms.

$$2x - 3 \overline{)6x^4 - 17x^3 \qquad\qquad + 28x - 17} (3x^3 - 4x^2 - 6x + 5$$
$$\underline{6x^4 - 9x^3}$$
$$ - 8x^3$$
$$\underline{ - 8x^3 + 12x^2}$$
$$-12x^2 + 28x$$
$$\underline{-12x^2 + 18x}$$
$$+ 10x - 17$$
$$\underline{+ 10x - 15}$$
$$- 2$$

$\therefore$ the quotient is $3x^3 - 4x^2 - 6x + 5$ and the remainder is -2.

Notice that each term in the quotient is obtained by making the first term in the divisor (i.e. $2x$) divide *exactly* each time, so that when the successive subtractions are done there is no remainder under $6x^4$, or under $-8x^3$, etc.

Exercise 16

Multiply
 1. $a^2 - 2a + 1$ by $2a - 3$
 2. $2d^2 + 5d - 3$ „ $5d + 3$
 3. $3m^2 - 1 - 2m$ „ $2m - 3$
 4. $u^2 + uv + 2v^2$ „ $u - v$
 5. $2x^2 - 3xy + y^2$ „ $3x + 4y$
 6. $m + n + 1$ „ $m - n - 1$
 7. $2a - b + 3$ „ $3a - 2b + 4$
 8. $c^3 + 1 - 3c^2$ „ $2c + 5$
 9. $2d^3 + 3d - 2$ „ $2d + d^2 - 3$
10. $5 + m^2 - 3m$ „ $2m - 3 + m^2$

Divide

11. $x^3 + x^2 - 10x + 8$ oy $x - 2$
12. $2m^3 - 5m^2 + 16$ „ $2m + 3$
13. $6a^3 + 20 - 27a - a^2$ „ $3a - 5$
14. $4d^3 - 21d - 4$ „ $2d - 5$
15. $2a^3 - 13ab^2 - 2b^3 + 2a^2b$ „ $a + 3b$
16. $6m^3 - 22n^3 - m^2n$ „ $2m - 3n$
17. $20x - 31x^2 - 3 + 10x^3$ „ $2x^2 + 1 - 5x$
18. $15c^3 + 31c^2d - 6d^3$ „ $3c^2 + 5cd - 2d^2$
19. $3x^4 - x^3 - 25x^2 - 13x + 25$ „ $3x + 5$
20. $15m + 8m^4 - 3 - 20m^2$ „ $2m^2 - 3m + 1$

Simplify

21. $(a^2 - 3a + 1)(2a - 1) - (2a^2 - 3)(a - 4)$

22. $\dfrac{2m^2 - m - 15}{m - 3} - \dfrac{3m^2 + 14m - 5}{3m - 1}$

23. $(3x - 2y - 1)^2 - (2x - 3y + 1)^2$

24. $(c^2 - cd + d^2)(c + d) + (c^2 + cd + d^2)(c - d)$

25. $\dfrac{3a^2 + 5ab - 2b^2}{a + 2b} + \dfrac{2a^2 - 3ab - 2b^2}{a - 2b}$

Chapter 17

Fractions

Example 1 *Simplify* $\dfrac{2x^2 - 5xy - 3y^2}{6y^2 + xy - x^2}$.

$$\frac{2x^2 - 5xy - 3y^2}{6y^2 + xy - x^2} = \frac{(x - 3y)(2x + y)}{(3y - x)(2y + x)} = -\frac{2x + y}{2y + x}$$

N.B. $x - 3y = -(3y - x)$

$$\therefore \quad \frac{x - 3y}{3y - x} = -1$$

Example 2 *Simplify* $\dfrac{a^2 - a - 6}{a^2 - 25} \times \dfrac{a^2 - 5a}{2a^2 - 7a + 3}$.

$$\frac{a^2 - a - 6}{a^2 - 25} \times \frac{a^2 - 5a}{2a^2 - 7a + 3} = \frac{(a - 3)(a + 2)}{(a - 5)(a + 5)} \times \frac{a(a - 5)}{(2a - 1)(a - 3)}$$

$$= \frac{a(a + 2)}{(a + 5)(2a - 1)}$$

Example 3 *Simplify* $\dfrac{p^3 - q^3}{p^2 + pq - qr - pr} \div \dfrac{p^2 + pq + q^2}{pr - r^2}$.

$$\frac{p^3 - q^3}{p^2 + pq - qr - pr} \div \frac{p^2 + pq + q^2}{pr - r^2}$$

$$= \frac{(p - q)(p^2 + pq + q^2)}{(p + q)(p - r)} \times \frac{r(p - r)}{p^2 + pq + q^2}$$

$$= \frac{r(p - q)}{p + q}$$

Exercise 17a

Simplify the following: if there is no simpler form, say so.

1. $\dfrac{ab + ac}{ab - ac}$

2. $\dfrac{a^2 + ab}{ab + b^2}$

3. $\dfrac{a^2 + b^2}{a + b}$

4. $\dfrac{a^2 - b^2}{ab - a^2}$

5. $\dfrac{x^2 - 4y^2}{x^2 + 2xy}$

6. $\dfrac{m^2 - 2mn + n^2}{m^2 - n^2}$

7. $\dfrac{pq - q^2}{(p - q)^2}$

8. $\dfrac{pq - q^2}{(p + q)^2}$

9. $\dfrac{a^3 - b^3}{a^2 - b^2}$

10. $\dfrac{6 - x - x^2}{x^2 - 4}$

11. $\dfrac{12xy}{9x^2 - 4y^2} \times \dfrac{6xy + 4y^2}{18x^2}$

12. $\dfrac{3ab}{3a^2 - 6ab} \div \dfrac{8ab}{4b^2 - 2ab}$

13. $\dfrac{2p^2 - 6pq}{12q^2} \times \dfrac{9q^2 + 3pq}{p^2 - 9q^2}$

14. $\dfrac{m^2 - 4n^2}{m^2 - 3mn} \times \dfrac{2m^2 - 5mn - 3n^2}{2m^2 - 3mn - 2n^2}$

15. $\dfrac{2x^2 + 3xy - 2y^2}{6x^2 - 5xy + y^2} \div \dfrac{3x^2 - 12y^2}{3x^2 - 7xy + 2y^2}$

16. $\dfrac{ac + bc - ad - bd}{ac - c^2 + cd - ad} \times \dfrac{ac - cd - c^2 + ad}{b^2 - ad + ab - bd}$

17. $\dfrac{x^2 - xy}{y^2 - yz} \div \dfrac{y^2 - xy}{xy - xz}$

18. $\dfrac{p^3 - q^3}{p^3 + q^3} \times \dfrac{p^3 - p^2q + pq^2}{q^3 + q^2p + qp^2}$

19. $\dfrac{a^2 - 2a + 4}{a^2 - 4} \div \dfrac{a^3 + 8}{a^2 + 4a + 4}$

20. $\dfrac{x^2 - xy - 2y^2}{x^2 + 2xy - 3y^2} \times \dfrac{x^2 + 5xy + 6y^2}{3x^2 - 5xy - 2y^2} \div \dfrac{x^2 + 3xy + 2y^2}{x^2 - 4xy + 3y^2}$

Example 4   *Simplify* $2 - \dfrac{4x - y}{2y} + \dfrac{6x^2 + 2y^2}{3xy}$.

$$2 - \frac{4x - y}{2y} + \frac{6x^2 + 2y^2}{3xy} = \frac{12xy - 3x(4x - y) + 2(6x^2 + 2y^2)}{6xy}$$

$$= \frac{12xy - 12x^2 + 3xy + 12x^2 + 4y^2}{6xy}$$

$$= \frac{15xy + 4y^2}{6xy}$$

$$= \frac{y(15x + 4y)}{6xy}$$

$$= \frac{15x + 4y}{6x}$$

Example 5   *Simplify* $\dfrac{3a - 2}{a^2 - 4a} + \dfrac{10}{16 - a^2} - \dfrac{a - 1}{a^2 + 4a}$.

$$\frac{3a - 2}{a^2 - 4a} + \frac{10}{16 - a^2} - \frac{a - 1}{a^2 + 4a}$$

$$= \frac{3a - 2}{a^2 - 4a} - \frac{10}{a^2 - 16} - \frac{a - 1}{a^2 + 4a}$$

$$= \frac{3a - 2}{a(a - 4)} - \frac{10}{(a - 4)(a + 4)} - \frac{a - 1}{a(a + 4)}$$

$$= \frac{(3a - 2)(a + 4) - 10a - (a - 1)(a - 4)}{a(a - 4)(a + 4)}$$

$$= \frac{3a^2 + 10a - 8 - 10a - (a^2 - 5a + 4)}{a(a - 4)(a + 4)}$$

$$= \frac{3a^2 - 8 - a^2 + 5a - 4}{a(a - 4)(a + 4)}$$

$$= \frac{2a^2 + 5a - 12}{a(a - 4)(a + 4)}$$

$$= \frac{(2a - 3)(a + 4)}{a(a - 4)(a + 4)}$$

$$= \frac{2a - 3}{a(a - 4)}$$

Example 6   *If* $x = \dfrac{3y - 2}{2y + 3}$, *express* $\dfrac{x + 1}{2x - 1}$ *in terms of* y.

$$x + 1 = \frac{3y - 2}{2y + 3} + 1 = \frac{3y - 2 + 2y + 3}{2y + 3} = \frac{5y + 1}{2y + 3}$$

$$2x - 1 = \frac{2(3y - 2)}{2y + 3} - 1 = \frac{2(3y - 2) - (2y + 3)}{2y + 3}$$

$$= \frac{6y - 4 - 2y - 3}{2y + 3} = \frac{4y - 7}{2y + 3}$$

$$\therefore \frac{x + 1}{2x - 1} = \frac{5y + 1}{2y + 3} \div \frac{4y - 7}{2y + 3} = \frac{5y + 1}{4y - 7}$$

Exercise 17b

Simplify

1. $\dfrac{2}{3xy} - \dfrac{3}{4yz}$

2. $3 - \dfrac{p - q}{q}$

3. $\dfrac{b}{a^2 - ab} + \dfrac{a + b}{ab}$

4. $\dfrac{1}{2a - 4b} - \dfrac{1}{6a - 12b}$

5. $\dfrac{2}{x + 2} - \dfrac{x - 6}{x^2 - 4}$

6. $\dfrac{2a + b}{a^2 - ab} - \dfrac{2b + a}{ab - b^2}$

7. $\dfrac{7}{2x^2 + x - 6} - \dfrac{3}{x^2 + x - 2}$

8. $\dfrac{7}{a^2 - a - 12} - \dfrac{1}{a^2 + 5a + 6}$

9. $\dfrac{2}{p^2 - 4pq + 4q^2} + \dfrac{3}{p^2 + pq - 6q^2}$

10. $\dfrac{7}{3a^2 + 5ab - 2b^2} - \dfrac{2}{a^2 + 2ab}$

11. $\dfrac{1}{1 - x} + \dfrac{1}{1 + x} + \dfrac{3x - x^2}{x^2 - 1}$

12. $\dfrac{x + 2y}{3x^2 + 2xy - y^2} - \dfrac{x + y}{3x^2 + 5xy - 2y^2}$

13. $a = \dfrac{2b - 3}{3b - 2}$. Express $\dfrac{a + 2}{a - 2}$ in terms of b.

14. $y = \dfrac{1 + 3x}{x - 3}$.   (i) Express x in terms of y.
                 (ii) Express $(x + y)$ in terms of y.

15. $y = \dfrac{3x - 2}{2x + 5}$.   (i) Express x in terms of y.
                 (ii) Find x if $x = 7y$.

Equations

Example 7   *Solve the equation* $\dfrac{3}{x^2 - x - 6} = \dfrac{2}{x^2 - 5x + 6}$.

$$\dfrac{3}{x^2 - x - 6} = \dfrac{2}{x^2 - 5x + 6}$$

$$\therefore \quad \dfrac{3}{(x - 3)(x + 2)} = \dfrac{2}{(x - 3)(x - 2)}$$

Multiply both sides by $(x - 3)(x + 2)(x - 2)$.
Then $3(x - 2) = 2(x + 2)$
$$\therefore \quad 3x - 6 = 2x + 4$$
$$\therefore \quad x = 10$$

Check.   If $x = 10$, $\dfrac{3}{x^2 - x - 6} = \dfrac{3}{100 - 10 - 6} = \dfrac{3}{84} = \dfrac{1}{28}$

$$\dfrac{2}{x^2 - 5x + 6} = \dfrac{2}{100 - 50 + 6} = \dfrac{2}{56} = \dfrac{1}{28}$$

Example 8 *Solve the equation* $\dfrac{2}{2a - 1} = \dfrac{3}{4a + 1} + \dfrac{1}{3}$.

$$\dfrac{2}{2a - 1} = \dfrac{3}{4a + 1} + \dfrac{1}{3} \qquad\qquad \times 3(2a - 1)(4a + 1)$$

$\therefore\ 6(4a + 1) = 9(2a - 1) + (2a - 1)(4a + 1)$

$\therefore\ 24a + 6 = 18a - 9 + 8a^2 - 2a - 1$

$\therefore\ 8a^2 - 8a - 16 = 0$

$\therefore\ a^2 - a - 2 = 0$

$\therefore\ (a - 2)(a + 1) = 0$

$\qquad\qquad \therefore\ a = 2 \text{ or } -1$

Check. If $a = 2$, L.H.S. $= \frac{2}{3}$
$\qquad\qquad$ R.H.S. $= \frac{3}{9} + \frac{1}{3} = \frac{2}{3}$
$\qquad$ If $a = -1$, L.H.S. $= -\frac{2}{3}$
$\qquad\qquad$ R.H.S. $= -\frac{3}{3} + \frac{1}{3} = -\frac{2}{3}$

Exercise 17c

Solve the following equations.

1. $\dfrac{2}{x} = 3 + 2x$
$\qquad\qquad\qquad$ **2.** $x = \dfrac{3}{x - 2}$

3. $a - 2 = \dfrac{3a - 2}{a + 4}$
$\qquad\qquad$ **4.** $p + 2 = \dfrac{4}{p + 2}$

5. $\dfrac{x}{x + 2} = \dfrac{x + 2}{2x + 1}$
$\qquad\qquad$ **6.** $\dfrac{1}{x} = \dfrac{4}{5} - \dfrac{6}{x + 5}$

7. $\dfrac{2}{9} + \dfrac{1}{p + 1} = \dfrac{1}{p - 5}$
$\qquad$ **8.** $\dfrac{b - 2}{b + 1} = \dfrac{b + 6}{2b + 5}$

9. $\dfrac{5}{x - 3} - \dfrac{7}{4x} = \dfrac{1}{x - 1}$
$\qquad$ **10.** $\dfrac{1}{m - 1} + \dfrac{9}{2m + 3} = \dfrac{8}{m + 4}$

11. $\dfrac{2x + 5}{x^2 - 4} = \dfrac{5}{x + 2}$

91

12. $\dfrac{5}{x^2 - 6x + 8} = \dfrac{4}{x^2 - 7x + 12}$

13. $\dfrac{a + 3}{a^2 - 1} = \dfrac{a + 1}{a^2 - 3a + 2} - \dfrac{3}{a^2 - a - 2}$

14. $\dfrac{7}{3x - 1} = \dfrac{x - 1}{x + 1} + \dfrac{12}{3x^2 + 2x - 1}$

15. $\dfrac{4x - 5}{x^2 + 3x + 2} = \dfrac{3}{x^2 + x - 2} + \dfrac{2x - 5}{x^2 - 1}$

Problems involving fractions

Example 9 *In a 60-km bicycle race a rider calculates that, if he can increase his speed by 6 km h^{-1} he will cut his time for the distance by 20 minutes. What was his original speed?*

Let original speed be v km h^{-1}:

$$\text{then time taken} = \frac{60}{v}h$$

Improved speed is $(v + 6)$ km h^{-1}:

$$\text{then time taken} = \frac{60}{v + 6}h$$

But the first time is $\frac{1}{3}$ h (20 min) longer than the second,

$\therefore \quad \dfrac{60}{v} - \dfrac{60}{v + 6} = \dfrac{1}{3} \qquad \times 3v(v + 6)$

$\therefore \quad 180(v + 6) - 180v = v(v + 6)$

$\therefore \quad 180v + 1\,080 - 180v = v^2 + 6v$

$\therefore \quad v^2 + 6v - 1\,080 = 0$

$\therefore \quad (v - 30)(v + 36) = 0$

$\therefore \quad v = 30 \text{ or } -36$

But -36 is an unsuitable result,
$\therefore$ original speed is 30 km h^{-1}.

Check.   Original time $= \frac{60}{30}\text{h} = 2\text{ h}$
Improved time $= \frac{60}{36}\text{h} = 1\frac{2}{3}\text{ h}$
Difference $= \frac{1}{3}\text{h} = 20\text{ min.}$

Alternatively the initial working may be tabulated:

	Speed (km h^{-1})	Distance (km)	Time (h)
Original	v	60	$\dfrac{60}{v}$
Improved	$v + 6$	60	$\dfrac{60}{v + 6}$

Hence $\dfrac{60}{v} - \dfrac{60}{v + 6} = \dfrac{1}{3}$ etc., as before.

Example 10   *A trader bought a barrel of apples for £6. He sold all but 5 kg at 3p per kg more than they cost him and his total profit was 30p. What was the mass of apples in the barrel originally?*

Let original mass be x kg.

	No. of kg	Total price (p)	Cost per kg (p)
Bought	x	600	$\dfrac{600}{x}$
Sold	$x - 5$	630	$\dfrac{630}{x - 5}$

$$\frac{630}{x - 5} - \frac{600}{x} = 3$$

$$\therefore \frac{210}{x - 5} - \frac{200}{x} = 1$$

$$\therefore 210x - 200(x - 5) = x(x - 5)$$

$$\therefore 210x - 200x + 1\,000 = x^2 - 5x$$

$$\therefore x^2 - 15x - 1\,000 = 0$$

$$\therefore (x - 40)(x + 25) = 0$$

$$\therefore x = 40 \text{ or } -25$$

But -25 is unsuitable,

$\therefore$ barrel originally held 40 kg.

Check.   40 kg for 600p = 15p per kg

35 kg for 630p = 18p per kg

$\therefore$ profit = 3p per kg.

Exercise 17d

1. A light aircraft has to travel to an airfield 320 km distant from the starting point, the wind blowing steadily from start to finish at 40 km h^{-1} along the line of flight. If the total travelling time out and back is 3 h 20 min, what is the speed of the aircraft in still air?

2. A woman giving a children's party bought a number of identical toys for £1·80. If these had cost 2p each less she could have bought one more toy than she did. How many did she buy?

3. In his will a man left £300 to be divided equally among his surviving grandchildren. By the time he died the number of grandchildren had increased by two, so that the individual shares went down by £25. How much did each grandchild get?

4. A cyclist planned a 60-km journey at a certain speed. If he had increased this speed by 4 km h^{-1} the time would have been less by half an hour. What was the planned speed?

5. My normal time from Rugby to London (135 km) is increased by 1 h 12 min owing to fog, which reduces my average speed by 30 km h⁻¹. What is my normal speed?

6. A man bought a job lot of secondhand golf balls for £1·20. Six of them were unsaleable but, by selling the rest at a profit of 4p each, his total profit on the deal was 20p. How many did he buy?

7. If the price of jam is reduced by two pence per pot you get four more pots than before for £1·60. What was the original price per pot?

8. Alf bicycles to a place 20 km away: Bert's route to the same place is 4 km longer, but he rides 2 km h⁻¹ faster than Alf and gets there 5 minutes later. What are their speeds?

9. A boat's crew can row at 14 km h⁻¹ in still water. If it takes them an hour and three quarters to row 10 km upstream and back again, how fast is the current?

10. When seaside 'rock' is made it is first made into thick ropes 3·6 m long and is then cut into lengths. A maker found that by shortening the lengths by $1\frac{1}{2}$ cm he could get one more piece out of a rope. What was the original length of a piece?

11. Two places are 270 km apart by rail and 288 km by road. A train averages 27 km h⁻¹ more than a car, and the car takes 2 h 24 min longer over the journey. What are the average speeds of train and car?

12. A motor-launch goes upstream from its moorings and back again on a river running at 3 km h⁻¹. Its average speed for the double journey is 14·4 km h⁻¹. What would be its speed in still water? Does the distance involved matter?

Chapter 18

Literal equations. Change of subject

Example 1   *Solve for x the following equations*:

$$\text{(i) } px - p^2 = qx - q^2$$

$$\text{(ii) } a = \frac{b + x}{b - x}$$

$$\text{(iii) } mn = \sqrt{m^2 - x^2}.$$

(i) $px - p^2 = qx - q^2$

$\therefore\ px - qx = p^2 - q^2$

$\therefore\ x(p - q) = (p + q)(p - q)$

$\therefore\ x = p + q$

(ii) $a = \dfrac{b + x}{b - x}$

$\therefore\ a(b - x) = b + x$

$\therefore\ ab - ax = b + x$

$\therefore\ ab - b = ax + x$

$\therefore\ b(a - 1) = x(a + 1)$

$\therefore\ x = \dfrac{b(a - 1)}{a + 1}$

(iii) $mn = \sqrt{m^2 - x^2}$

$\therefore\ m^2 n^2 = m^2 - x^2$

$\therefore\ x^2 = m^2 - m^2 n^2$

$\qquad = m^2(1 - n^2)$

$\therefore\ x = \pm m\sqrt{1 - n^2}$

Exercise 18a

Solve for x the following equations:

1. $px + q = x$

2. $\dfrac{m}{x} + n = p$

3. $\dfrac{x}{a} - \dfrac{x}{b} = c$

4. $m(x + n) = n$

5. $mx = n(m + x)$

6. $x(a + b) = b(c - x)$

7. $p = \dfrac{2q + 3x}{3q - 2x}$

8. $\sqrt{x} = a$

9. $a\sqrt{x} = b$

10. $\sqrt{ax} = 2b$

11. $\sqrt{x + a} = b$

12. $\sqrt{x} + a = b$

13. $\sqrt{x^2 + a^2} = b$

14. $p\sqrt{x - 1} = q$

15. $\dfrac{p}{p + x} = \dfrac{q}{q - x}$

16. $\dfrac{p}{q - x} = \dfrac{q}{p + x}$

17. $a(a^2 - x) = b(b^2 - x)$

18. $\dfrac{x}{x + p} - \dfrac{p}{q + x} = 1$

19. $\sqrt{a^2 - bx} = a - b$

20. $\dfrac{1}{p} - \dfrac{2}{2x - p} = \dfrac{1}{x + p}$

Formulae, change of subject

Example 2 *Make P the subject of the formula* $R = \dfrac{Q^2 - PR}{Q + P}$

$R = \dfrac{Q^2 - PR}{Q + P}$

$\therefore\ RQ + RP = Q^2 - PR$

$\therefore\ 2PR = Q^2 - RQ$

$\therefore\ P = \dfrac{Q^2 - RQ}{2R} = \dfrac{Q(Q - R)}{2R}$

Example 3 *Make r the subject of the formula* $V = \frac{4}{3}\pi r^3$.

$$V = \frac{4}{3}\pi r^3$$

$$\therefore\ r^3 = \frac{3V}{4\pi}$$

$$\therefore\ r = \sqrt[3]{\frac{3V}{4\pi}}$$

Exercise 18b

Rearrange the following formulae, taking as 'subject' the letter printed in heavy type after each one. If there are two letters make each in turn the subject.

1. $R = \dfrac{N - M}{D}$ **M**

2. $T = a + bN^2$ **N**

3. $\dfrac{P + 3Q}{Q - 3P} = \dfrac{x}{y}$ **Q**

4. $v^2 = u^2 - 2as$ **s, u**

5. $E = \dfrac{m}{2g}(v^2 - u^2)$ **u**

6. $e = \dfrac{P - p}{PT - pt}$ **p**

7. $T - W = \dfrac{Wv^2}{gx}$ **W**

8. $t = 2\pi\sqrt{\dfrac{l}{g}}$ **g**

9. $V = \pi r^2(h + \frac{2}{3}r)$ **h**

10. $v = \sqrt{gd\left(1 + \dfrac{3h}{d}\right)}$ **h, d**

11. $A = \pi r\sqrt{h^2 - r^2}$ **h**

12. $d = \sqrt[3]{\dfrac{P}{Q - P}}$ **Q, P**

13. $T = 2\pi\sqrt{\dfrac{h^2 + k^2}{2gh}}$ **k**

14. $e = \sqrt{\dfrac{t - k}{k(1 + kt)}}$ **t**

15. $n = \sqrt{\dfrac{m^2 - 2p^2}{2m^2 + p^2}}$ **p**

16. $C = 2\pi r$, $V = \pi r^2 h$.

Express r in terms of C and π. Hence find a formula with V as subject, eliminating r.

17. $A = \pi r(r + 2h)$, $C = r + h$.

Find a formula   (i) with subject A, eliminating h,

(ii) with subject A, eliminating r.

18. $V = \pi r^2(h + \frac{2}{3}r)$, $S = \pi r(3r + 2h)$.

Eliminate h and deduce a formula expressing V in terms of S, r and π.

Chapter 19

Circle theorems

Chords of a circle

(i) The line joining the centre of a circle to the mid-point of a chord is perpendicular to the chord.
(ii) Equal chords are equidistant from the centre (and conversely).
(iii) In equal circles equal chords are equidistant from the centres (and conversely).

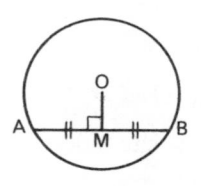

Fig. 21

Example 1 *A 7-cm chord is 2 cm from the centre of a circle. How far is a 1-cm chord from the centre?*

From Fig. 22
$$r^2 = 2^2 + 3.5^2 = x^2 + 0.5^2$$
$$\therefore x^2 = 4 + 12.25 - 0.25$$
$$= 16$$
$$\therefore x = 4$$
∴ the 1-cm chord is 4 cm from the centre.

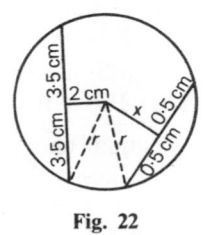

Fig. 22

Exercise 19a

1. A chord 8·4 cm long is 5·6 cm from the centre of a circle. Find the radius of the circle.

2. How far from the centre of a circle of radius 6·5 cm is a chord of length 5 cm?

3. A chord of a circle of radius 8·5 cm is 4 cm from the centré. How long is the chord?

4. A straight line cuts off chords of lengths 14 cm and 2 cm on two equal circles (Fig. 23), the distance of the line from one centre being twice that from the other. What are these distances?

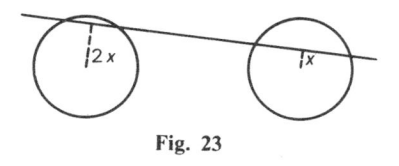

Fig. 23

5. How far apart are opposite sides of a regular hexagon with sides 5 cm long? (3 sig. fig.)

6. Two concentric circles have a common centre O. A straight line $\overline{PXYQ}$ cuts one circle at P and Q and the other at X and Y. Prove PX = QY.

7. Two circles with centres A and B intersect at X and Y. Prove that $\overline{AB}$ bisects $\overline{XY}$ at right angles.

8. Two circles with centres X and Y intersect at A and B, and $\overline{AXM}$, $\overline{AYN}$ are diameters of the circles. Assuming the result of no. 7, prove that the straight line $\overline{MN}$ passes through B and that MN = 2XY.

9. $\overline{AB}$ and $\overline{DC}$ are equal chords of a circle ABCD. $\overline{AB}$ and $\overline{DC}$, when produced, intersect at X. Prove XB = XC.

10. Two circles APQC and BPQD intersect at P and Q. The lines $\overline{APB}$ and $\overline{CQD}$ are parallel. Prove that AC = BD.

11. In a circle with centre O equal chords $\overline{AB}$ and $\overline{CD}$ intersect inside the circle at Q, and O lies within the angle $A\hat{Q}C$. Prove AQ = CQ.

12. AB and CD are parallel chords of a circle, on opposite sides of the centre O, and $\overline{OP}$, $\overline{OQ}$ are the perpendiculars from O on to $\overline{AB}$ and $\overline{CD}$ respectively. Prove $AB^2 - CD^2 = 4PQ(OQ - OP)$. Find a similar result if the chords are on the same side of O.

Circle theorems

Theorem. The angle which an arc of a circle subtends at the centre of the circle is twice that which it subtends at any point on the remaining part of the circumference.

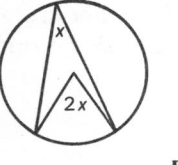 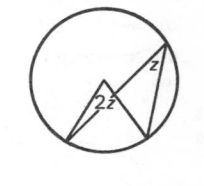

Fig. 24

Theorem. Angles in the same segment of a circle are equal.

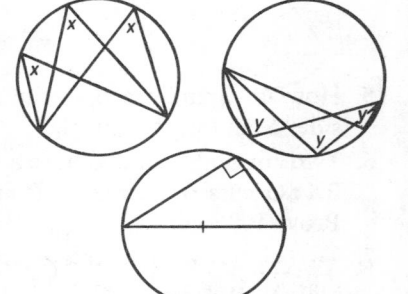

Theorem. The angle in a semi-circle is a right angle.

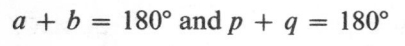

Theorem. The opposite angles of a cyclic quadrilateral are supplementary.

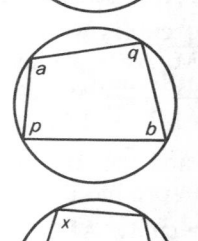

$a + b = 180°$ and $p + q = 180°$

Corollary. If one side of a cyclic quadrilateral is produced, the exterior angle so formed is equal to the interior opposite angle.

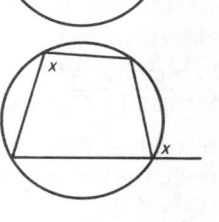

Fig. 25

Exercise 19b

In each of the following figures find the marked angle (some construction lines may be necessary). Simply draw the figures and mark in the angles as they are found: no 'proof' required.

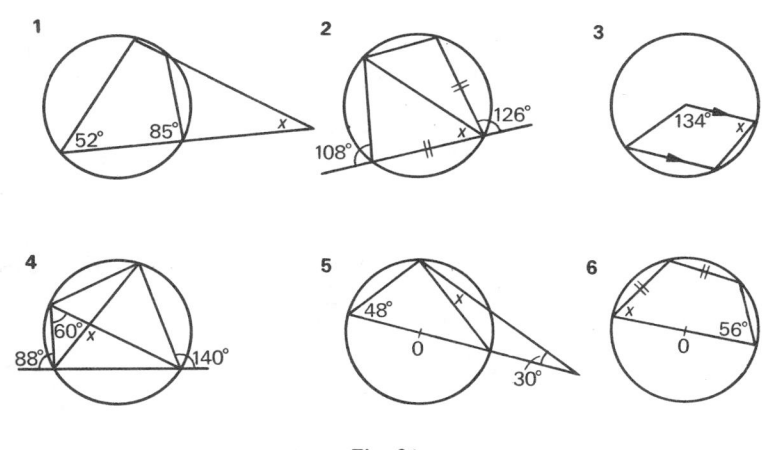

Fig. 26

7. Two circles AXYD and BXYC intersect in X and Y, and $\overline{AXB}$ is a straight line. If $\overline{AD}/\!/\overline{BC}$ prove that $\overline{CYD}$ is also a straight line.

8. Two circles PABY and QABZ intersect at A and B, and $\overline{YBZ}$ is a straight line. $\overline{YP}$ produced cuts $\overline{ZQ}$ produced at X. Prove that XPAQ is a cyclic quadrilateral.

9. PABR and QABS are two circles intersecting at A and B, and $\overline{PAQ}$, $\overline{RBS}$ are straight lines. Prove $P\hat{B}Q = R\hat{A}S$.

10. ADC is an isosceles triangle having DA = DC, and B is any point on $\overline{AC}$. The circle on $\overline{AB}$ as diameter cuts $\overline{DA}$ at E. If O is the centre of this circle prove that OEDC is a cyclic quadrilateral.

11. $\overline{OA}$ and $\overline{OB}$ are radii of a circle centre O and $A\hat{O}B$ is obtuse. X is a point on the minor arc AB such that $\overline{AX}/\!/\overline{OB}$. Prove that $A\hat{O}B = 2O\hat{B}X$.

103

12. $\overline{AOB}$ is a diameter of a circle centre O. Any chord $\overline{XY}$ of the circle is produced to cut $\overline{AOB}$ produced at Z. Prove that $\widehat{XYB} = 90° + X\widehat{B}A$.

13. Two circles ABCD and ABPQ cut at A and B, and $\overline{ACP}$, $\overline{BDQ}$ are straight lines. Prove $\overline{CD}/\!/\overline{PQ}$.

14. AFBCD is a cyclic pentagon; $\overline{BA}$ is produced to E; $\overline{FA}$ produced bisects $E\widehat{A}D$. Prove that $\overline{FC}$ bisects $B\widehat{C}D$.

15. Two circles S_1 and S_2 intersect at A and B, and the centre O of circle S_2 lies on the circumference of circle S_1. $\overline{PQOR}$ is a straight line, P lying on S_1, Q and R on S_2. Prove that $\overline{QA}$ bisects $P\widehat{A}B$.

16. ABCD is a rectangle. A straight line through C at right angles to $\overline{AC}$ cuts $\overline{AB}$ produced and $\overline{AD}$ produced at P and Q respectively. Prove B, D, Q, P concyclic.

17. ABC is any triangle. A circle cuts internally the sides $\overline{AB}$, $\overline{BC}$, $\overline{CA}$ of the triangle at P, U; T, S; R, Q respectively. Prove that $A\widehat{P}Q + C\widehat{R}S + B\widehat{T}U = 180°$.

18. $\overline{AB}$ is a diameter of a circle ABCD. $\overline{CA}$ bisects $B\widehat{A}D$, and $\overline{BC}$ produced cuts $\overline{AD}$ produced at E. Prove that the triangle CDE is isosceles.

19. $\overline{AB}$ is a diameter of a circle ABCD, and AD = DC. $\overline{AC}$ and $\overline{BD}$ intersect at P. Prove $A\widehat{P}B = D\widehat{C}B$.

20. Two equal circles XAB and ZABY intersect at A and B, and $\overline{XAZ}$, $\overline{XBY}$ are straight lines. If $\overline{AY}$ and $\overline{BZ}$ intersect at P, prove that $A\widehat{P}B = 3\widehat{X}$.

Chapter 20

Surds

Example 1 *Simplify* $\sqrt{72} \times \sqrt{75}$.

Simplify each surd first. Then take whole numbers with whole numbers and surds with surds.

$$\sqrt{72} \times \sqrt{75} = \sqrt{36 \times 2} \times \sqrt{25 \times 3}$$
$$= 6\sqrt{2} \times 5\sqrt{3}$$
$$= 30\sqrt{6}$$

Example 2 *Express the fraction* $\dfrac{3}{\sqrt{5}}$ *with a rational denominator.*

$$\frac{3}{\sqrt{5}} = \frac{3 \times \sqrt{5}}{\sqrt{5} \times \sqrt{5}}$$
$$= \frac{3\sqrt{5}}{5}$$

Example 3 *Simplify* $5\sqrt{18} - 3\sqrt{72} + 4\sqrt{50}$.

$$5\sqrt{18} - 3\sqrt{72} + 4\sqrt{50} = 5\sqrt{9 \times 2} - 3\sqrt{36 \times 2} + 4\sqrt{25 \times 2}$$
$$= 5 \times 3\sqrt{2} - 3 \times 6\sqrt{2} + 4 \times 5\sqrt{2}$$
$$= 15\sqrt{2} - 18\sqrt{2} + 20\sqrt{2}$$
$$= 17\sqrt{2}$$

Example 4 *Simplify* $\dfrac{2\sqrt{5} \times 7\sqrt{2}}{\sqrt{14} \times \sqrt{45}}$.

$$\frac{2\sqrt{5} \times 7\sqrt{2}}{\sqrt{14} \times \sqrt{45}} = \frac{2\sqrt{5} \times 7\sqrt{2}}{\sqrt{7 \times 2} \times \sqrt{9 \times 5}}$$

$$= \frac{2\sqrt{5} \times 7\sqrt{2}}{\sqrt{7} \times \sqrt{2} \times 3\sqrt{5}}$$

$$= \frac{2 \times 7}{3\sqrt{7}}$$

$$= \frac{2\sqrt{7}}{3}$$

Exercise 20

Simplify the following by making the number under the square root sign as small as possible:

1. $\sqrt{18}$ **2.** $\sqrt{28}$ **3:** $\sqrt{108}$ **4.** $\sqrt{44}$ **5.** $\sqrt{175}$

Express each of the following as the square root of a single number:

6. $2\sqrt{6}$ **7.** $3\sqrt{7}$ **8.** $5\sqrt{6}$ **9.** $12\sqrt{2}$ **10.** $7\sqrt{3}$

Simplify the following by rationalising the denominators:

11. $\dfrac{2}{\sqrt{3}}$ **12.** $\dfrac{8}{\sqrt{2}}$ **13.** $\dfrac{21}{\sqrt{7}}$ **14.** $\dfrac{10\sqrt{2}}{\sqrt{12}}$ **15.** $\dfrac{2\sqrt{5}}{\sqrt{10}}$

Simplify the following (all denominators in the answers should be rational):

16. $\sqrt{20} + \sqrt{5}$ **17.** $4\sqrt{3} - \sqrt{12}$ **18.** $\dfrac{20}{\sqrt{45}}$ **19.** $\sqrt{\dfrac{72}{75}}$

20. $5\sqrt{7} - \sqrt{28}$ **21.** $\sqrt{11} + \sqrt{44} - \sqrt{99}$

22. $\sqrt{18} - \sqrt{32} + \sqrt{50}$

23. $\dfrac{4\sqrt{5}}{3\sqrt{10}}$ **24.** $\dfrac{12}{\sqrt{162}}$ **25.** $\dfrac{2\sqrt{18}}{3\sqrt{12}}$

26. $3\sqrt{27} - \sqrt{48} - 2\sqrt{75} + \sqrt{108}$

27. $\sqrt{3} \times \sqrt{27}$ **28.** $\sqrt{18} \times \sqrt{8}$ **29.** $\sqrt{27} \times \sqrt{15}$

30. $\sqrt{5} \times \sqrt{6} \times \sqrt{10} \times \sqrt{12}$

31. $(\sqrt{3})^3$ **32.** $(\sqrt{2})^6$ **33.** $(3\sqrt{2})^3$

34. $4\sqrt{28} + 5\sqrt{112} - 6\sqrt{63}$ **35.** $3\sqrt{24} - 2\sqrt{216} + 3\sqrt{54}$

36. $2\sqrt{3} - \dfrac{6}{\sqrt{3}} + \dfrac{3}{\sqrt{27}}$ **37.** $\dfrac{3\sqrt{15} \times 2\sqrt{22}}{7\sqrt{2} \times \sqrt{165}}$

38. $\dfrac{3\sqrt{8} \times 5\sqrt{3} \times \sqrt{7}}{\sqrt{42} \times 2\sqrt{3} \times \sqrt{15}}$ **39.** $\dfrac{20}{5\sqrt{20} - 2\sqrt{45}}$

40. $\dfrac{2\sqrt{45} \times 3\sqrt{20} \times 4\sqrt{18}}{\sqrt{6} \times 5\sqrt{27} \times \sqrt{240}}$

Chapter 21

Angles of 45°, 60°, 30°, 0°, 90°

45°   In Fig. 27, ABCD is a square with sides each 1 unit in length.

$$\sin 45° = \frac{CB}{DB} = \frac{1}{\sqrt{2}}$$

$$\cos 45° = \frac{DC}{DB} = \frac{1}{\sqrt{2}}$$

$$\tan 45° = \frac{CB}{DC} = \frac{1}{1} = 1$$

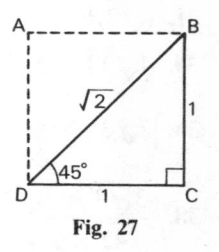

Fig. 27

60°   In Fig. 28, EFG is an equilateral triangle with sides each 2 units in length.

$$\sin 60° = \frac{HE}{FE} = \frac{\sqrt{3}}{2}$$

$$\cos 60° = \frac{FH}{FE} = \frac{1}{2}$$

$$\tan 60° = \frac{HE}{FH} = \frac{\sqrt{3}}{1} = \sqrt{3}$$

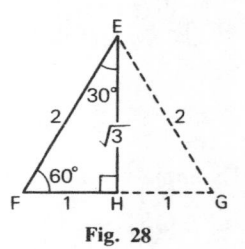

Fig. 28

30°   In Fig. 28,

$$\sin 30° = \frac{FH}{FE} = \frac{1}{2}$$

$$\cos 30° = \frac{HE}{FE} = \frac{\sqrt{3}}{2}$$

$$\tan 30° = \frac{FH}{HE} = \frac{1}{\sqrt{3}}$$

$\boxed{0°}$ In Fig. 29, the angle K is nearly 0°.

$$\sin 0° = \frac{LJ}{KJ} = \frac{0}{1} = 0$$

$$\cos 0° = \frac{KL}{KJ} = \frac{1}{1} = 1$$

$$\tan 0° = \frac{LJ}{KL} = \frac{0}{1} = 0$$

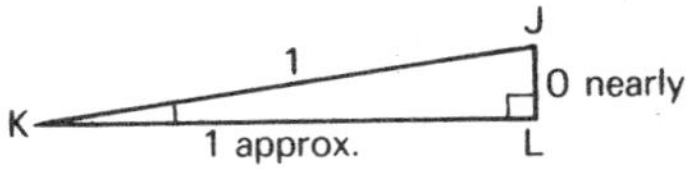

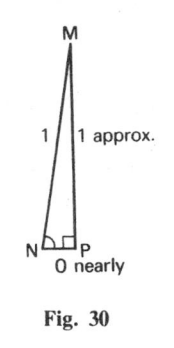

Fig. 29

$\boxed{90°}$ In Fig. 30, the angle N is nearly 90°.

$$\sin 90° = \frac{PM}{NM} = \frac{1}{1} = 1$$

$$\cos 90° = \frac{NP}{NM} = \frac{0}{1} = 0$$

$$\tan 90° = \frac{PM}{NP} = \frac{1}{0} = \infty$$

Fig. 30

Example *In Fig. 31, if* SQ $= 8$ *cm, calculate* RQ *and* RS.

In $\triangle$QST, with angles 30°, 60°, 90°, the sides are in the ratio $1:2:\sqrt{3}$,

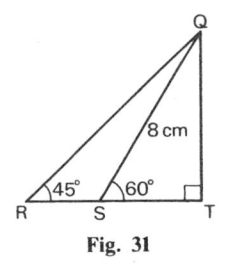

Fig. 31

109

i.e. ST = $\frac{1}{2}$SQ and TQ = $\sqrt{3}$ times ST.

∴ since SQ = 8 cm,

ST = 4 cm and TQ = $4\sqrt{3}$ cm.

In △QRT, with angles 45°, 45°, 90°, the sides are in the ratio 1:1:$\sqrt{2}$,

i.e. RT = TQ and RQ = $\sqrt{2}$ times TQ.

∴ since TQ = $4\sqrt{3}$ cm,

RT = $4\sqrt{3}$ cm and RQ = $4\sqrt{3} \times \sqrt{2}$ cm = $4\sqrt{6}$ cm.

Also RS = RT − ST = $4\sqrt{3}$ cm − 4 cm = $4(\sqrt{3} - 1)$ cm.

Exercise 21

No tables or decimals should be used in this exercise. Answers which are not rational numbers should be given in surd form. Denominators of fractions should be rationalised where necessary.

In nos. 1–9 the length of one side of a triangle is given in centimetres. Find the lengths of the other two sides.

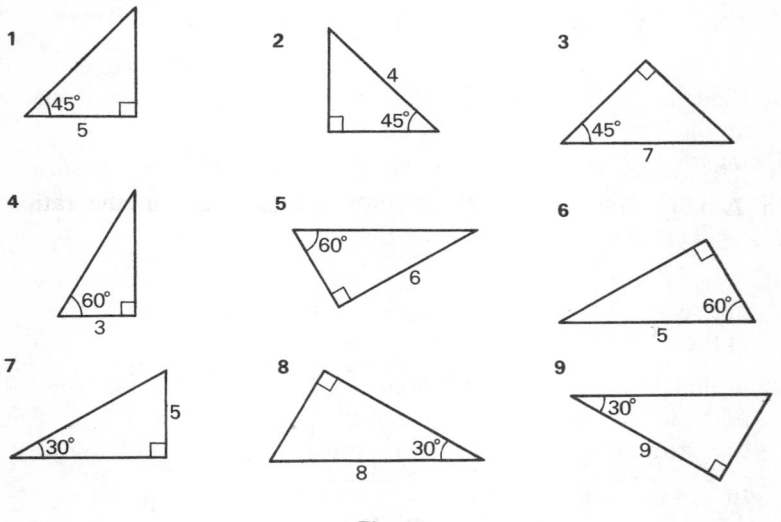

Fig. 32

In nos. 10–18, find the lengths marked *x*. (All lengths given are in cm.)

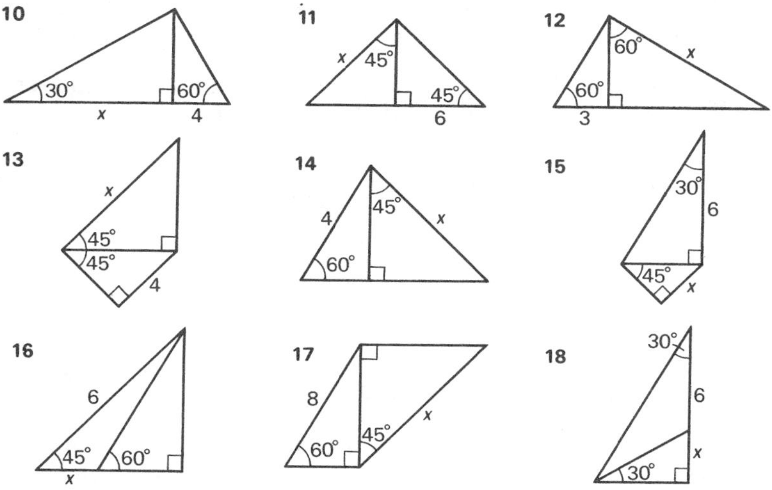

Fig. 33

19. Find the height of a tree which throws a shadow 42 m long on the level ground when the altitude of the sun is 30°.

20. AB is a diameter of a circle, and C is a point on the circumference such that $A\widehat{B}C = 60°$. If the radius of the circle is 3 cm, calculate the lengths of the chords AC and BC.

21. A buoy B is 270 m due east of a buoy A, and a boat which is due south of B is on a bearing of 120° from A. Find the distance of the boat from A.

22. A and B are two observation points 400 m apart, B being north-west of A. A target is north-east of B and on a bearing of 015° from A. Find the distances of the target from A and from B.

23. In △ABC, AB = 7 cm, BC = 5 cm, CA = 3 cm. The altitude AD meets BC produced at D. Calculate CD, and hence find

111

AĈD. (*Let* CD = x cm, *and write down the value of* AD² *in two ways.*)

24. If a mast is 15 m high, how much longer is its shadow when the sun's altitude is 30° than it is when the sun's altitude is 60°?

25. In Fig. 34, $\overline{AB}$ is a rugger goal, and P is the position of a player. If PB = 16 m, calculate the width of the goal.

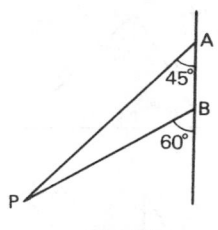

Fig. 34

26. The angle of elevation of the top of a flagstaff from a point at ground level is 30°. From another point on the horizontal ground, 20 m nearer the flagstaff, the angle of elevation is 60°. Find the height of the flagstaff.

27. The triangle ABC is right-angled at A, and $\hat{B}$ = twice $\hat{C}$. $\overline{AD}$ is an altitude. If BD = x cm, calculate DC.

28. Fig. 35 represents a jib-crane. The post is vertical, the tie-rod slopes at 30° to the horizontal, and the jib, which is 12 m long, slopes at 45° to the horizontal. Find the length of the tie-rod, and the height of the top of the jib above the ground.

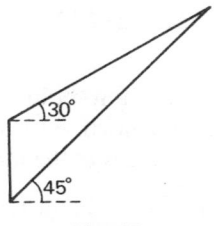

Fig. 35

Chapter 22

Theory of logarithms

If $a^x = N$, then $\log_a N = x$.

Example 1   *Evaluate* (*i*) $\log_3 27$, (*ii*) $\log_4 8$, (*iii*) $\log_5 0.04$.

(i) Let $\log_3 27 = x$
   Then $3^x = 27 = 3^3$
   $\therefore\ x = 3$

(ii) Let $\log_4 8 = x$
   Then $4^x = 8$
   $\therefore\ 2^{2x} = 2^3$
   $\therefore\ 2x = 3$
   $\therefore\ x = 1\frac{1}{2}$

(iii) Let $\log_5 0.04 = x$
   Then $5^x = 0.04 = \frac{1}{25} = 5^{-2}$
   $\therefore\ x = -2$

Exercise 22a

Evaluate the following:

1. $\log_4 16$	**2.** $\log_5 125$	**3.** $\log_9 3$	**4.** $\log_8 32$
5. $\log_{36} 216$	**6.** $\log_{100} 0.1$	**7.** $\log_8 0.25$	**8.** $\log_7 \frac{1}{49}$
9. $\log_{0.2} 25$	**10.** $\log_4 0.125$		

Basic laws

1. $\log(MN) = \log M + \log N$ $a^x \times a^y = a^{x+y}$

2. $\log\left(\dfrac{M}{N}\right) = \log M - \log N$ $a^x \div a^y = a^{x-y}$

3. $\log(M^p) = p \log M$ $(a^x)^p = a^{xp}$

Example 2 *Assuming only that* $\log_{10} 2 = 0{\cdot}301\,0$ *and* $\log_{10} 3 = 0{\cdot}477\,1$, *evaluate* (i) $\log_{10} 9$, (ii) $\log_{10} 12$, (iii) $\log_{10} 15$.

(i) $\log_{10} 9 = \log_{10} 3^2 = 2\log_{10} 3 = 2 \times 0{\cdot}477\,1 = 0{\cdot}954\,2$

(ii) $\log_{10} 12 = \log_{10}(2^2 \times 3) = 2\log_{10} 2 + \log_{10} 3$
$$= 0{\cdot}602\,0 + 0{\cdot}477\,1 = 1{\cdot}079\,1$$

(iii) $\log_{10} 15 = \log_{10}\left(\tfrac{30}{2}\right) = \log_{10} 3 + \log_{10} 10 - \log_{10} 2$
$$= 0{\cdot}477\,1 + 1 - 0{\cdot}301\,0 = 1{\cdot}176\,1$$

Example 3 *Evaluate to 2 decimal places* $\log_4 5{\cdot}83$.

Let $\log_4 5{\cdot}83 = x$

Then $4^x = 5{\cdot}83$

$\therefore\ x\log_{10} 4 = \log_{10} 5{\cdot}83$

$\therefore\ x = \dfrac{\log_{10} 5{\cdot}83}{\log_{10} 4} = \dfrac{0{\cdot}765\,7}{0{\cdot}602\,1} \fallingdotseq 1{\cdot}27$

No.	Log.
0·765 7	$\bar{1}$·884 1
0·602 1	$\bar{1}$·779 7
1·272	0·104 4

Exercise 22b

1. Assuming only that $\log_{10} 2 = 0{\cdot}301\,0$, $\log_{10} 3 = 0{\cdot}477\,1$, $\log_{10} 7 = 0{\cdot}845\,1$, evaluate

    (i) $\log_{10} 8$ (ii) $\log_{10} 81$ (iii) $\log_{10} 8{\cdot}1$ (iv) $\log_{10} 40$
    (v) $\log_{10} 21$ (vi) $\log_{10} \sqrt{60}$ (vii) $\log_{10} 37{\cdot}5$ (viii) $\log_{10} 12{\cdot}25$

2. Evaluate to 3 significant figures

    (i) $\log_2 6$ (ii) $\log_6 2$ (iii) $\log_7 38$ (iv) $\log_{12} 0{\cdot}86$

3. Express as logarithms of single numbers or fractions, all logarithms being to base 10:

    (i) $\log 5 + \log 6$ (ii) $\log 8 - \log 6$ (iii) $3\log 6$
    (iv) $\tfrac{1}{2}\log 49$ (v) $-2\log 4$ (vi) $1 + \log 5$
    (vii) $1 - \log 2$ (viii) $\log 18 - 2\log 2$ (ix) $2 - 2\log 5$
    (x) $\tfrac{3}{5}\log 32$

4. Solve for x
    (i) $\log_{10} x = 3$ (ii) $\log_x 27 = 3$ (iii) $\log_x \tfrac{1}{16} = -\tfrac{1}{2}$

5. Simplify without using tables

(i) $\dfrac{\log 8}{\log 2}$ (ii) $\dfrac{\log 27}{\log 9}$ (iii) $\dfrac{\log \sqrt{8}}{\log 4}$

(iv) $\dfrac{\log 5}{\log 0 \cdot 2}$ (v) $\dfrac{\log 8 - \log 4}{\log 6 - \log 3}$ (vi) $\dfrac{\log 12 - \log 3}{\log 8}$

6. Express the following equations in index form:

(i) $\log_a x = b$ (ii) $\log_a x - \log_a y = 1$ (iii) $\log_a x + 1 = 0$
(iv) $\log_a x = 3 + 2 \log_a y$ (v) $\log_a x - \log_a y = 2 \log_a z$

7. Solve for x the following equations:

(i) $3^x = 1$ (ii) $4^{x+1} = 8^x$
(iii) $2^x \times 2^{3x-1} = 1$ (iv) $2^{2x} - 3 \times 2^x + 2 = 0$
(v) $3^{2x} + 6 \times 3^x - 27 = 0$ (vi) $2^{2x+1} - 9 \times 2^x + 4 = 0$

8. Solve the equation $x + \dfrac{1}{x} = 3\frac{1}{3}$.

Hence find y, correct to 2 decimal places, if $e^y + e^{-y} = 3\frac{1}{3}$ and $e = 2 \cdot 718$.

Chapter 23

Mensuration

Circles, rings, arcs and segments

Area of circle $= \pi r^2$

Circumference of circle $= 2\pi r$

Area of sector $= \dfrac{\theta}{360}$ of πr^2

Length of arc $= \dfrac{\theta}{360}$ of $2\pi r$

π is often taken as $\frac{22}{7}$, as in the following examples.

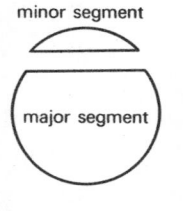

Fig. 36

Example 1   *Find the diameter of a circle of area* 1 386 m^2.

$$\pi r^2 = 1\,386$$
$$\therefore \tfrac{22}{7}r^2 = 1\,386$$
$$\therefore r^2 = 1\,386 \times \tfrac{7}{22} = 63 \times 7 = 9 \times 7^2$$
$$\therefore r = 3 \times 7 = 21$$
$$\therefore \text{diameter} = 42 \text{ m}$$

Example 2   *What is the area of a flat circular disc* 88 *mm in outside diameter with a central hole* 38 *mm in diameter?*

Area $= \pi 44^2 \text{ mm}^2 - \pi 19^2 \text{ mm}^2$
$= \pi (44^2 - 19^2) \text{ mm}^2$
$= \pi (44 + 19)(44 - 19) \text{ mm}^2$
$= \frac{22}{7} \times 63 \times 25 \text{ mm}^2$
$= 4\,950 \text{ mm}^2$

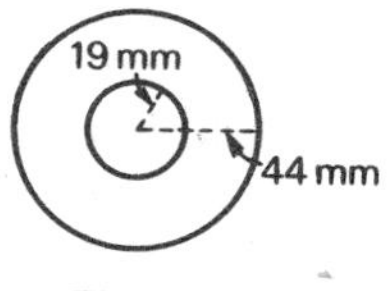

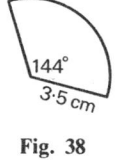

Fig. 37

Example 3 *Find the area and perimeter of a sector of a circle of radius 3·5 cm, the angle of the sector being 144°.*

Area $= \frac{144}{360}$ of $\pi \times 3 \cdot 5^2 \text{ cm}^2 = \frac{144}{360} \times \frac{22}{7} \times \frac{49}{4} \text{ cm}^2 = 15 \cdot 4 \text{ cm}^2$
Arc $= \frac{144}{360}$ of $2\pi \times 3 \cdot 5 \text{ cm} = \frac{144}{360} \times 2 \times \frac{22}{7} \times \frac{7}{2} \text{ cm} = 8 \cdot 8 \text{ cm}$

$\therefore$ perimeter $=$ arc $+ 2r = (8 \cdot 8 + 7) \text{ cm} = 15 \cdot 8 \text{ cm}$

Fig. 38

Exercise 23a

1. The minute-hand of a wall clock is 10·5 cm long. How far does its tip travel in the course of 24 hours?

2. Through what angle does the minute-hand of a clock move in 25 minutes?

3. How many revolutions does a bicycle wheel of diameter 70 cm make in travelling 110 m?

4. Circular discs of diameter 4 cm are punched out of a sheet of brass of mass 0·84 g per cm². What is the mass of 500 discs?

5. If 350 of the discs in no. 4 are obtained from a sheet of brass 80 cm square, what percentage of the sheet is scrap?

6. The winding barrel of a church clock is 17·5 cm in diameter and it requires 18 turns of the winding-handle every day to

117

raise the weight. As the weight hangs in a loop, the length of cord needed is twice as much as the distance the weight has to rise. What length of cord is necessary, allowing an extra 20 cm for clearances?

7. The handle in no. 6 is 35 cm long. How far does the winder's hand travel when winding the clock?

8. What is the diameter to the nearest metre of a circular lake of area exactly one hectare?

9. In a circle of radius 12 cm a chord is drawn which is 6 cm from the centre. What angle does the chord subtend at the centre, and what is the length of the minor arc cut off by the chord?

10. What is the area of the minor segment cut off by the chord in no. 9? (Take $\pi = 3{\cdot}142$ and answer to 3 sig. fig.)

11. A steel washer 3 mm thick is 4·5 cm in diameter with a central hole of diameter 1·5 cm. What is the volume of steel used for 100 washers? ($\pi = 3{\cdot}142$; answer in cm^3 to 3 sig. fig.)

12. The end of a temporary building is in the form of a major segment of a 6-m diameter circle, the chord being 3 m long. What is the area of the segment in square metres? ($\pi = 3{\cdot}142$, answer to 3 sig. fig.)

Cylinders, tanks, etc.

Example 4 *An open rectangular box has external dimensions 32 cm long, 27 cm wide and 15 cm deep. If the box is made of wood 1 cm thick, what area of wood has been used?*

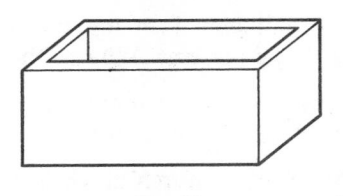

Fig. 39

The internal dimensions are respectively 30 cm, 25 cm and 14 cm.

External volume $= 32 \times 27 \times 15 \text{ cm}^3 = 12\,960 \text{ cm}^3$
Internal volume $= 30 \times 25 \times 14 \text{ cm}^3 = 10\,500$ „
$\therefore$ volume of wood $= 2\,460$ „
$\therefore$ area used $= 2\,460 \text{ cm}^2$

Cylinder

Volume $=$ base area $\times$ height $= \pi r^2 h$

Curved surface area $= 2\pi rh$

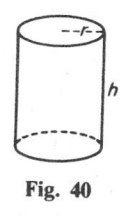

Fig. 40

Example 5 *How many litres of oil does a cylindrical drum* 28 *cm in diameter and* 50 *cm deep hold?*

Volume of drum $= \pi r^2 h = \frac{22}{7} \times 14^2 \times 50 \text{ cm}^3 = 30\,800 \text{ cm}^3$
$\therefore$ capacity $= 30{\cdot}8$ litres.

Example 6 *A cylindrical metal bar* 50 *cm long and* 6 *cm in diameter is pulled out to form a wire of diameter* 3 *mm. What length of wire is produced? How does the curved surface area of the wire compare with that of the bar?*

Let length of wire be x cm.

Then volume of wire $= \pi \left(\dfrac{3}{20}\right)^2 \times x \text{ cm}^3$

But volume of bar $= \pi 3^2 \times 50 \text{ cm}^3$

$\therefore \ \pi \dfrac{9x}{400} = \pi 9 \times 50$

$\therefore \ x = 450\pi \times \dfrac{400}{9\pi} = 20\,000$

$\therefore$ length $= 20\,000 \text{ cm} = 200 \text{ m}$

Bar surface area = $2\pi 3 \times 50 \text{ cm}^2 = 300\pi \text{ cm}^2$

Wire surface area = $2\pi \frac{3}{20} \times 20\,000 \text{ cm}^2 = 6\,000 \text{ cm}^2$

∴ surface of wire = 20 × that of bar.

NB. Never substitute a numerical value for π if it can be avoided.

Exercise 23b

In nos. 1–10 take $\pi = \frac{22}{7}$ *unless otherwise instructed.*

1. Liquid in a 14 mm diameter pipe flows at 2 ms^{-1}. How many litres per minute are discharged from the pipe?

2. What is the mass in kilograms of a cylindrical brass bar 35 cm long and 3 cm in diameter if the density of the metal is 8 g cm^{-3}?

3. The plan of a small plunge-bath consists of a rectangle with a semicircular end (dimensions in metres in Fig. 41). The bath is uniformly 1·7 m deep and is filled up to 10 cm from the top. How many litres does the bath then hold?

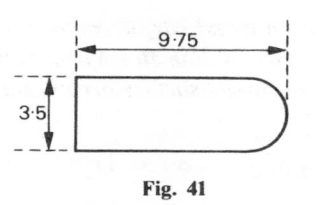

Fig. 41

4. 154 litres of oil are poured into a drum of diameter 35 cm. To what depth is the drum filled?

5. A casting of the form shown in Fig. 42 (dimensions in mm) is made of iron of density $7·2 \text{ g cm}^{-3}$. What is the mass of the casting in kilograms?

6. 6·6 millimetres of rain fall on to a flat roof 8 m long and 6 m wide, and discharge into a cylindrical water-butt of diameter 60 cm. How far does the water level rise in the butt?

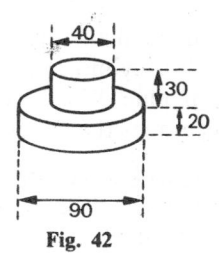

Fig. 42

7. An open rectangular box made of wood 1·5 cm thick has external dimensions 63 cm long, 48 cm wide and 50 cm deep. What is the volume of wood in the box, and what is its mass if the density of the wood is $0·8\,\mathrm{g\,cm^{-3}}$?

8. The most economical shape for a closed cylindrical tin is one in which the height and diameter are equal. What is the capacity in litres of such a tin 10 cm high? (2 sig. fig.)

9. What depth of tin in no. 8 will hold exactly 2 litres? (Take $\log \pi = 0·497\,1$ and answer to 3 sig. fig.)

10. What is the mass of a one-metre length of a cylindrical iron pipe of external diameter 10 cm and internal diameter 8 cm if the specific gravity of iron is 7·2? (Take $\log \pi = 0·497\,1$ and answer to 3 sig. fig.)

No numerical substitution for π in nos. 11–15.

11. How many times can a cylindrical tumbler 8 cm high and 6 cm in diameter be filled from a cylindrical jug 18 cm high and 10 cm in diameter?

12. A lead cylinder 15 cm in diameter and 9 cm thick is melted down and cast into cylindrical rods 1·5 cm in diameter. What total length of rod results?

13. A cylindrical water-butt is 60 cm in diameter and the water contained is 120 cm deep. The water is let out through a 2-cm diameter tube in the bottom of the butt. If the water flows at $2·5\,\mathrm{m\,s^{-1}}$ how long does it take to empty the butt?

14. A cylindrical can 8 cm in diameter and 10 cm high contains 4 cm depth of water. If a cylindrical wooden rod 4 cm in diameter and 6 cm long is placed in the can it floats exactly half-submerged. How much does the water-level rise?

15. If the wooden rod in no. 14 is replaced by a heavy metal bar of the same size, how much does the level rise if the bar is placed (i) horizontally, (ii) vertically?

Cones and frusta

Volume of cone $= \frac{1}{3}$ **base area** $\times$ **perpendicular height** $= \frac{1}{3}\pi r^2 h$

Curved surface area $= \pi r l$

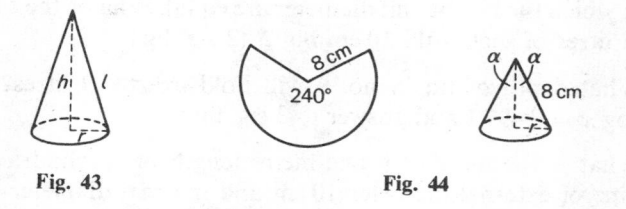

Fig. 43   Fig. 44

Example 7   *A 240° sector of a circle of radius 8 cm is bent round to form a cone. Find the radius of the base of this cone and its vertical angle.*

Let radius of base be r cm and vertical angle 2α.

Since the circumference of base circle of cone = arc of original sector

$$2\pi r = \frac{240}{360} \times 2\pi 8$$

$$\therefore r = \frac{16}{3}$$

$$\therefore \sin \alpha = \frac{r}{8} = \frac{2}{3} = 0.6667$$

∴ α = 41° 49′

∴ 2α = 83° 38′

Ans.   Base radius = $5\frac{1}{3}$ cm and vertical angle = 83° 38′.

When dealing with a **frustum** of a cone it is usually necessary to consider the frustum as part of a whole cone, as in the example which follows.

Example 8   *Find the capacity in litres of a bucket 24 cm in diameter at the top, 16 cm at the bottom and 18 cm deep.*

Complete the cone as in Fig. 45 and let the depth of the extension be *x* cm.

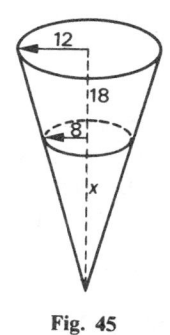

Fig. 45

Then $\dfrac{x}{8} = \dfrac{x + 18}{12}$ *similar* △*s*

∴ x = 36

∴ volume of frustum = $\frac{1}{3}\pi 12^2 \times 54\,\text{cm}^3 - \frac{1}{3}\pi 8^2 \times 36\,\text{cm}^3$

$= \frac{1}{3}\pi 4^2 (3^2 \times 54 - 2^2 \times 36)\,\text{cm}^3$

$= \dfrac{16\pi}{3} \times 342\,\text{cm}^3$

$\simeq 5\,730\,\text{cm}^3$

∴ capacity of bucket = 5·73 litres.

123

Exercise 23c

In this set leave π in the answer if π is involved (e.g. 235π cm².)

1. Find the base-radii and the vertical angles of cones formed from
   (i) a semicircle of radius 16 cm,
   (ii) a sector of radius 8 cm and angle 270°,
   (iii) a sector of radius 15 cm and angle 150°.

2. What are the curved surface area and volume of a cone of height 8 cm and base-diameter 12 cm?

3. If the cone in no. 2 is made of paper and the paper is slit and opened out into a sector, what is the angle of the sector?

4. A lampshade is in shape the frustum of a cone, the top and bottom diameters being 10 cm and 20 cm and the height 12 cm. Find the area of material required to cover the shade and also its volume.

5. A flower-pot is 12 cm diameter at the top, 8 cm at the bottom, and is 10 cm deep. What is its volume? How many such pots could be filled to the brim with earth from a cart holding one-tenth of a cubic metre? (Take log π = 0·497 1.)

6. A pile of sand is in the form of a cone 20 m in diameter at the bottom and 6 m high. What is the mass of the sand in tonnes if the mass of one litre is 2·5 kg?

Summary

Rectangular block or cuboid

Volume = abh
Surface area = $2(ab + ah + bh)$

Prism

Volume = base area × perpendicular height

Pyramid

Volume = $\frac{1}{3}$ base area × perpendicular height

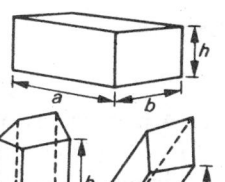

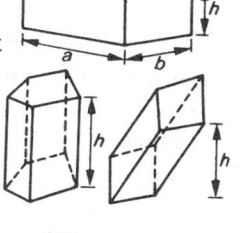

Cone

Volume = $\frac{1}{3}\pi r^2 h$
Curved surface area = πrl

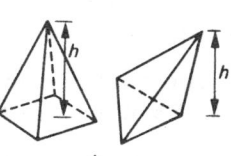

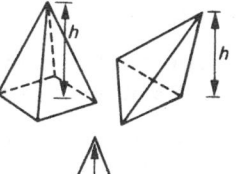

Right circular cylinder

Volume = $\pi r^2 h$
Curved surface area = $2\pi rh$
Total surface area = $2\pi rh + 2\pi r^2$
$= 2\pi r(h + r)$

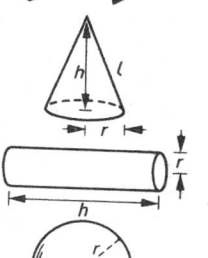

Sphere

Volume = $\frac{4}{3}\pi r^3$
Surface area = $4\pi r^2$

Fig. 46

Example 9 *What is the mass of metal in a hollow sphere 10 cm in external diameter, the shell being 1 mm thick and the density of the metal 7·1 g cm⁻³? Take log π = 0·497 1.*

Volume of outer sphere = $\frac{4}{3}\pi 5^3$ cm³
   „   „   inner   „ = $\frac{4}{3}\pi 4·9^3$ cm³
∴   „   „   metal   „ = $\frac{4}{3}\pi(5^3 - 4·9^3)$ cm³
                        $= \frac{4}{3}\pi(125 - 117·7)$ cm³
                        $= \frac{4}{3}\pi \times 7·3$ cm³

∴   mass of metal $= \dfrac{29·2\pi}{3} \times 7·1$ g

                  $\simeq 217$ g

125

Exercise 23d

In nos. 1–5 do not use any numerical value for π.

1. A hemispherical bowl of diameter 36 cm is full of water which is subsequently drained off into an empty cylindrical can of diameter 24 cm. How deep is the water in the can?

2. How many ladlefuls of soup can be got out of a cylindrical saucepan 30 cm in diameter and full to a depth of 20 cm if the ladle is a hemisphere 10 cm in diameter?

3. A lead ball of diameter 6 cm is melted down and cast into balls 5 mm in diameter. How many of the smaller balls are' there?

4. A heavy 9-cm diameter ball is placed in an empty cylindrical can of diameter 12 cm, and enough water is poured into the can to cover the ball. If the ball is then removed, how far does the water-level fall?

5. In Fig. 47 what fraction of the volume of the cylinder is (i) the sphere? (ii) the cone? What is the relation between the curved surface areas of the sphere and the cylinder?

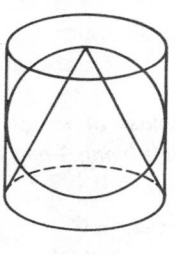

Fig. 47

In nos. 6–12 take π = $\frac{22}{7}$ *or* 3·142, *or* log π = 0·497 1 *as may be appropriate. All answers to 3 sig. fig.*

6. Five kilometres of paper 0·018 mm thick are wound on to a wooden roller of diameter 15 cm. What is the diameter of the full roll?

7. A lead plummet consists of a cone attached to a hemisphere (Fig. 48); the diameter of the hemisphere is 3 cm and the height of the cone is 4 cm. What is the mass of the plummet if the density of the lead is $11 \cdot 3$ g cm^{-3}?

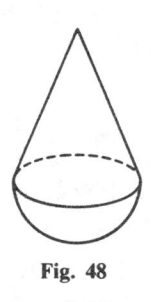

Fig. 48

8. A pyramid 7 cm high stands on a base 12 cm square. Find the lengths of the slant-edges of the pyramid, and also its volume.

9. Find the approximate mass in kilograms of an earthenware drainpipe 2 m long and 18 cm in external diameter if the material is $1 \cdot 5$ cm thick and is of density $1 \cdot 3$ g cm^{-3}.

10. A lampshade in the form of a frustrum of a cone is formed from a sector cut from a thin copper disc as in Fig. 49. Find the mass of the completed shade if the copper is $0 \cdot 7$ mm thick and its density $8 \cdot 94$ g cm^{-3}.

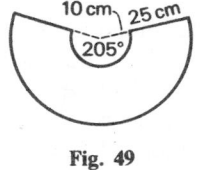

10 cm   25 cm
205°

Fig. 49

11. The 'Wall of Death' on a permanent fairground is a concrete cylinder 4 m deep and 4 m in internal diameter. If the concrete is 50 cm thick in both walls and base, how many cubic metres of it are used in the construction?

12. A hollow metal sphere is of external diameter 12 cm, the metal being 4 mm thick and of density $8·9 \text{ g cm}^{-3}$. What is the mass of the ball?

13. A steel component is machined into a cylindrical form of which the diametrical section is shown in Fig. 50, all dimensions given being in mm. Calculate the volume of the component in cm^3.

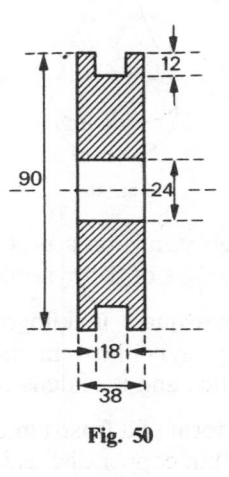

Fig. 50

14. A cylindrical drainpipe made of lead has an outside diameter of 11 cm, the lead itself being 3 mm thick. Taking the density of lead as $11·3 \text{ g cm}^{-3}$, find the mass per metre length of the pipe.

15. A concrete road-block, intended as a tank-trap, is in the form of a frustum of a square pyramid, the base being 50 cm square, the top 30 cm square, and these two surfaces ,60 cm apart. If the density of the concrete is $2\,300 \text{ kg m}^{-3}$, find the mass of one frustum (to 3 sig. fig.) in kilograms.

Chapter 24

Graphs

Example 1 *Draw the graph of $y = x^2 + 3x - 4$ for values of x from -5 to $+2$. Read off the values of (i) y when $x = 1.5$ (ii) y when $x = -2.5$ (iii) x when $y = 4$ (iv) the least value of $x^2 + 3x - 4$ (v) the value of x for which y is least.*

The values of y are obtained by adding the values of x^2, of $3x$, and -4, and setting out the table of values as follows:

x	-5	-4	-3	-2	-1	0	1	2
x^2 $+3x$ -4	25 -15 -4	16 -12 -4	9 -9 -4	4 -6 -4	1 -3 -4	0 0 -4	1 3 -4	4 6 -4
y	6	0	-4	-6	-6	-4	0	6

It is convenient to use a scale of 2 cm for units on the x-axis, and 1 cm for units on the y-axis. See Fig. 51 overleaf.

Ans. (i) $y = 2.75$ (ii) $y = -5.25$ (iii) $x = 1.7$ or -4.7
(iv) -6.25 (v) $x = -1.5$

Exercise 24a

Draw the graphs of the following functions ($y =$ the function in each case):

1. $x^2 - 3x - 4$ for values of x from -2 to $+5$. Read off the values of y when $x = 4.5$, 2.5, -0.7; also of x when $y = 4$, 0, -3. For what value of x is $x^2 - 3x - 4$ a minimum, and what is this minimum value?

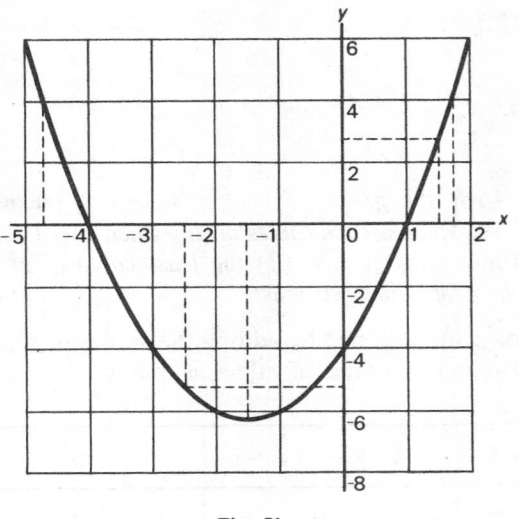

Fig. 51

2. $4x - x^2$ for values of x from -1 to $+5$. Read off the values of y when $x = 3.5$, -0.5; also of x when $y = 2$, -3. For what value of x does $4x - x^2$ have its greatest value, and what is this greatest value?

3. $x(x - 5)$ for values of x from -1 to $+6$. Read off the values of y when $x = 5.6$, 1.2; also of x when $y = 2$, -5.2. Find the minimum value of y and the value of x for which this occurs.

4. $(x + 1)(x - 2)$ for values of x from -3 to $+4$. Read off the values of y when $x = 3.2$, 1.3, -2.5; also of x when $y = 7$, -1, 2.

5. $4 - 2x - x^2$ for values of x from -4 to $+2$. Read off the values of y when $x = 1.6$, -1.6, -2.8; also of x when $y = 3$, 0, -3. For what value of x is y a maximum, and what is this maximum value?

Graphical solution of quadratic equations

Example 2 *Solve graphically the equation* $2x^2 + 3x - 6 = 0$. *From the same graph read off the roots of the equations*

(i) $2x^2 + 3x - 11 = 0$ (ii) $2x^2 + 3x - 3 = 0$
(iii) $2x^2 + 3x + 3 = 0$.

x	-4	-3	-2	-1	0	1	2
$2x^2$ $+3x$ -6	32 -12 -6	18 -9 -6	8 -6 -6	2 -3 -6	0 0 -6	2 3 -6	8 6 -6
$2x^2 + 3x - 6$	14	3	-4	-7	-6	-1	8

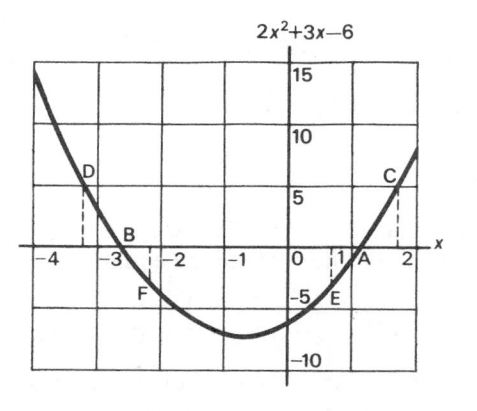

Fig. 52

$2x^2 + 3x - 6$ is equal to 0 along the x-axis. Hence the points on the curve at which $2x^2 + 3x - 6 = 0$ are A and B.

At these points $x = 1·14$ or $-2·64$.

131

(i) $2x^2 + 3x - 11 = 0$
   $\therefore 2x^2 + 3x \quad\quad = 11$
   $\therefore 2x^2 + 3x - 6 \ = 11 - 6$
   i.e. $2x^2 + 3x - 6 = 5$

This is true at the points C and D.
   Hence $x = 1.71$ or -3.21.

(ii) $2x^2 + 3x - 3 = 0$
   $\therefore 2x^2 + 3x \quad\quad = 3$
   $\therefore 2x^2 + 3x - 6 = 3 - 6$
   i.e. $2x^2 + 3x - 6 = -3$

This is true at the points E and F.
   Hence $x = 0.69$ or -2.19.

(iii) $2x^2 + 3x + 3 = 0$
   $\therefore 2x^2 + 3x \quad\quad = -3$
   $\therefore 2x^2 + 3x - 6 = -3 - 6$
   i.e. $2x^2 + 3x - 6 = -9$

   There is no point on the graph at which $2x^2 + 3x - 6$ is equal to -9.
$\therefore$ the roots are imaginary.

Exercise 24b

1. Draw the graph of $x^2 - 3x - 2$, taking values of x from -1 to 4, and from it read off the roots of the equations

   $x^2 - 3x - 2 = 0$ $x^2 - 3x + 1 = 0$ $x^2 - 3x - 1 = 0$
   $x^2 - 3x = 0$ $x^2 - 3x - 3 = 0$ $x^2 - 3x - 4 = 0$

2. Draw the graph of $x^2 + 4x + 1$ for values of x from -5 to 1, and from it read off the roots of the equations

   $x^2 + 4x + 1 = 0$ $x^2 + 4x - 1 = 0$ $x^2 + 4x + 2 = 0$
   $x^2 + 4x + 4 = 0$ $x^2 + 4x + 5 = 0$ $x^2 + 4x - 3 = 0$

3. Solve graphically the equation $2x^2 - 4x - 5 = 0$ (take values of x from -2 to 4), and using the same graph solve the

equations

$$2x^2 - 4x - 7 = 0 \quad 2x^2 - 4x - 3 = 0 \quad 2x^2 - 4x + 3 = 0$$
$$2x^2 - 4x + 1 = 0 \quad 2x^2 - 4x - 11 = 0$$

4. Taking values of x from -3 to 2 solve graphically the equation $3x^2 + 2x - 1 = 0$. Using the same graph read off the roots of the equations

$$3x^2 + 2x = 0 \quad\quad 3x^2 + 2x + 4 = 0 \quad 3x^2 + 2x - 7 = 0$$
$$3x^2 + 2x - 3 = 0 \quad 3x^2 + 2x - 12 = 0$$

5. Draw the graph of $3x^2 - 5x + 3$, and from it read off the roots of the equations

$$3x^2 - 5x + 3 = 0 \quad 3x^2 - 5x = 0 \quad\quad 3x^2 - 5x - 1 = 0$$
$$3x^2 - 5x - 4 = 0 \quad 3x^2 - 5x - 7 = 0 \quad 3x^2 - 5x - 11 = 0$$

Example 3 *Draw the graphs of the equations $y = x(x + 1)(x - 2)$ and $y = 2x - 2$. Read off the values of x at the points at which the straight line cuts the curve. Of what equation in x are these values the roots?*

x	-2	-1	0	1	2	3	$-\frac{1}{2}$	$\frac{1}{2}$	$1\frac{1}{2}$
$x + 1$	-1	0	1	2	3	4	$\frac{1}{2}$	$1\frac{1}{2}$	$2\frac{1}{2}$
$x - 2$	-4	-3	-2	-1	0	1	$-2\frac{1}{2}$	$-1\frac{1}{2}$	$-\frac{1}{2}$
y	-8	0	0	-2	0	12	$0{\cdot}625$	$-1{\cdot}125$	$-1{\cdot}875$

For the curve the values of y for the integral values of x are first plotted. It can then be seen that additional values of y for $x = -\frac{1}{2}, \frac{1}{2}, 1\frac{1}{2}$ will be helpful in drawing the curve accurately.

The straight line is then drawn by plotting the values:

x	-2	0	3
y	-6	-2	4

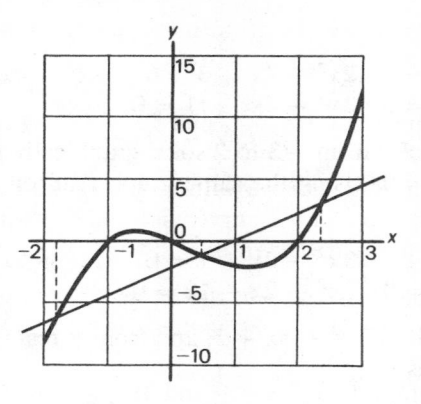

Fig. 53

Reading from the graph, the values of x at the intersections of the curve and the straight line are 2.34, 0.47, -1.81.

At these intersections,

$$y = x(x + 1)(x - 2) \text{ and } y = 2x - 2$$
$$\therefore \; x(x + 1)(x - 2) = 2x - 2$$
$$\therefore \; x^3 - x^2 - 2x = 2x - 2$$
$$\therefore \; x^3 - x^2 - 4x + 2 = 0$$

which is the required equation.

Exercise 24c

1. Draw the graph of $y = x(x - 1)$ for values of x from -2 to 3, and read off the values of x at the points at which it is cut by the line $y = 3 - x$. Of what equation in x are these values the roots?

2. Draw the graphs of $y = 2x^2 - 3x - 6$ and $y = 1 - 3x$ for values of x from -2 to 3. Read off the values of x at the intersections of the line and the curve. Find the equation in x of which these values are the roots.

3. Solve the equation $x^2 = \frac{1}{2}x + 4$ by drawing the graphs of $y = x^2$ and $y = \frac{1}{2}x + 4$ for values of x from -3 to 3, and

reading off the values of x at the intersections of the line and the curve.

4. Draw the graphs of $y = \dfrac{3x}{x + 3}$ and $5y = 3x - 2$ for values of x from -1 to 5. Read off the values of x at the points of intersection of the line and the curve, and find the equation in x of which these values are the roots.

5. Find the values of x and y at the intersections of the graphs of $xy = 2$ and $2x - 3y = 1$. (Take values of x from -3 to 3.)

6. Draw the graphs of $y = \dfrac{2x - 1}{x + 2}$ and $2x + 3y = 6$ for values of x from -1 to 4. Read off the values of x and y at the intersection of the graphs.

7. Read off the values of x and y at the intersections of the graphs of $y = \dfrac{x^2}{x + 2}$ and $x = 2y - 2$. (Take values of x from -1 to 5.)

8. Draw the graphs of $y = x(x - 1)(x - 3)$ and $y = 3x - 5$ for values of x from -1 to 4. Read off the values of x at the intersections of the curve and the straight line. Of what equation in x are these values the roots?

9. Draw the graphs of $y = x^3$ and $3x - y + 2 = 0$ for values of x from -3 to 3. Read off the values of x at the intersections of the graphs, and find the equation in x of which these values are the roots.

10. Solve the equation $x^3 - 4x - 1 = 0$ by drawing the graphs of $y = x^3$ and $y = 4x + 1$ for values of x from -3 to 3, and reading off the values of x at the intersections of the graphs.

Chapter 25

Tangents. Contact of circles. Alternate segment

Tangents

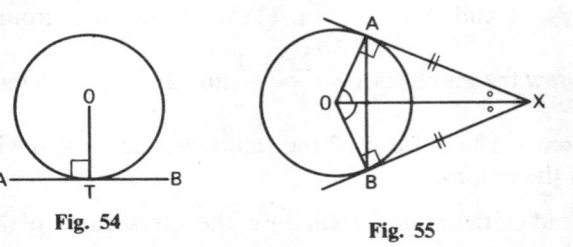

Fig. 54

$\overline{OT} \perp \overline{ATB}$

Fig. 55

(i)   XA = XB
(ii)   OX̂A = OX̂B
(iii) AÔX = BÔX
(iv) $\overline{OX}$ bisects $\overline{AB}$ at
        right angles

Construction

To construct tangents from a point to a circle.

P is the point, O the centre of the circle. The dotted lines indicate the construction which is necessary.

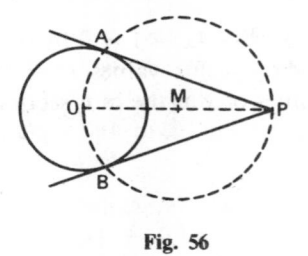

Fig. 56

Contact of circles

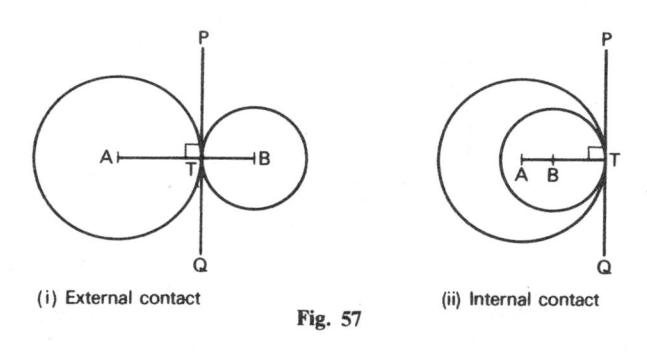

(i) External contact   (ii) Internal contact

Fig. 57

In both cases $\overline{AB}$, the line joining the centres of the circles, passes through T, their point of contact, and is at right angles to the common tangent $\overline{PTQ}$.

Exercise 25a

1. Three circles touch one another externally, and their centres form a triangle with sides 10 cm, 9 cm and 7 cm. What are the radii of the circles?

2. Two circles touch one another externally and both touch a third circle internally. If the sides of the triangle formed by the three centres are 5 cm, 6 cm and 9 cm, what are the radii of the circles?

3. What are the lengths of the tangents from a point X to a circle centre O and radius 6 cm if OX = 11 cm? (2 dec. places)

137

4. In Fig. 58 find $\hat{C}$.

5. A circle is drawn inside a triangle ABC to touch the sides $\overline{BC}$, $\overline{CA}$ and $\overline{AB}$ at P, Q and R respectively. If $\hat{A} = 56°$ and $\hat{B} = 68°$, find the angles of the triangle PQR.

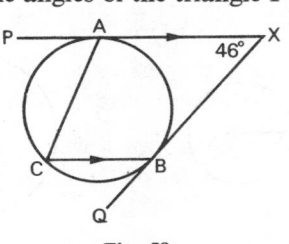

Fig. 58

6. In a figure lettered like Fig. 58 $\overline{BC}/\!/\overline{XA}$ and $\hat{CBQ} = 52°$. Find $\hat{CAP}$. (**NB.** $\hat{X}$ is not 46° in this example.)

7. In Fig. 59 the circle touches the sides of the triangle at X, Y, Z. If BC = 11 cm, CA = 10 cm and AB = 9 cm, find AY and BX.

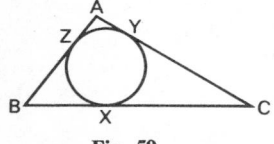
Fig. 59

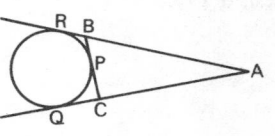
Fig. 60

8. In Fig. 60 the circle touches the sides of the triangle ABC (two of the sides being produced) at P, Q and R. If BC = 7 cm, CA = 6 cm and AB = 5 cm, find BP and CP.

9. $\overline{XA}$ and $\overline{XB}$ are tangents from X to a circle ABC, centre O: $\overline{BC}/\!/\overline{XA}$. Prove that, if C lies in the major segment cut off by $\overline{AB}$, $\hat{AOC} = \hat{AOB}$.

10. $\overline{XA}$ and $\overline{XB}$ are tangents from X to a circle ABC and $\overline{BC}/\!/\overline{XA}$. Prove that $\overline{AB}$ bisects $\hat{XBC}$ and that AB = AC.

11. A quadrilateral ABCD is drawn round a given circle so that its sides touch the circle. Prove that AB + CD = BC + AD.

12. Two circles touch externally at T, and a straight line $\overline{XTY}$ cuts the circles at X and Y. If tangents are drawn to the circles at X and Y prove that these tangents are parallel.

13. $\overline{AB}$ is a diameter of a circle ABC and $\overline{AT}$ the tangent at A. If $\hat{CAT}$ is acute prove that $\hat{CAT} = \hat{CBA}$.

14. $\overline{TA}$ and $\overline{TC}$ are tangents from a point T to a circle ABC, centre O, $\overline{AB}$ being a diameter. Prove $\overline{TO}/\!/\overline{CB}$ and $\hat{ATC} = 2\hat{CAB}$.

15. $\overline{XP}$ and $\overline{XQ}$ are tangents from X to a circle centre O, P and Q being the points of contact of the tangents. If $\overline{PX}$ is produced to R prove that $\hat{QXR} = 2\hat{POX}$.

16. Two circles touch externally at A, and $\overline{PQ}$ is a straight line touching one circle at P and the other at Q. Prove that $\hat{PAQ}$ is a right angle.

Alternate segment

In Fig. 61 (i) and (ii) $x_1 = x_2$ and $y_1 = y_2$.

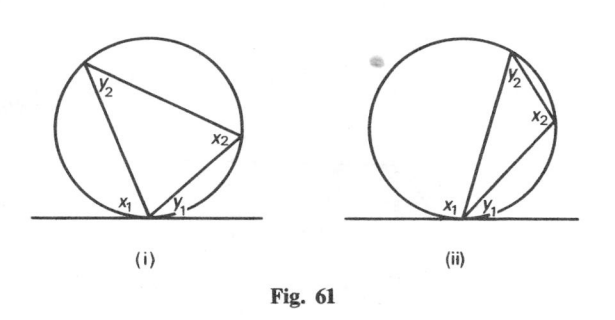

(i)   (ii)

Fig. 61

The angles between a tangent to a circle and a chord through the point of contact are equal respectively to the angles in the alternate (or opposite) segments.

Exercise 25b

1. In Fig. 62 find the angles a, b, c; x, y, z; p; q; r.

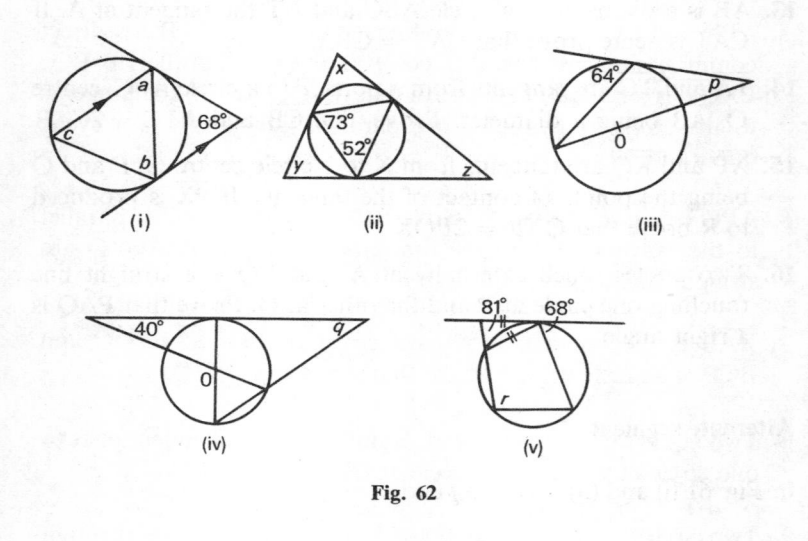

(i)   (ii)   (iii)

(iv)   (v)

Fig. 62

2. In Fig. 63 show that $2b - a = 180°$.

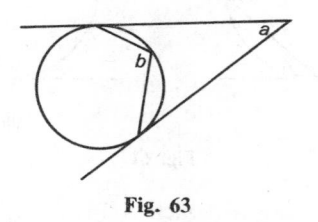

Fig. 63

3. ABC is a circle and the tangent at B cuts $\overline{AC}$ produced at T. If $\widehat{ABC} = \widehat{T}$, prove that $\overline{AB}$ is a diameter of the circle.

140

4. ABC is a triangle, and a circle through A touches $\overline{BC}$ at X and cuts $\overline{AB}$, $\overline{AC}$ at Y, Z respectively. If $\overline{AX}$ bisects $B\hat{A}C$, prove $\overline{YZ}/\!\!/\overline{BC}$.

5. APX and BQY are two non-intersecting circles: $\overline{AB}$ is a direct common tangent (see Fig. 66(i)) and $\overline{AP}$ is parallel to $\overline{BQ}$: $\overline{PXQY}$ is a straight line. Prove that (i) $\overline{AX}/\!\!/\overline{BY}$, (ii) the tangents to the circle at P and Q are parallel, (iii) ABQX is a cyclic quadrilateral.

6. APQ is a circle having a circle BCYX inside it. $\overline{BC}$ is parallel to the tangent at A to the first circle and $\overline{ABXP}$, $\overline{ACYQ}$ are straight lines. Prove $\overline{XY}/\!\!/\overline{PQ}$.

7. $\overline{XAB}$ is the tangent at A to a circle ACPD. $\overline{XAB}/\!\!/\overline{DC}$ and $\overline{BCP}$ is a straight line. Prove that $\overline{AP}$ bisects $C\hat{P}D$.

8. Two equal circles intersect at A and B, and the tangent at B to one circle cuts the other circle at C. Prove AB = AC.

9. Two circles S_1 and S_2 intersect at A and B, and S_2 passes through the centre O of S_1. A radius $\overline{OC}$ of S_1, $A\hat{O}C$ being obtuse, is the tangent to S_2 at O. Prove that $\overline{AC}$ bisects $O\hat{A}B$.

10. $\overline{AB}$ is a diameter of a circle ABC: the tangents to the circle at B and C intersect at T, and $\overline{AC}$ produced cuts $\overline{BT}$ produced at D. Prove that TC = TD.

11. Two circles ABCD and ABX intersect at A and B, and $\overline{AC}$ is the tangent at A to the circle ABX. $\overline{XAD}$ and $\overline{XBC}$ are straight lines. Prove that CA = CD.

12. ABCD is a trapezium in which $\overline{AB}$ is parallel to $\overline{DC}$. A circle through A and B touches $\overline{DC}$ at R and cuts $\overline{AD}$, $\overline{BC}$ respectively at P, Q. Prove that (i) PQCD is a cyclic quadrilateral, (ii) $R\hat{Q}C = R\hat{P}D$.

13. Two circles intersect at A and B, and $\overline{PQ}$ is a common tangent (Fig. 64). PAX and QAY are straight lines. $\overline{YP}$ produced and $\overline{XQ}$ produced cut at T. Prove TP = TQ.

14. Two circles touch externally at A. $\overline{TA}$ is the common tangent to the circles at A, and $\overline{TB}$ is another tangent to one of them. $\overline{BA}$ produced cuts the other circle at C, and $\overline{TC}$ cuts this circle at D. Prove that TBAD is a cyclic quadrilateral, and also that the circle through B, C and D touches $\overline{TB}$ at B.

15. In Fig. 65 the circles touch at A; $\overline{TA}$, $\overline{TB}$, $\overline{TC}$ are tangents; $\overline{BAY}$ and $\overline{CAX}$ are straight lines. Prove that $\overline{BX}$ and $\overline{CY}$ are both perpendicular to $\overline{BC}$.

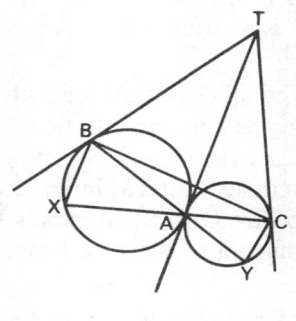

Fig. 64   Fig. 65

Common tangents

In Fig. 66 (i) shows the **direct** common tangent to two circles,

(ii) shows the **transverse** common tangent to two circles.
The dotted lines indicate the procedure for constructing these tangents, the radii of the dotted circles being (i) $r_1 - r_2$, (ii) $r_1 + r_2$.

142

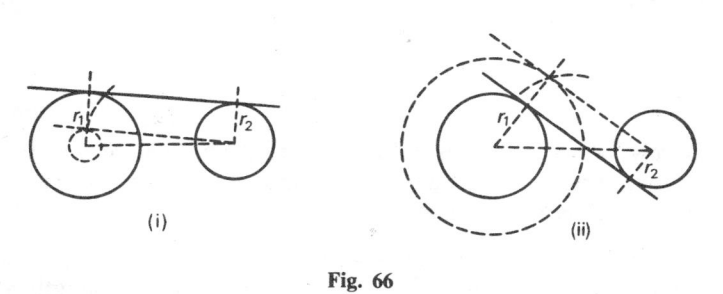

Fig. 66

Circumcircle, incircle and e-circle

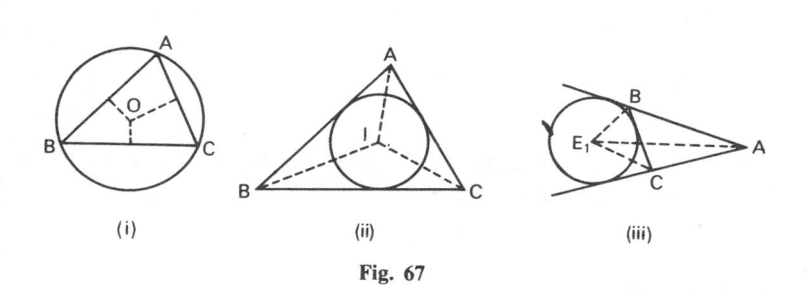

Fig. 67

Fig. 67 (i) shows the **circumcentre** O of triangle ABC, which is the centre of the circle ABC. The perpendicular bisectors of the sides of the triangle meet at O.

(ii) shows the **incentre** I, which is the centre of the circle which touches internally the sides of the triangle. The bisectors of the angles of the triangle meet at I.

(iii) shows one of the three **e-circles** which touch the three sides of the triangle, one of them externally and the other two internally after they have been produced. The bisectors of one internal and two external angles of the triangles meet at E_1.

143

Exercise 25c

Common tangents

1. Draw two circles with radii 5 cm and 3 cm, their centres being 9 cm apart. Construct a direct common tangent and measure its length. Check by calculation.

2. Using the same dimensions as in no. 1 construct a transverse common tangent to the two circles. Measure its length and check as before.

3. Circles radii 6 cm and 4 cm; centres 8 cm apart. Construct direct common tangent; measure and check.

4. Circles radii 3 cm and 4 cm; centres 10 cm apart. Construct transverse common tangent; measure and check.

Circumcircle

Construct the circumcircles of the triangles whose sides are given in nos. 5–7 and measure their radii.

5. 5 cm, 6 cm, 7 cm.

6. 6 cm, 7 cm, 10 cm.

7. 5 cm, 6 cm, 10 cm.

Incircle and e-circle

Construct the incircles of the triangles whose sides are given in nos. 8–10 and measure their radii.

8. 6 cm, 7 cm, 9 cm.

9. 7 cm, 10 cm, 13 cm.

10. 7 cm, 9 cm, 12 cm.

11. Draw a triangle with sides 2 cm, 3 cm and 4 cm and construct the e-circle touching the 3-cm side. Measure its radius.

12. Draw a triangle with sides 4 cm, 5 cm and 6 cm. Draw all three e-circles and measure their radii.

13. In a $\triangle ABC$ $AB = 5$ cm, $BC = 7$ cm, $AC = 6$ cm. The incircle touches $\overline{BC}$, $\overline{CA}$, $\overline{AB}$ at P, Q, R respectively. Calculate AR, BP, CQ.

14. In a $\triangle ABC$ dimensioned as in no. 13 the smallest of the three e-circles touches $\overline{AB}$ at Z and $\overline{CB}$ produced, $\overline{CA}$ produced at X, Y respectively. Calculate AY.

15. In Fig. 67 (ii) prove that $\widehat{BIC} = 90° + \frac{1}{2}A$.

16. In Fig. 67 (iii) prove that $A\widehat{E}_1B = \frac{1}{2}C$.

17. $\overline{XA}$ and $\overline{XB}$ are the tangents from X to a circle, and M is the mid-point of the minor arc AB. Prove that M is the incentre of $\triangle ABX$.

18. An isosceles triangle of height 16 cm has an incircle of radius 4 cm. If a line is drawn parallel to the base to touch this circle, what will be the radius of the incircle of the triangle thus formed? (Fig. 68).

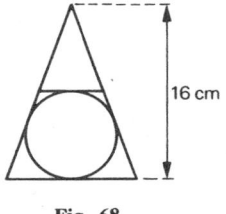

Fig. 68

19. The **orthocentre** of a triangle is the point at which the three altitudes meet. ABC is any triangle and another triangle PQR is formed by drawing $\overline{RAQ}/\!/\overline{BC}$, $\overline{QCP}/\!/\overline{AB}$, $\overline{PBR}/\!/\overline{CA}$. Show that the orthocentre of $\triangle ABC$ is the circumcentre of $\triangle PQR$.

20. Three circles are drawn so that each touches the other two externally. Show that the common tangents at the points of contact meet in a point, and that this point is the incentre of the triangle formed by the centres of the circles.

Chapter 26

Miscellaneous arithmetical problems

Speed, time and distance

Distance = Speed × Time

Speed = Distance ÷ Time

Time = Distance ÷ Speed

The relative speed of two moving objects is the rate at which the distance between them is increasing or decreasing.

Example 1 *A car and a motor-cycle are travelling on a straight road at speeds of 65 km h^{-1} and 85 km h^{-1} respectively, and are 1 500 m apart. How much time elapses before they are level with one another if they are travelling (i) towards one another? (ii) in the same direction, with the car in front?*

(i) Relative speed = $(65 + 85)$ km h^{-1} = 150 km h^{-1}
Distance apart = 1 500 m = 1·5 km

$$\therefore \quad \text{time} = \frac{1·5}{150}\,\text{h} = \frac{1}{100}\,\text{h} = 0·6\,\text{min} = 36\,\text{seconds}$$

(ii) Relative speed = $(85 - 65)$ km h^{-1} = 20 km h^{-1}

Distance apart = 1·5 km

$$\therefore \quad \text{time} = \frac{1·5}{20}\,\text{h} = 4·5\,\text{minutes}$$

Example 2 *A passenger train 233 m long travelling at 96 km h^{-1} is overtaking a goods train 369 m long travelling at 40 km h^{-1}. How long does it take the passenger train to pass the goods train completely?*

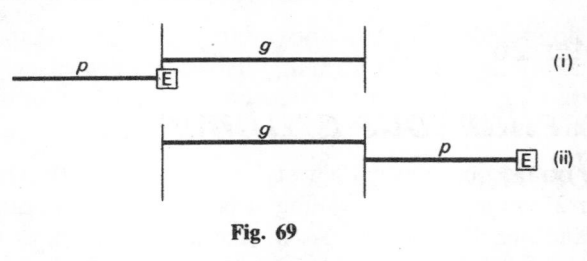

Fig. 69

The engine $\boxed{E}$ of the passenger train has to travel the distance $(g + p)$ before this train has completely passed the other.

$g + p = (369 + 233)\,\text{m} = 602\,\text{m}$

Relative speed $= (96 - 40)\,\text{km h}^{-1}$

$$= 56\,\text{km h}^{-1} = \frac{56\,000}{3\,600}\,\text{m s}^{-1} = \frac{140}{9}\,\text{m s}^{-1}$$

$\therefore$ time to change from position (i) to position (ii)

$$= 602 \times \frac{9}{140}\,\text{seconds} = 38 \cdot 7\,\text{seconds}.$$

Exercise 26a

1. If telegraph poles along a road are 20 m apart and a car travels from the first to the fifteenth in $10\frac{1}{2}$ seconds, what is its speed in km h^{-1}?

2. Two cars travelling at $70\,\text{km h}^{-1}$ and $80\,\text{km h}^{-1}$ respectively are 250 m apart and are approaching one another on a straight road. In what time will they be level with one another?

3. A police car capable of $185\,\text{km h}^{-1}$ is on a motorway half a kilometre behind a stolen vehicle with a top speed of $113\,\text{km h}^{-1}$. If both cars are going as fast as possible how long will it take the police car to catch the other, and how far will it have travelled in this time?

4. How long does it take a train 236 m long to pass completely through a station with a platform 214 m long if the train is travelling at $120\,\text{km h}^{-1}$?

5. Two 'long vehicles' on a motorway are each 25 m long and one is overtaking the other at 6 km h^{-1}. How long does the complete process of overtaking last if 20 seconds are allowed for drawing out and pulling in again?

6. Two trains, one 200 m long and travelling at 90 km h^{-1}, the other 275 m long and travelling at 60 km h^{-1}, are approaching one another. How long does it take for (i) the trains to pass completely? (ii) the slower train to pass a passenger in the faster one?

7. The University Boat Race is rowed in slack water over a course roughly 7 km long: the time taken is 20 minutes. What is the speed in km h^{-1}? How long would the course take if there were a following tide of 3 km h^{-1}?

8. A launch capable of a speed in still water of 15 km h^{-1} has to travel 10 km upstream, turn round and come back again. If the stream runs at 3 km h^{-1} and the turn round takes a quarter of an hour, how long does the whole journey take?

9. How fast is the earth travelling in its orbit round the sun if the orbit is approximately a circle of radius 150 million km and the time taken to cover it is $365\frac{1}{4}$ days? Answer in standard form in km h^{-1}.

10. A nose-to-tail convoy of army vehicles 180 m long is travelling on a motorway at 60 km h^{-1}. How long will it take a motorist to overtake the convoy if he is moving at 80 km h^{-1}?

Mixtures

Example 3 *In what proportion must teas costing 75p and 83p a kilo be mixed to produce a blend costing 80p per kilo?*

On each kilo at 75p there is a gain of 5p
On each kilo at 83p there is a loss of 3p
∴ 3 kilo of the first must be taken with 5 kilo of the second to ensure that gains and losses are balanced.
∴ required proportion is 3:5.

Exercise 26b

1. In what proportion must teas at 86p and 77p per kilo be mixed to produce a blend worth 83p per kilo?

2. How must two sorts of wine at respectively 12F and 8·50F per litre be mixed to produce a blend costing 11F per litre?

3. Two kinds of sugar at $10\frac{1}{2}$p and 14p per kilo were accidentally poured into the same container, and the mixture worked out at 12p per kilo. In what proportion were the sugars mixed?

4. Equal numbers of sweets at two a penny and six a penny are mixed together. How many of the mixed sweets do you get for a penny?

5. In what proportion should butter at $12\frac{1}{2}$p a packet and margarine at 7p be mixed to produce a blend costing $10\frac{1}{2}$p?

6. At the end of a market day a stallholder has left on his hands 5 boxes of apples at £2·32, 3 at £2·20 and 4 at £1·60. He mixes them all up together and offers the mixture at £2 a box. How much is this price more or less than the actual price per box?

7. Three kinds of tea normally sold at 83p, 79p and 75p per kilo are to be mixed to produce a blend at 78p per kilo. If one kilo of the most expensive brand goes with three of the cheapest, what is the complete ratio of the three in the mixture?

8. Wines at £1·20 and £1·07 per litre are mixed with a third wine in the ratio 2:3:4, and the blend works out at £1·05 per litre. What is the cost per litre of the third wine?

9. Acid costing 90p per litre is added to water in the ratio 1:5 by volume. The resulting solution is sold at 24p per litre. What is the profit per cent?

10. A bottle of vermouth is larger than a bottle of gin in the ratio 5:4, the respective costs being £1·25 and £2·55 per bottle. A cocktail is to be mixed consisting of two bottles of vermouth to one of gin. If there are 25 'glasses' to a vermouth bottle, what is the cost per glass of the cocktail (nearest $\frac{1}{2}$p)?

Work, pipes

Example 4 *Alf can complete a labouring job in* 15 *hours, but Bert takes only* 12 *hours for the same job. How long would they take if they worked together?*

In 1 hour Alf does $\frac{1}{15}$ of the job.
In 1 hour Bert does $\frac{1}{12}$ of the job.
∴ in one hour, working together, they do $\frac{1}{15} + \frac{1}{12} = \frac{3}{20}$ of the job
∴ together they do the job in $\frac{20}{3}$ hours = 6 h 40 min.

Exercise 26c

1. One tap can fill a bath in 5 minutes and another in $7\frac{1}{2}$ minutes. How long does it take to fill the bath if both taps are turned on?

2. The flow through the inlet valve fills a cistern in 4 minutes. If the outlet valve is opened a full tank empties in 6 minutes. How long will it take to fill the tank if both valves are opened?

3. A hose-pipe can fill a water-butt in 5 minutes, and the tap in the butt will empty it in 6 minutes. The hose-pipe is started with the tank empty and the tap open, but this is noticed after three minutes and the tap is then closed. How much longer does the butt take to fill?

4. A can build a wall in 9 days and B the same length in 12 days. They work together for 4 days, and then B is moved to another job. How long does it take A to finish the wall alone?

5. Three labourers could each do a certain job in 10, $7\frac{1}{2}$ and 6 days respectively, if working alone. How long will they take working together?

6. If in no. 5 the two fastest workers were taken off after two days, how much longer would it take the slowest to finish the job?

7. Nobby can do a job in 8 days and Pete in 6. Nobby starts alone and is joined by Pete at the start of the second day. How long does the job take altogether?

8. A contractor undertakes to complete a certain job in 6 days, and puts two workmen on to begin with who could do the whole thing in 15 and 12 days respectively if working alone. Realising that the job is not going to be completed on time, he puts in a third man at the start of the 6th day and just fulfils his contract. How long would the third man take, working alone?

9. A and B working together can dig a ditch in 3 days: A would take 5 days working alone. How long would B take?

10. It takes Beryl and Penny working together 20 hours to produce a quota of small articles in a factory; Penny and Irene 18 hours; Irene and Beryl 15 hours. Which of the three girls is the fastest worker, and how long would it take her to produce the quota if she were working alone?

Chapter 27

Matrices

Addition

$$\begin{pmatrix} a & b & c \\ d & e & f \end{pmatrix} + \begin{pmatrix} g & h & i \\ j & k & l \end{pmatrix} = \begin{pmatrix} a+g & b+h & c+i \\ d+j & e+k & f+l \end{pmatrix}$$

Subtraction

$$\begin{pmatrix} a & b \\ c & d \\ e & f \end{pmatrix} - \begin{pmatrix} g & h \\ i & j \\ k & l \end{pmatrix} = \begin{pmatrix} a-g & b-h \\ c-i & d-j \\ e-k & f-l \end{pmatrix}$$

Multiplication

$$3\begin{pmatrix} a & b & c \\ d & e & f \\ g & h & i \end{pmatrix} = \begin{pmatrix} 3a & 3b & 3c \\ 3d & 3e & 3f \\ 3g & 3h & 3i \end{pmatrix}$$

$$\begin{pmatrix} a & b \\ c & d \\ e & f \end{pmatrix}\begin{pmatrix} g & h & i \\ j & k & l \end{pmatrix} = \begin{pmatrix} ag+bj & ah+bk & ai+bl \\ cg+dj & ch+dk & ci+dl \\ eg+fj & eh+fk & ei+fl \end{pmatrix}$$

$$\begin{pmatrix} g & h & i \\ j & k & l \end{pmatrix}\begin{pmatrix} a & b \\ c & d \\ e & f \end{pmatrix} = \begin{pmatrix} ag+ch+ei & bg+dh+fi \\ aj+ck+el & bj+dk+fl \end{pmatrix}$$

Note that for two matrices to be added or subtracted they must have the same number of rows and of columns and for two matrices to be multiplied the number of rows in the first must be equal to the number of columns in the second.

Example 1 $A = \begin{pmatrix} 4 & 2 \\ 1 & 3 \end{pmatrix}$, $B = \begin{pmatrix} 3 & -1 \\ 2 & 1 \end{pmatrix}$. *Find* $A + B$, $A - B$, AB

and BA.

$$A + B = \begin{pmatrix} 4 & 2 \\ 1 & 3 \end{pmatrix} + \begin{pmatrix} 3 & -1 \\ 2 & 1 \end{pmatrix} = \begin{pmatrix} 7 & 1 \\ 3 & 4 \end{pmatrix}$$

$$A - B = \begin{pmatrix} 4 & 2 \\ 1 & 3 \end{pmatrix} - \begin{pmatrix} 3 & -1 \\ 2 & 1 \end{pmatrix} = \begin{pmatrix} 1 & 3 \\ -1 & 2 \end{pmatrix}$$

$$AB = \begin{pmatrix} 4 & 2 \\ 1 & 3 \end{pmatrix}\begin{pmatrix} 3 & -1 \\ 2 & 1 \end{pmatrix} = \begin{pmatrix} 16 & -2 \\ 9 & 2 \end{pmatrix}$$

$$BA = \begin{pmatrix} 3 & -1 \\ 2 & 1 \end{pmatrix}\begin{pmatrix} 4 & 2 \\ 1 & 3 \end{pmatrix} = \begin{pmatrix} 11 & 3 \\ 9 & 7 \end{pmatrix}$$

Exercise 27a

In nos. 1–10 find the sum, difference and the two products of each pair of matrices, stating why some cannot be found.

1. $\begin{pmatrix} 2 & 3 \\ 1 & -1 \end{pmatrix}$, $\begin{pmatrix} 5 & -2 \\ 1 & 3 \end{pmatrix}$

2. $\begin{pmatrix} 3 & 1 & 1 \\ 2 & 2 & 1 \end{pmatrix}$, $\begin{pmatrix} -1 & 0 & 3 \\ 4 & 9 & 7 \end{pmatrix}$

3. $\begin{pmatrix} 6 & 10 & 11 \\ 2 & 3 & -4 \end{pmatrix}$, $\begin{pmatrix} -1 & 0 \\ 7 & 13 \\ 19 & 2 \end{pmatrix}$

4. $\begin{pmatrix} 2 & 8 & 1 & 0 \\ -1 & 0 & 3 & 2 \end{pmatrix}$, $\begin{pmatrix} 6 & 3 & 1 \\ 2 & 4 & 2 \\ 3 & 1 & 6 \\ 2 & 0 & 6 \end{pmatrix}$

5. $\begin{pmatrix} 6 & 3 \\ -1 & 2 \end{pmatrix}$, $\begin{pmatrix} 2 & -3 \\ 1 & 6 \end{pmatrix}$

6. $\begin{pmatrix} 1 & 0 & 2 \\ 3 & -1 & 6 \\ 5 & 2 & -1 \end{pmatrix}, \begin{pmatrix} 1 & -1 & 7 \\ 0 & 2 & 1 \\ 9 & 8 & 0 \end{pmatrix}$

7. $(2 \quad 1 \quad -1), (3 \quad 2 \quad 1)$

8. $(2 \quad 1 \quad -1), \begin{pmatrix} 3 \\ 2 \\ 1 \end{pmatrix}$

9. $\begin{pmatrix} 4 & 6 & 2 \\ 7 & 2 & 1 \\ 8 & -9 & 0 \end{pmatrix}, \begin{pmatrix} 6 & 1 \\ 2 & 5 \\ -1 & -2 \end{pmatrix}$

10. $\begin{pmatrix} 1 & 0.5 \\ -0.5 & 1 \end{pmatrix}, \begin{pmatrix} 1.5 & -1 \\ -1 & 1.5 \end{pmatrix}$

11. On Monday a man posts 10 letters under 50 g, 5 under 100 g and 2 under 150 g. On Tuesday he posts 12 letters under 50 g, 3 under 100 g and 3 under 150 g.

   The postage for 50 g, 100 g and 150 g letters by first class mail is $4\frac{1}{2}$p, $6\frac{1}{2}$p and 10p respectively, and second class mail $3\frac{1}{2}$p, 5p and 7p. Set up matrices to represent these numbers and by multiplication show the costs on each day by either first or second class mail.

12. On Wednesday a woman buys 6 oranges, 5 bananas, 4 apples and 3 pears. On Thursday she buys 10 oranges, 4 bananas, 3 apples and 2 pears. On Friday she buys 8 oranges, 3 bananas, 6 apples and no pears.

   At the market the prices for the fruit are: oranges $2\frac{1}{2}$p, bananas $3\frac{1}{2}$p, apples 3p and pears 4p. In a shop the prices are respectively 3p, $4\frac{1}{2}$p, 4p and 5p.

   Show this in matrix form and by multiplication calculate the cost on each day in the market and in the shop.

New General Mathematics Revision

Simultaneous equations

The **inverse** of $\begin{pmatrix} a & b \\ c & d \end{pmatrix}$ is $\dfrac{1}{ad - bc} \begin{pmatrix} d & -b \\ -c & a \end{pmatrix}$

i.e. $\dfrac{1}{ad - bc} \begin{pmatrix} d & -b \\ -c & a \end{pmatrix} \begin{pmatrix} a & b \\ c & d \end{pmatrix} = \begin{pmatrix} 1 & 0 \\ 0 & 1 \end{pmatrix}.$

$ad - bc$ is the **determinant** of $\begin{pmatrix} a & b \\ c & d \end{pmatrix}.$

$\begin{pmatrix} 1 & 0 \\ 0 & 1 \end{pmatrix}$ is called the **identity** matrix   i.e. $\begin{pmatrix} 1 & 0 \\ 0 & 1 \end{pmatrix} \begin{pmatrix} x \\ y \end{pmatrix} = \begin{pmatrix} x \\ y \end{pmatrix}.$

The equations $ax + by = p$
$\qquad\qquad\quad cx + dy = q$

can be written $\begin{pmatrix} a & b \\ c & d \end{pmatrix} \begin{pmatrix} x \\ y \end{pmatrix} = \begin{pmatrix} p \\ q \end{pmatrix}.$

Pre-multiplying both sides by the inverse of $\begin{pmatrix} a & b \\ c & d \end{pmatrix},$

$$\dfrac{1}{ad - bc} \begin{pmatrix} d & -b \\ -c & a \end{pmatrix} \begin{pmatrix} a & b \\ c & d \end{pmatrix} \begin{pmatrix} x \\ y \end{pmatrix} = \dfrac{1}{ad - bc} \begin{pmatrix} d & -b \\ -c & a \end{pmatrix} \begin{pmatrix} p \\ q \end{pmatrix}$$

$$\therefore \begin{pmatrix} 1 & 0 \\ 0 & 1 \end{pmatrix} \begin{pmatrix} x \\ y \end{pmatrix} = \dfrac{1}{ad - bc} \begin{pmatrix} dp - bq \\ -cp + aq \end{pmatrix}$$

$$\therefore \quad x = \dfrac{dp - bq}{ad - bc}$$

$$\text{and} \quad y = \dfrac{aq - cp}{ad - bc}.$$

Note that if the determinant $ad - bc = 0$ there are no solutions.

Example 2   *Solve the equations* $2x + 3y = 1$ *and* $5x - 4y = 37$.

The equations are $\begin{pmatrix} 2 & 3 \\ 5 & -4 \end{pmatrix} \begin{pmatrix} x \\ y \end{pmatrix} = \begin{pmatrix} 1 \\ 37 \end{pmatrix}.$

156

Pre-multiplying by the inverse,

$$\frac{1}{-8-15}\begin{pmatrix} -4 & -3 \\ -5 & 2 \end{pmatrix}\begin{pmatrix} 2 & 3 \\ 5 & -4 \end{pmatrix}\begin{pmatrix} x \\ y \end{pmatrix} = \frac{1}{-23}\begin{pmatrix} -4 & -3 \\ -5 & 2 \end{pmatrix}\begin{pmatrix} 1 \\ 37 \end{pmatrix}$$

$$\therefore \frac{1}{-23}\begin{pmatrix} -23 & 0 \\ 0 & -23 \end{pmatrix}\begin{pmatrix} x \\ y \end{pmatrix} = \frac{1}{-23}\begin{pmatrix} -115 \\ 69 \end{pmatrix}$$

$$\therefore \begin{pmatrix} 1 & 0 \\ 0 & 1 \end{pmatrix}\begin{pmatrix} x \\ y \end{pmatrix} = \begin{pmatrix} 5 \\ -3 \end{pmatrix}$$

$$\therefore x = 5, y = -3.$$

Check $2 \times 5 + 3 \times (-3) = 1$ and $5 \times 5 - 4 \times (-3) = 37$.

Exercise 27b

Solve the following simultaneous equations, where possible, using the matrix method.

1. $3x + 2y = 7$
   $4x + 3y = 10$

2. $6x + 5y = 8$
   $5x + 4y = 7$

3. $7x - 2y = 27$
   $3x + 5y = 35$

4. $9x + 5y = 7$
   $8x - 3y = -31$

5. $10x - 7y = 4$
   $8x - 11y = -13$

6. $2x + 3y = 4$
   $4x + 6y = 9$

7. $12a - 9b = 18$
   $13a - 8b = 23$

8. $16p + 17q = 15$
   $7p + 6q = 8$

9. $7u - 9v = 4$
   $12u + 8v = 42$

10. $6s - 10t = 3$
    $12s - 14t = 9$

11. What is the inverse of $\begin{pmatrix} 5 & 3 \\ 3 & 2 \end{pmatrix}$?

    Hence find the matrix $\begin{pmatrix} a & b \\ c & d \end{pmatrix}$ where

    $$\begin{pmatrix} 5 & 3 \\ 3 & 2 \end{pmatrix}\begin{pmatrix} a & b \\ c & d \end{pmatrix} = \begin{pmatrix} 6 & 7 \\ 5 & 1 \end{pmatrix}.$$

12. Use the method of no. 11 to solve

$$\begin{pmatrix} 7 & 3 \\ 4 & 2 \end{pmatrix} \begin{pmatrix} a & b \\ c & d \end{pmatrix} = \begin{pmatrix} 6 & 8 \\ 4 & 10 \end{pmatrix}.$$

Mapping

Any set of points can be transformed into another set of points by being multiplied by a matrix. For example $\begin{pmatrix} 0 & 1 \\ -1 & 0 \end{pmatrix}$ transforms $\begin{pmatrix} 1 \\ 0 \end{pmatrix}$ into $\begin{pmatrix} 0 & 1 \\ -1 & 0 \end{pmatrix} \begin{pmatrix} 1 \\ 0 \end{pmatrix} = \begin{pmatrix} 0 \\ -1 \end{pmatrix}$, and $\begin{pmatrix} 0 \\ 1 \end{pmatrix}$ into $\begin{pmatrix} 0 & 1 \\ -1 & 0 \end{pmatrix} \begin{pmatrix} 0 \\ 1 \end{pmatrix} = \begin{pmatrix} 1 \\ 0 \end{pmatrix}$. It transforms the general point $\begin{pmatrix} x \\ y \end{pmatrix}$ into $\begin{pmatrix} 0 & 1 \\ -1 & 0 \end{pmatrix} \begin{pmatrix} x \\ y \end{pmatrix} = \begin{pmatrix} y \\ -x \end{pmatrix}$. This is a rotation of one right angle clockwise about the origin.

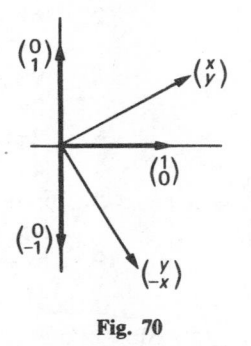

Fig. 70

If it is required to find a matrix operator to perform a particular mapping it is usual to consider the effect on $\begin{pmatrix} 1 \\ 0 \end{pmatrix}$ and $\begin{pmatrix} 0 \\ 1 \end{pmatrix}$.

For example if it is required to calculate *M*, the matrix which reflects all points in the x-axis, let *M* be $\begin{pmatrix} a & b \\ c & d \end{pmatrix}$ and consider the following

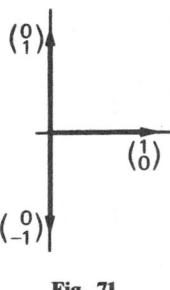

Fig. 71

equations:

$$\begin{pmatrix} a & b \\ c & d \end{pmatrix}\begin{pmatrix} 1 \\ 0 \end{pmatrix} = \begin{pmatrix} 1 \\ 0 \end{pmatrix}$$

$$\begin{pmatrix} a & b \\ c & d \end{pmatrix}\begin{pmatrix} 0 \\ 1 \end{pmatrix} = \begin{pmatrix} 0 \\ -1 \end{pmatrix}$$

$$\therefore \quad a + 0b = 1$$
$$c + 0d = 0$$
$$0a + b = \quad 0$$
$$0c + d = -1$$

$$\therefore \quad M = \begin{pmatrix} 1 & 0 \\ 0 & -1 \end{pmatrix}.$$

Note that $MM = M^2 = I$ where I is the identity matrix. In general the inverse of a matrix has the effect of mapping the image of a point back into the object. In this case, as $M^2 = I$, M is the inverse of itself.

Example 3 *If the triangle ABC where A is $\begin{pmatrix} 1 \\ 3 \end{pmatrix}$, B is $\begin{pmatrix} 3 \\ 5 \end{pmatrix}$ and C is $\begin{pmatrix} -1 \\ 4 \end{pmatrix}$ is reflected in the line $y = x$ what are the co-ordinates of the vertices of the resulting triangle?*

First the operator M for reflection in $y = x$ must be found. $\begin{pmatrix} 1 \\ 0 \end{pmatrix}$ is mapped into $\begin{pmatrix} 0 \\ 1 \end{pmatrix}$, and $\begin{pmatrix} 0 \\ 1 \end{pmatrix}$ is mapped into $\begin{pmatrix} 1 \\ 0 \end{pmatrix}$.

Let M be $\begin{pmatrix} p & q \\ r & s \end{pmatrix}$,

then $\begin{pmatrix} p & q \\ r & s \end{pmatrix}\begin{pmatrix} 1 \\ 0 \end{pmatrix} = \begin{pmatrix} 0 \\ 1 \end{pmatrix}$

and $\begin{pmatrix} p & q \\ r & s \end{pmatrix}\begin{pmatrix} 0 \\ 1 \end{pmatrix} = \begin{pmatrix} 1 \\ 0 \end{pmatrix}$.

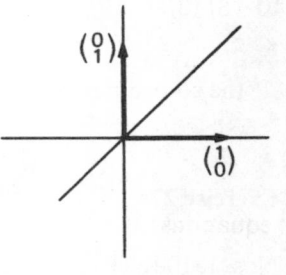

Fig. 72

$\therefore$ $p = 0, r = 1, q = 1$ and $s = 0$ and hence $M = \begin{pmatrix} 0 & 1 \\ 1 & 0 \end{pmatrix}$.

$\begin{pmatrix} 0 & 1 \\ 1 & 0 \end{pmatrix}\begin{pmatrix} 1 \\ 3 \end{pmatrix} = \begin{pmatrix} 3 \\ 1 \end{pmatrix}$, $\begin{pmatrix} 0 & 1 \\ 1 & 0 \end{pmatrix}\begin{pmatrix} 3 \\ 5 \end{pmatrix} = \begin{pmatrix} 5 \\ 3 \end{pmatrix}$ and $\begin{pmatrix} 0 & 1 \\ 1 & 0 \end{pmatrix}\begin{pmatrix} -1 \\ 4 \end{pmatrix} = \begin{pmatrix} 4 \\ -1 \end{pmatrix}$.

$\therefore$ the co-ordinates of the resulting triangle are $\begin{pmatrix} 3 \\ 1 \end{pmatrix}$, $\begin{pmatrix} 5 \\ 3 \end{pmatrix}$ and $\begin{pmatrix} 4 \\ -1 \end{pmatrix}$.

Example 4 *Find the enlargement of the triangle* ABC *of Example 3 in the ratio* $3:1$ *with centre at the origin.*

Let $E = \begin{pmatrix} a & b \\ c & d \end{pmatrix}$ be the required operator.

Then $\begin{pmatrix} a & b \\ c & d \end{pmatrix}\begin{pmatrix} 1 \\ 0 \end{pmatrix} = \begin{pmatrix} 3 \\ 0 \end{pmatrix}$

and $\begin{pmatrix} a & b \\ c & d \end{pmatrix}\begin{pmatrix} 0 \\ 1 \end{pmatrix} = \begin{pmatrix} 0 \\ 3 \end{pmatrix}$

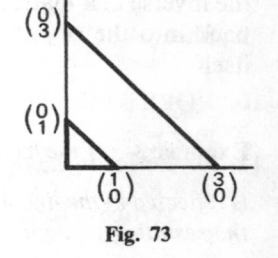

Fig. 73

$\therefore$ $a = 3, c = 0, b = 0$ and $d = 3$ and hence $\mathbf{E} = \begin{pmatrix} 3 & 0 \\ 0 & 3 \end{pmatrix} = 3\mathbf{I}$.

$$\begin{pmatrix} 3 & 0 \\ 0 & 3 \end{pmatrix}\begin{pmatrix} 1 \\ 3 \end{pmatrix} = \begin{pmatrix} 3 \\ 9 \end{pmatrix}, \begin{pmatrix} 3 & 0 \\ 0 & 3 \end{pmatrix}\begin{pmatrix} 3 \\ 5 \end{pmatrix} = \begin{pmatrix} 9 \\ 15 \end{pmatrix} \text{ and } \begin{pmatrix} 3 & 0 \\ 0 & 3 \end{pmatrix}\begin{pmatrix} -1 \\ 4 \end{pmatrix} = \begin{pmatrix} -3 \\ 12 \end{pmatrix}.$$

$\therefore$ the co-ordinates of the resulting triangle are $\begin{pmatrix} 3 \\ 9 \end{pmatrix}, \begin{pmatrix} 9 \\ 15 \end{pmatrix}$ and $\begin{pmatrix} -3 \\ 12 \end{pmatrix}$.

Exercise 27c

Nos. 1–10 refer to a rectangle ABCD whose vertices are at $\begin{pmatrix} 1 \\ 1 \end{pmatrix}, \begin{pmatrix} 3 \\ 1 \end{pmatrix}$, $\begin{pmatrix} 3 \\ 2 \end{pmatrix}$ and $\begin{pmatrix} 1 \\ 2 \end{pmatrix}$. Write down the co-ordinates of the vertices of the new figure after the stated operation has been carried out.

1. Rotate ABCD through one right angle clockwise.
2. Rotate ABCD through one right angle anti-clockwise.
3. Rotate ABCD through two right angles.
4. Reflect ABCD in the x-axis.
5. Reflect ABCD in the y-axis.
6. Reflect ABCD in the line $y = -x$.
7. Enlarge ABCD in the ratio $2:1$, centre the origin.
8. Stretch ABCD with the operator $\begin{pmatrix} 3 & 1 \\ 1 & 3 \end{pmatrix}$. Sketch the result.
9. Shear ABCD with the operator $\begin{pmatrix} 1 & 2 \\ 0 & 1 \end{pmatrix}$. Sketch the result.
10. PQRS is the reflection of ABCD in the line $y = x$. Reflect PQRS in $y = x$.
11–20. Perform the operations of nos. 1–10 on the rhombus whose vertices are at $\begin{pmatrix} 2 \\ 1 \end{pmatrix}, \begin{pmatrix} 3 \\ -1 \end{pmatrix}, \begin{pmatrix} 4 \\ 1 \end{pmatrix}, \begin{pmatrix} 3 \\ 3 \end{pmatrix}$.

Compound mapping

Example 5 *Enlarge the triangle whose vertices are at* $\begin{pmatrix} 2 \\ 4 \end{pmatrix}, \begin{pmatrix} 5 \\ 1 \end{pmatrix}, \begin{pmatrix} 7 \\ 6 \end{pmatrix}$ *in the ratio* 4:1, *and rotate it through 2 right angles.*

Enlargement in the ratio 4:1 is performed by the operator E, $\begin{pmatrix} 4 & 0 \\ 0 & 4 \end{pmatrix}$.

Rotation through 2 right angles is performed by the operator R, $\begin{pmatrix} -1 & 0 \\ 0 & -1 \end{pmatrix}$.

Enlarging first, $\begin{pmatrix} 2 \\ 4 \end{pmatrix}$ is mapped into $\begin{pmatrix} 4 & 0 \\ 0 & 4 \end{pmatrix}\begin{pmatrix} 2 \\ 4 \end{pmatrix} = \begin{pmatrix} 8 \\ 16 \end{pmatrix}$,

$\begin{pmatrix} 5 \\ 1 \end{pmatrix}$ is mapped into $\begin{pmatrix} 4 & 0 \\ 0 & 4 \end{pmatrix}\begin{pmatrix} 5 \\ 1 \end{pmatrix} = \begin{pmatrix} 20 \\ 4 \end{pmatrix}$,

and $\begin{pmatrix} 7 \\ 6 \end{pmatrix}$ is mapped into $\begin{pmatrix} 4 & 0 \\ 0 & 4 \end{pmatrix}\begin{pmatrix} 7 \\ 6 \end{pmatrix} = \begin{pmatrix} 28 \\ 24 \end{pmatrix}$.

Then rotating, $\begin{pmatrix} 8 \\ 16 \end{pmatrix}$ is mapped into $\begin{pmatrix} -1 & 0 \\ 0 & -1 \end{pmatrix}\begin{pmatrix} 8 \\ 16 \end{pmatrix} = \begin{pmatrix} -8 \\ -16 \end{pmatrix}$,

$\begin{pmatrix} 20 \\ 4 \end{pmatrix}$ is mapped into $\begin{pmatrix} -1 & 0 \\ 0 & -1 \end{pmatrix}\begin{pmatrix} 20 \\ 4 \end{pmatrix} = \begin{pmatrix} -20 \\ -4 \end{pmatrix}$,

and $\begin{pmatrix} 28 \\ 24 \end{pmatrix}$ is mapped into $\begin{pmatrix} -1 & 0 \\ 0 & -1 \end{pmatrix}\begin{pmatrix} 28 \\ 24 \end{pmatrix} = \begin{pmatrix} -28 \\ -24 \end{pmatrix}$.

This process can be described in general terms as $RE(a) = b$.

The product RE is $\begin{pmatrix} -1 & 0 \\ 0 & -1 \end{pmatrix}\begin{pmatrix} 4 & 0 \\ 0 & 4 \end{pmatrix} = \begin{pmatrix} -4 & 0 \\ 0 & -4 \end{pmatrix}$.

Using this operator, $\begin{pmatrix} 2 \\ 4 \end{pmatrix}$ is mapped into $\begin{pmatrix} -4 & 0 \\ 0 & -4 \end{pmatrix}\begin{pmatrix} 2 \\ 4 \end{pmatrix} = \begin{pmatrix} -8 \\ -16 \end{pmatrix}$,

$$\binom{5}{1} \text{ is mapped into } \begin{pmatrix} -4 & 0 \\ 0 & -4 \end{pmatrix}\binom{5}{1} = \binom{-20}{-4}$$

$$\text{and } \binom{7}{6} \text{ is mapped into } \begin{pmatrix} -4 & 0 \\ 0 & -4 \end{pmatrix}\binom{7}{6} = \binom{-28}{-24}.$$

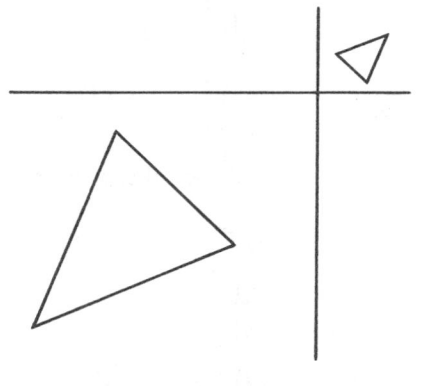

Fig. 74

Note that RE means perform E first and then R because $RE(a) = b$ means $R(E(a)) = b$.

Example 6   *The square whose vertices are at* $\binom{2}{1}$, $\binom{4}{1}$, $\binom{4}{3}$ *and* $\binom{2}{3}$ *is*

reflected in the line $y = -x$ *and then sheared by the operator* $\begin{pmatrix} 1 & 3 \\ 0 & 1 \end{pmatrix}$.

Find the vertices of the resulting figure. What would be the result if the shearing were performed first followed by the reflection?

Reflection in the line $y = -x$ is performed by $\begin{pmatrix} 0 & -1 \\ -1 & 0 \end{pmatrix}$.

The combined operation is performed by

$$\begin{pmatrix} 1 & 3 \\ 0 & 1 \end{pmatrix}\begin{pmatrix} 0 & -1 \\ -1 & 0 \end{pmatrix} = \begin{pmatrix} -3 & -1 \\ -1 & 0 \end{pmatrix}.$$

163

$\begin{pmatrix} 2 \\ 1 \end{pmatrix}$ is mapped into $\begin{pmatrix} -3 & -1 \\ -1 & 0 \end{pmatrix}\begin{pmatrix} 2 \\ 1 \end{pmatrix} = \begin{pmatrix} -7 \\ -2 \end{pmatrix}$,

$\begin{pmatrix} 4 \\ 1 \end{pmatrix}$ is mapped into $\begin{pmatrix} -3 & -1 \\ -1 & 0 \end{pmatrix}\begin{pmatrix} 4 \\ 1 \end{pmatrix} = \begin{pmatrix} -13 \\ -4 \end{pmatrix}$,

$\begin{pmatrix} 4 \\ 3 \end{pmatrix}$ is mapped into $\begin{pmatrix} -3 & -1 \\ -1 & 0 \end{pmatrix}\begin{pmatrix} 4 \\ 3 \end{pmatrix} = \begin{pmatrix} -15 \\ -4 \end{pmatrix}$,

$\begin{pmatrix} 2 \\ 3 \end{pmatrix}$ is mapped into $\begin{pmatrix} -3 & -1 \\ -1 & 0 \end{pmatrix}\begin{pmatrix} 2 \\ 3 \end{pmatrix} = \begin{pmatrix} -9 \\ -2 \end{pmatrix}$.

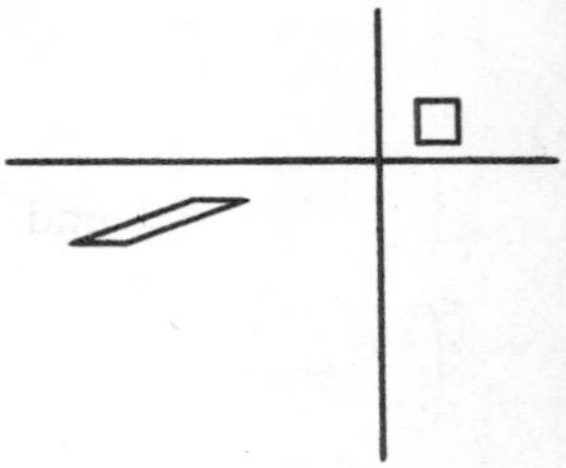

Fig. 75

If the operations are performed the other way round the combined operator is $\begin{pmatrix} 0 & -1 \\ -1 & 0 \end{pmatrix}\begin{pmatrix} 1 & 3 \\ 0 & 1 \end{pmatrix} = \begin{pmatrix} 0 & -1 \\ -1 & -3 \end{pmatrix}$.

$\begin{pmatrix} 2 \\ 1 \end{pmatrix}$ is mapped into $\begin{pmatrix} 0 & -1 \\ -1 & -3 \end{pmatrix}\begin{pmatrix} 2 \\ 1 \end{pmatrix} = \begin{pmatrix} -1 \\ -5 \end{pmatrix}$,

$\begin{pmatrix} 4 \\ 1 \end{pmatrix}$ is mapped into $\begin{pmatrix} 0 & -1 \\ -1 & -3 \end{pmatrix}\begin{pmatrix} 4 \\ 1 \end{pmatrix} = \begin{pmatrix} -1 \\ -7 \end{pmatrix}$,

$\begin{pmatrix} 4 \\ 3 \end{pmatrix}$ is mapped into $\begin{pmatrix} 0 & -1 \\ -1 & -3 \end{pmatrix}\begin{pmatrix} 4 \\ 3 \end{pmatrix} = \begin{pmatrix} -3 \\ -13 \end{pmatrix}$,

$\begin{pmatrix} 2 \\ 3 \end{pmatrix}$ is mapped into $\begin{pmatrix} 0 & -1 \\ -1 & -3 \end{pmatrix}\begin{pmatrix} 2 \\ 3 \end{pmatrix} = \begin{pmatrix} -3 \\ -11 \end{pmatrix}$.

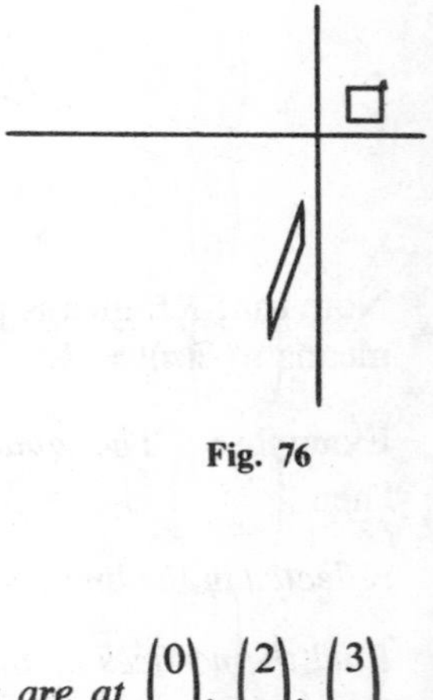

Fig. 76

Example 7 *The quadrilateral whose vertices are at* $\begin{pmatrix} 0 \\ 0 \end{pmatrix}$, $\begin{pmatrix} 2 \\ 3 \end{pmatrix}$, $\begin{pmatrix} 3 \\ 2 \end{pmatrix}$ *and* $\begin{pmatrix} 4 \\ -2 \end{pmatrix}$ *is enlarged in the ratio* $3:2$ *centre* $\begin{pmatrix} 1 \\ 2 \end{pmatrix}$. *What are the vertices of the resulting figure?*

This can be performed by translating $\begin{pmatrix} 1 \\ 2 \end{pmatrix}$ to the origin, enlarging and then translating back as follows:

164

$\begin{pmatrix} 0 \\ 0 \end{pmatrix}$ is mapped into $\begin{pmatrix} 0 \\ 0 \end{pmatrix} - \begin{pmatrix} 1 \\ 2 \end{pmatrix} = \begin{pmatrix} -1 \\ -2 \end{pmatrix},$

$\begin{pmatrix} 2 \\ 3 \end{pmatrix}$ is mapped into $\begin{pmatrix} 2 \\ 3 \end{pmatrix} - \begin{pmatrix} 1 \\ 2 \end{pmatrix} = \begin{pmatrix} 1 \\ 1 \end{pmatrix},$

$\begin{pmatrix} 3 \\ 2 \end{pmatrix}$ is mapped into $\begin{pmatrix} 3 \\ 2 \end{pmatrix} - \begin{pmatrix} 1 \\ 2 \end{pmatrix} = \begin{pmatrix} 2 \\ 0 \end{pmatrix},$

$\begin{pmatrix} 4 \\ -2 \end{pmatrix}$ is mapped into $\begin{pmatrix} 4 \\ -2 \end{pmatrix} - \begin{pmatrix} 1 \\ 2 \end{pmatrix} = \begin{pmatrix} 3 \\ -4 \end{pmatrix}.$

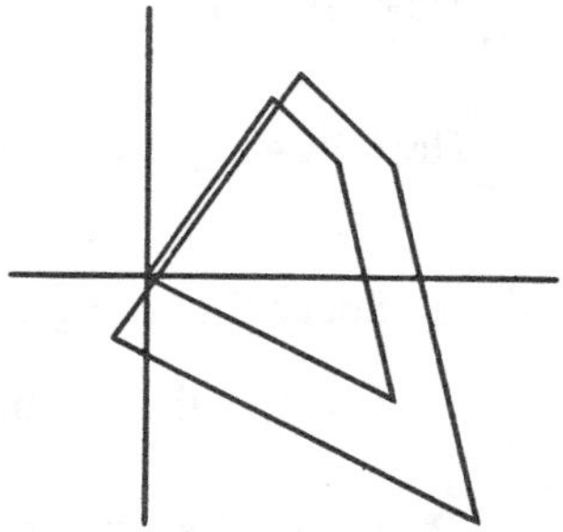

Fig. 77

Then $\begin{pmatrix} -1 \\ -2 \end{pmatrix}$ is mapped into $\begin{pmatrix} 1\frac{1}{2} & 0 \\ 0 & 1\frac{1}{2} \end{pmatrix}\begin{pmatrix} -1 \\ -2 \end{pmatrix} = \begin{pmatrix} -1\frac{1}{2} \\ -3 \end{pmatrix},$

$\begin{pmatrix} 1 \\ 1 \end{pmatrix}$ is mapped into $\begin{pmatrix} 1\frac{1}{2} & 0 \\ 0 & 1\frac{1}{2} \end{pmatrix} \begin{pmatrix} 1 \\ 1 \end{pmatrix} = \begin{pmatrix} 1\frac{1}{2} \\ 1\frac{1}{2} \end{pmatrix},$

$\begin{pmatrix} 2 \\ 0 \end{pmatrix}$ is mapped into $\begin{pmatrix} 1\frac{1}{2} & 0 \\ 0 & 1\frac{1}{2} \end{pmatrix} \begin{pmatrix} 2 \\ 0 \end{pmatrix} = \begin{pmatrix} 3 \\ 0 \end{pmatrix},$

$\begin{pmatrix} 3 \\ -4 \end{pmatrix}$ is mapped into $\begin{pmatrix} 1\frac{1}{2} & 0 \\ 0 & 1\frac{1}{2} \end{pmatrix}\begin{pmatrix} 3 \\ -4 \end{pmatrix} = \begin{pmatrix} 4\frac{1}{2} \\ -6 \end{pmatrix}.$

Then $\begin{pmatrix} -1\frac{1}{2} \\ -3 \end{pmatrix}$ is mapped into $\begin{pmatrix} -1\frac{1}{2} \\ -3 \end{pmatrix} + \begin{pmatrix} 1 \\ 2 \end{pmatrix} = \begin{pmatrix} -\frac{1}{2} \\ -1 \end{pmatrix},$

$\begin{pmatrix} 1\frac{1}{2} \\ 1\frac{1}{2} \end{pmatrix}$ is mapped into $\begin{pmatrix} 1\frac{1}{2} \\ 1\frac{1}{2} \end{pmatrix} + \begin{pmatrix} 1 \\ 2 \end{pmatrix} = \begin{pmatrix} 2\frac{1}{2} \\ 3\frac{1}{2} \end{pmatrix},$

$\begin{pmatrix} 3 \\ 0 \end{pmatrix}$ is mapped into $\begin{pmatrix} 3 \\ 0 \end{pmatrix} + \begin{pmatrix} 1 \\ 2 \end{pmatrix} = \begin{pmatrix} 4 \\ 2 \end{pmatrix},$

$\begin{pmatrix} 4\frac{1}{2} \\ -6 \end{pmatrix}$ is mapped into $\begin{pmatrix} 4\frac{1}{2} \\ -6 \end{pmatrix} + \begin{pmatrix} 1 \\ 2 \end{pmatrix} = \begin{pmatrix} 5\frac{1}{2} \\ -4 \end{pmatrix}.$

The vertices of the image are $\begin{pmatrix} -\frac{1}{2} \\ -1 \end{pmatrix}, \begin{pmatrix} 2\frac{1}{2} \\ 3\frac{1}{2} \end{pmatrix}, \begin{pmatrix} 4 \\ 2 \end{pmatrix}$ and $\begin{pmatrix} 5\frac{1}{2} \\ -4 \end{pmatrix}.$

165

Exercise 27d

The following refer to a triangle whose vertices are at $\begin{pmatrix} 1 \\ 2 \end{pmatrix}, \begin{pmatrix} 5 \\ 3 \end{pmatrix}, \begin{pmatrix} 3 \\ -2 \end{pmatrix}$.

1. Shear the triangle with the operator $\begin{pmatrix} 1 & 4 \\ 0 & 1 \end{pmatrix}$. Find the operator which will map the image back into the object.

2. Stretch the triangle with the operator $\begin{pmatrix} 1 & 3 \\ 3 & 1 \end{pmatrix}$. Find the operator which will map the image back into the object.

3. Find the result of first shearing the triangle as in no. 1 and then stretching it as in no. 2.

4. Map the triangle with the operator $\begin{pmatrix} 1 & 3 \\ 3 & 9 \end{pmatrix}$. Is it possible to find an operator which will map the image back into the object?

5. Enlarge the triangle with the operator $\begin{pmatrix} 6 & 0 \\ 0 & 6 \end{pmatrix}$. Find the operator which will map the image back into the object.

6. Enlarge the triangle as in no. 5 and then shear it as in no. 1.

7. Rotate the triangle about the origin through one right angle anti-clockwise and reflect it in the x-axis.

8. Rotate the triangle about the origin through two right angles and reflect it in the line $y = -x$.

9. Rotate the triangle about the origin through one right angle clockwise and enlarge it in the ratio $3:1$ with centre the origin.

10. Reflect the triangle in the x-axis and rotate it through one right angle anti-clockwise.

11. Reflect the triangle in the line $y = x$ and enlarge it in the ratio $5:1$ centre the origin.

12. Reflect the triangle in the y-axis and shear it with the operator $\begin{pmatrix} 1 & 3 \\ 0 & 1 \end{pmatrix}$.

13. Reflect the triangle in the x-axis and translate it through $\begin{pmatrix} 3 \\ 4 \end{pmatrix}$.

14. Shear the triangle with $\begin{pmatrix} 1 & 4 \\ 0 & 1 \end{pmatrix}$ and rotate it through one right angle clockwise about the origin.

15. Shear the triangle with $\begin{pmatrix} 1 & 5 \\ 0 & 1 \end{pmatrix}$ and reflect it in the line $y = -x$.

16. Use the method of Example 7 to enlarge the triangle in the ratio $3:1$ centre $\begin{pmatrix} 2 \\ 1 \end{pmatrix}$.

17. Rotate the triangle through one right angle clockwise about $\begin{pmatrix} -1 \\ 3 \end{pmatrix}$.

18. Rotate the triangle through two right angles about $\begin{pmatrix} 1 \\ 2 \end{pmatrix}$.

19. Rotate the triangle through two right angles about the origin, enlarge it in the ratio $2:1$ centre the origin, and stretch it with the operator $\begin{pmatrix} 1 & 3 \\ 3 & 1 \end{pmatrix}$.

20. Enlarge the triangle in the ratio $3:1$ centre $\begin{pmatrix} 4 \\ 2 \end{pmatrix}$ and shear it with the operator $\begin{pmatrix} 1 & 5 \\ 0 & 1 \end{pmatrix}$.

Chapter 28

Compound interest

Four per cent of a given number is found by multiplying the number by 4, and moving the digits two places to the right (to divide by 100), e.g. 4% of $163 \cdot 72 = 1 \cdot 637\ 2 \times 4$
$$= 6 \cdot 548\ 8.$$

Example 1 *Find to the nearest penny the compound interest on £236·73 for 3 years at 6% per annum.*

1st year	Principal	£236·73
	Interest 6%	14·203 8
2nd year	Principal	250·933 8
	Interest 6%	15·055 8 ...
3rd year	Principal	265·989 6
	Interest 6%	15·958 8
	Amount	281·948 4

$\qquad\qquad\quad = £281 \cdot 95$ to nearest penny

Principal $= £236 \cdot 73$

Compound Interest $= £45 \cdot 22.$

Example 2 *Find to the nearest penny the amount of £128·64 in 2 years at $4\frac{3}{4}\%$ per annum compound interest.*

1st year	Principal		£128·64
		$\begin{cases} 4\% \\ \frac{1}{2}\% \\ \frac{1}{4}\% \end{cases}$	
	Interest	4%	5·145 6
		$\frac{1}{2}\%$	0·643 2
		$\frac{1}{4}\%$	0·321 6
2nd year	Principal		134·750 4
	Interest	4%	5·390 0 ...
		$\frac{1}{2}\%$	0·673 7 ...
		$\frac{1}{4}\%$	0·336 8 ...
	Amount		141·150 9

$\qquad\qquad\quad = £141 \cdot 15$ to nearest penny.

If the interest is to be added half-yearly and the rate is 6% per annum, then the interest must be calculated and added each half-year at the rate of 3%.

Example 3 *A man borrows £3 650 at 8% per annum, interest to be added half-yearly, and arranges to pay back £240 at the end of each half-year. How much does he still owe after 1½ years?*

1st half-year	Total debt	£3 650
	Interest 4%	146
		3 796
	Repayment	240
2nd half-year	Total debt	3 556
	Interest 4%	142·24
		3 698·24
	Repayment	240
3rd half-year	Total debt	3 458·24
	Interest 4%	138·329 6
		3 596·569 6
	Repayment	240
Total debt after 1½ years		3 356·569 6
		= £3 356·57 to nearest penny.

Exercise 28

In this exercise all answers should be to the nearest penny.

Find the amount at compound interest for each of the following:

1. £123·62 for 2 years at 5% per annum.

2. £47·28 „ 3 „ „ 6% „ „

3. £865·47 „ 2 „ „ 4% „ „

4. £507·75 „ 4 „ „ 4% „ „

5. £82·64 „ 2 „ „ 2¾% „ „

6. £270·35 „ 2 „ „ 5½% „ „

Find the compound interest on

7. £211·36 for 2 years at 7% per annum.

8. £357·11 „ 3 „ „ 5% „ „

9. £19·57 „ 3 „ „ 3% „ „

10. £182·91 „ 4 „ „ 8% „ „

11. £973·76 „ 2 „ „ $3\frac{1}{2}$% „ „

12. £2 062·48 „ 3 „ „ $4\frac{2}{3}$% „ „

13. Find the amount of £308·60 in 2 years at 6% per annum, compound interest being added half-yearly.

14. Find the compound interest on £243·21 for $1\frac{1}{2}$ years at 7% per annum, interest being added half-yearly.

15. A man borrows £2 400 at 8% per annum compound interest. After a year he borrows a further £300, and a year later he borrows another £300. How much does he then owe?

16. A man borrows £2 540 at 9% per annum compound interest. After a year he repays £300, and a year later he repays a further £300. How much does he then owe?

17. Find the amount of £198·75 after 1 year at 8% per annum, compound interest being added quarterly.

18. The value of a car depreciates by 20% in the first year, 15% in the second, and $12\frac{1}{2}$% in each subsequent year. If the car cost £1 450 when new, find its value after 4 years (nearest £).

19. A man invests £2 750 at 7% per annum compound interest, and adds a further £650 to his investment at the end of each year. How much stands to his credit immediately after he has added his third £650?

20. A man invested £4 860 at 7% per annum, interest to be added half-yearly. After 6 months the rate was increased to 8%, and after another year it rose to 9% per annum. How much was standing to the investor's credit 2 years after his initial investment?

Chapter 29

Shares and stocks

Shares

Example 1 *An investor buys* 300 50p *shares when their price is* 75p, *and receives a dividend of* 9%.

  (i) *How much does he pay for the shares?*

 (ii) *What is his dividend in cash?*

(iii) *What yield per cent does he receive on his investment?*

  (i) Cost of shares = 300 × 75p = £225

 (ii) Nominal value of shares = 300 × 50p = £150

    ∴ dividend = 9% of £150 = £13·50

(iii) £225 cash earns £13·50

∴ £100 „   „ £13·50 × $\frac{100}{225}$ = £$\frac{1350}{225}$ = £6

    ∴ yield = 6%.

Alternatively

(iii) Dividend on one share = 9% of 50p = $4\frac{1}{2}$p

    ∴   75p cash earns $4\frac{1}{2}$p

    ∴ 100p „   „ $4\frac{1}{2}$p × $\frac{100}{75}$ = 6p

    ∴ yield = 6%.

Example 2 *A* 40p *share stands at* 25p. *Find the yield per cent on money invested if the dividend is* 7%.

Dividend on one share = 7% of 40p = 2·8p

∴   25p cash earns 2·8p

∴ 100p „   „   2·8p × $\frac{100}{25}$ = 11·2p

∴ yield = 11·2%.

Alternatively

    Since the nominal value of the shares is **greater** than their cash value in the ratio $\frac{40}{25}$, the yield is **more** than 7% in the ratio $\frac{40}{25}$.

∴ yield = 7% × $\frac{40}{25}$ = 7% × $\frac{8}{5}$ = 11·2%.

N.B. From Example 2 and Example 1(iii) it can be seen that

$$\text{yield } \% = \frac{\text{nominal value}}{\text{cash value}} \times \text{dividend } \%,$$

and this is usually the simplest way of calculating the yield per cent.

Example 3 *A man invests £520 in 25p shares when their price is 80p. A dividend of 19% is declared and he subsequently sells the shares at $92\frac{1}{2}$p.*
 (i) *How many shares does he buy?*
 (ii) *What is his cash dividend?*
(iii) *What is the yield per cent?*
(iv) *What cash profit does he make on the sale?*

 (i) Number of shares $= \dfrac{£520}{80\text{p}} = \dfrac{52\,000}{80} = 650$

 (ii) Nominal value of shares $= 650 \times 25\text{p} = £162\cdot50$
  $\therefore$ dividend $= 19\%$ of £162·50
   $= 19 \times £1\cdot625 = £30\cdot875 \simeq £30\cdot88$

(iii) Yield $\% = \dfrac{\text{nominal value}}{\text{cash value}} \times \text{dividend } \%$

  $= \frac{25}{80} \times 19\% = \frac{475}{80}\% \simeq 5\cdot94\%$

(iv) Profit on one share $= 92\frac{1}{2}\text{p} - 80\text{p} = 12\frac{1}{2}\text{p}$
  $\therefore$ profit on 650 shares $= 650 \times 12\frac{1}{2}\text{p} = £81\cdot25$.

Exercise 29a

1. Calculate the cost of
   (i) 240 Shell £1 shares at 164p.
   (ii) 125 Lake George 25p shares at 45p.
   (iii) 600 Anglo-Oriental Rubber 10p shares at $26\frac{1}{2}$p.
   (iv) 72 S. and N. Breweries £1 shares at 313p.
   (v) 120 British Leyland 25p shares at $27\frac{3}{4}$p.

2. Find how many shares can be bought for £270 invested in
   (i) British American Tobacco 50p shares at 540p.
   (ii) Lotus 25p shares at $67\frac{1}{2}$p.

    (iii) Barclays Bank £1 shares at 375p.
    (iv) Cunard £1 shares at $62\frac{1}{2}$p.
    (v) Cerebos 25p shares at $56\frac{1}{4}$p.

3. In the following cases find the actual dividend paid, and the percentage yield on money invested.

    (i) 350 £1   shares bought at 125p; dividend 10%.

(ii)	250	40p	„	„	„	75p;	„	$12\frac{1}{2}$%.
(iii)	350	50p	„	„	„	45p;	„	3%.
(iv)	280	25p	„	„	„	18p;	„	$4\frac{1}{2}$%.
(v)	450	20p	„	„	„	192p;	„	72%.

4. Find the profit made by buying 250 G.E.C. shares at $132\frac{1}{2}$p and selling them at 149p.

5. An investor bought 600 E.M.I. shares at 198p and sold them when the price had fallen to $152\frac{1}{2}$p. How much did he lose?

6. A man bought 350 Plessey 50p shares at 115p and received a dividend of $11\frac{1}{2}$%. Find the percentage yield on cash invested.

7. Some Johnson Matthey £1 shares were bought at 420p, and the dividend declared produced a yield of $3\frac{3}{4}$% on the investment. Find the dividend per cent.

8. An investor bought some Thomas Tilling 20p shares and received a dividend of $40\frac{1}{2}$%. The actual return on money invested was $7\frac{1}{2}$%. Find the price at which he bought the shares.

9. A man sold 180 Whitbread Brewery shares at 95p, and made a profit of £29·70. Find the price at which he bought them.

10. A holder of 240 Marks and Spencer 25p shares sold them at 264p and re-invested the proceeds in Smith and Nephew 10p shares at 55p. How many of the latter shares did he buy?

11. In 1963 a man bought 400 Allied Breweries 25p shares at 65p. He sold them in 1971 at $129\frac{1}{2}$p and invested the proceeds in Crest Timber 20p shares at 74p. How many Crest Timber shares did he buy? If he sold these in 1973 at $51\frac{1}{2}$p, find his total capital gain?

12. In 1969 an investor bought 540 British Leyland 25p shares at 87p and some Ready Mixed Concrete 25p shares at 85p. In 1972 he sold the British Leyland shares at 32p and the R.M.C. shares at 217p. If he neither gained nor lost, how many R.M.C. shares did he buy?

13. A man holding 300 Carlton Shoe 25p shares received a dividend of 18%. He sold the shares at 81p and re-invested the cash in Automat 50p shares at 75p. If Automat declared a dividend of $8\frac{1}{3}$%, was his income greater or less than before?

14. Some £1 Preference shares pay an annual dividend of $4\frac{3}{4}$% and they stand at 72p. How many shares must an investor buy to obtain an annual income of £114, and how much will he have to pay for them? What will be his percentage return on the money invested? (3 sig. fig.)

15. A man bought 600 25p shares at 35p. He sold half of them at 41p, and two days later when the price had risen to 45p he sold the remainder. He re-invested the proceeds of the two sales in some £1 shares at 172p. If he received a half-yearly dividend of $3\frac{1}{2}$% on the first investment, and then a half-yearly dividend of $7\frac{1}{2}$% on the second, express his total income as a percentage yield on his original cash outlay.

Stock

The price of stock is based on a **par** value of £100, so that if a stock is quoted at $84\frac{3}{4}$, then £100 stock can be bought or sold for £84·75 cash.

It is important to use the words **cash** and **stock** to avoid confusion.

Example 4 *How much Treasury 4% stock at 68 can be bought for £253·30? What annual income is received, and what is the yield per cent on cash invested?*

(i)   £68 cash buys £100 stock

∴ £253·30 cash buys £100 × $\dfrac{253\cdot30}{68}$ stock

= £372·50 stock

(ii) The income is £4 on £100 stock,
        i.e. £4 on £68 cash.
      On £100   stock the income is £4

$$\therefore \text{ on } £372{\cdot}50 \text{ stock the income is } £4 \times \frac{372{\cdot}50}{100}$$

$$= £14{\cdot}90$$

Alternatively
      On £68 cash the income is £4

$$\therefore \text{ on } £253{\cdot}30 \text{ cash the income is } £4 \times \frac{253{\cdot}30}{68}$$

$$= £14{\cdot}90$$

(iii)   On £68 cash the income is £4
      $\therefore$ on £100 cash the income is £4 $\times \frac{100}{68} \simeq £5{\cdot}88$
      $\therefore$ the yield is 5·88%.

Alternatively, since the nominal value of the stock is **greater** than its cash value in the ratio $\frac{100}{68}$, the yield is **more** than 4% in the ratio $\frac{100}{68}$.
$\therefore$ the yield is 4% $\times \frac{100}{68} \simeq 5{\cdot}88\%$.

Example 5   *A man holding £840 of Dover Harbour $3\frac{3}{4}\%$ stock sold it at 77 and re-invested the proceeds in Canadian Pacific 4% stock at 85. By what amount was his income reduced?*

Original income $= 3\frac{3}{4}\%$ of £840
               $= £31{\cdot}50$
    £100 of D.H. stock is sold for £77 cash
$\therefore$ £840 of D.H. stock is sold for £77 $\times \frac{840}{100}$ cash
                      $= £646{\cdot}80$ cash
    In C.P. stock   £85   cash yields an income of £4

$$\therefore \text{ in C.P. stock } £646{\cdot}80 \text{ cash yields an income of } £4 \times \frac{646{\cdot}80}{85}$$

$$\simeq £30{\cdot}44$$

$\therefore$ reduction in income $= £31{\cdot}50 - £30{\cdot}44$
                     $= £1{\cdot}06$.

Exercise 29b

Give the answers to the nearest penny where necessary.

1. Find the cost of

    (i) £400 of 3% stock at 60.
    (ii) £250 „ 7% „ „ 105.
    (iii) £320 „ 6% „ „ 96.
    (iv) £560 „ $3\frac{3}{4}$% „ „ $62\frac{1}{2}$.
    (v) £360 „ $5\frac{1}{4}$% „ „ $94\frac{1}{2}$.

2. Find the income from each of the investments in no. 1.

3. Find the yield per cent from each of the investments in no. 1.

4. Find how much stock is obtained by investing

    (i) £480 in a $2\frac{1}{2}$% stock at 64.
    (ii) £300 „ „ 3% „ „ 72.
    (iii) £420 „ „ 6% „ „ 108.
    (iv) £250 „ „ 4% „ „ 88.
    (v) £500 „ „ $4\frac{1}{2}$% „ „ 96.

5. Find the income from each of the investments in no. 4.

6. Find the yield per cent from each of the investments in no. 4 (2 dec. places).

7. How much cash must be invested in Birmingham $2\frac{3}{4}$% loan at $98\frac{1}{2}$ to obtain an annual income of £55?

8. Find the price of Norvic 5% loan if an investment of £1 395 cash provides an annual income of £75.

9. Find the annual income obtained by investing £950 in Odeon $3\frac{1}{4}$% stock at 67.

10. Find the rate per cent paid by Neville Loan at 93 if an investment of £837 cash provides an income of £45 annually.

11. A man invested £400 in a 3% stock at 72 and sold out at 76. How much did he gain?

12. Find the price of British Gas $3\frac{1}{2}\%$ stock if money invested gives a yield of $4\frac{3}{8}\%$.

13. Find the rate per cent paid by Brown debentures at 104 if an investment of £676 cash yields an annual income of £35·75.

14. Find the cash value of an investment in a $3\frac{1}{2}\%$ stock at $82\frac{1}{2}$ if it produces an annual income of £36·40.

15. An investment of £1 200 in Dunlop $3\frac{1}{2}\%$ stock provides an annual income of £58·33. Find the price of the stock.

Chapter 30

Simultaneous equations

Solution by substitution

Example 1 *Solve the equations* $3x + y = 11$, $5x - 3y = 9$.

$$3x + y = 11 \qquad \text{(i)}$$
$$5x - 3y = 9 \qquad \text{(ii)}$$

From (i) $\qquad y = 11 - 3x \quad \text{(iii)}$

Substituting this value for y in (ii),

$5x - 3(11 - 3x) = 9$

$\therefore \ 5x - 33 + 9x = 9$

$\qquad \therefore \ 14x = 42$

$\qquad \therefore \qquad x = 3$

Substituting this value for x in (iii),

$y = 11 - 3 \times 3 = 11 - 9 = 2$

$\therefore \ x = 3, y = 2.$

Check by substituting both values in (i) and (ii),

(i) $3x + y = 3 \times 3 + 2 = 9 + 2 = 11$

(ii) $5x - 3y = 5 \times 3 - 3 \times 2 = 15 - 6 = 9.$

Solution by elimination

Example 2 *Solve the equations* $2x - 3y = 13$, $5x + 2y = 4$.

$$2x - 3y = 13 \qquad \text{(i)}$$
$$5x + 2y = 4 \qquad \text{(ii)}$$

(i) $\times 2 \quad 4x - 6y = 26$

(ii) $\times 3 \quad \underline{15x + 6y = 12}$

Add $\ 19x \qquad = 38$

$\qquad \therefore \ x = 2$

Substitute in (ii) $5 \times 2 + 2y = 4$

$$\therefore\ 2y = 4 - 10 = -6$$
$$\therefore\ y = -3$$

$\therefore\ x = 2,\ y = -3.$

Check in (i) $2x - 3y = 2 \times 2 - 3 \times (-3) = 4 + 9 = 13$

(ii) $5x + 2y = 5 \times 2 + 2 \times (-3) = 10 - 6 = 4.$

Alternatively, instead of substituting $x = 2$ to find y, it may be simpler to start again with the original equations and eliminate x to find y: e.g.

(i) $\times 5 \qquad 10x - 15y = 65$
(ii) $\times 2 \qquad\ \ 10x + 4y = \ \ 8$
$\qquad\qquad$ Subtract $-19y = 57$
$$\therefore\ y = -3$$

Exercise 30a

Use the method of substitution to solve:

1. $x + y = 6$ 2. $2x - y = 11$ 3. $3x - 4y = 7$
   $2x + 3y = 14$ $x + 2y = -7$ $x - 2y = 5$

Use the method of elimination to solve:

4. $3x + 2y = 7$ 5. $5x - 2y = -23$ 6. $3x - 2y = 4$
   $7x - 3y = 1$ $3x + 4y = 7$ $2x - 7y = 31$

Solve the following pairs of equations:

7. $x - 2y = 1$ 8. $a + 3b = -13$ 9. $4c - 3d = 1$
   $x + 2y = 9$ $2a - 9b = 4$ $2c + 4d = 17$

10. $3x + 4y = -1$ 11. $5m - 2n = 15$ 12. $3x + 7y = -8$
    $3x + 8y = 4$ $3m + 5n = 9$ $5y = 2x + 15$

13. $3a + 4m = 0$ 14. $5d = 4n + 8$ 15. $5x + 3y - 2 = 0$
    $a = 2m - 5$ $5n + 10 = 4d$ $3x - 32 = 7y$

Example 3   *Solve the equations* $\frac{2}{3}x - \frac{1}{2}y = 2$, $\frac{3}{4}x - \frac{1}{3}y = 3\frac{1}{6}$.

$\frac{2}{3}x - \frac{1}{2}y = 2$ (i)
$\frac{3}{4}x - \frac{1}{3}y = 3\frac{1}{6}$ (ii)

First simplify the equations separately by clearing the fractions.

(i) $\times 6$ $4x - 3y = 12$ (iii)

(ii) $\times 12$ $9x - 4y = 38$ (iv)

Now solve in the usual way.

(iii) $\times 4$ $16x - 12y = 48$

(iv) $\times 3$ $27x - 12y = 114$

     Subtract $-11x = -66$

            $\therefore x = 6$

Substitute in (iii) $24 - 3y = 12$

           $\therefore -3y = -12$

              $\therefore y = 4$

$\therefore x = 6, y = 4.$

Alternatively

$$4x - 3y = 12$$
$$9x - 4y = 38$$

$$\therefore \begin{pmatrix} 4 & -3 \\ 9 & -4 \end{pmatrix} \begin{pmatrix} x \\ y \end{pmatrix} = \begin{pmatrix} 12 \\ 38 \end{pmatrix}$$

$$\therefore \frac{1}{11}\begin{pmatrix} -4 & 3 \\ -9 & 4 \end{pmatrix}\begin{pmatrix} 4 & -3 \\ 9 & -4 \end{pmatrix} \begin{pmatrix} x \\ y \end{pmatrix} = \frac{1}{11}\begin{pmatrix} -4 & 3 \\ -9 & 4 \end{pmatrix}\begin{pmatrix} 12 \\ 38 \end{pmatrix}$$

$$\therefore \frac{1}{11}\begin{pmatrix} 11 & 0 \\ 0 & 11 \end{pmatrix}\begin{pmatrix} x \\ y \end{pmatrix} = \frac{1}{11}\begin{pmatrix} 66 \\ 44 \end{pmatrix}$$

$$\therefore \begin{pmatrix} 1 & 0 \\ 0 & 1 \end{pmatrix}\begin{pmatrix} x \\ y \end{pmatrix} = \begin{pmatrix} 6 \\ 4 \end{pmatrix}$$

$$\therefore x = 6, y = 4.$$

Check   (i) $\frac{2}{3}x - \frac{1}{2}y = 4 - 2 = 2$

          (ii) $\frac{3}{4}x - \frac{1}{3}y = 4\frac{1}{2} - 1\frac{1}{3} = 3\frac{1}{6}.$

Example 4   *Solve the equations* $\dfrac{4}{x} + \dfrac{1}{y} = 4$, $\dfrac{2}{x} - \dfrac{3}{y} = 9.$

Instead of treating x and y as the unknowns, use $\dfrac{1}{x}$ and $\dfrac{1}{y}$.

$$\frac{4}{x} + \frac{1}{y} = 4 \qquad \text{(i)}$$

$$\frac{2}{x} - \frac{3}{y} = 9 \qquad \text{(ii)}$$

(i) $\qquad \dfrac{4}{x} + \dfrac{1}{y} = 4$

(ii) $\times 2 \qquad \dfrac{4}{x} - \dfrac{6}{y} = 18$

Subtract $\qquad \dfrac{7}{y} = -14$

$$\therefore \frac{1}{y} = -2 \quad \text{i.e. } y = -\tfrac{1}{2}$$

Substitute in (ii) $\quad \dfrac{2}{x} - 3 \times (-2) = 9$

$$\therefore \frac{2}{x} + 6 = 9$$

$$\therefore \frac{2}{x} = 3$$

$$\therefore \frac{1}{x} = 1\tfrac{1}{2} \quad \text{i.e. } x = \tfrac{2}{3}$$

$$\therefore x = \tfrac{2}{3}, \; y = -\tfrac{1}{2}.$$

Check (i) $\dfrac{4}{x} + \dfrac{1}{y} = 4 \times 1\tfrac{1}{2} - 2 = 6 - 2 = 4$

(ii) $\dfrac{2}{x} - \dfrac{3}{y} = 2 \times 1\tfrac{1}{2} - 3 \times (-2) = 3 + 6 = 9.$

Example 5 *Solve the equations*
$$3x - 2y + 1 = 2x + 5y - 10 = 4x - 3y.$$

Pair the three equal algebraic expressions in any two different ways.

$3x - 2y + 1 = 4x - 3y$
$\therefore\ x - y = 1$ (i)
$2x + 5y - 10 = 4x - 3y$
$\therefore 2x - 8y = -10$
$\therefore\ x - 4y = -5$ (ii)

Equations (i) and (ii) are then solved in the usual way, and $x = 3$, $y = 2$.

Exercise 30b

Solve the following pairs of equations:

1. $\frac{3}{4}x + \frac{1}{5}y = 4$
$\frac{1}{2}x = \frac{3}{5}y - 1$

2. $\dfrac{4}{x} - \dfrac{3}{y} = 1$

$\dfrac{5}{x} - \dfrac{6}{y} = \dfrac{1}{2}$

3. $1\cdot2x - 1\cdot1y = 7\cdot9$
$1\cdot8x + 0\cdot7y = 0\cdot1$

4. $\dfrac{d}{4} - \dfrac{n}{3} = 6$

$\dfrac{3d}{2} + \dfrac{5n}{6} = 2$

5. $3x - y + 12 = 5x + 2y + 4 = x + y$

6. $5(a + b) = 2(a + 3b) + 1$
$3(a + 2b) - 7 = a + 3b + 1$

7. $\dfrac{3}{x} + \dfrac{7}{y} = \dfrac{3}{2}$

$\dfrac{1}{x} + \dfrac{4}{y} = \dfrac{4}{3}$

8. $2\cdot5d - 1\cdot5g = -2$
$1\cdot3d + g + 4\cdot6 = 0$

9. $\dfrac{5}{x} - \dfrac{2}{y} = 7$

$\dfrac{2}{x} + 6 = \dfrac{3}{y}$

10. $\frac{2}{3}(a - 6) = m - 3$
$\frac{3}{5}(a + 2) = 2m + 1$

11. $c + d + 6 = 2c - 5d - 3 = 3c - 4d + 2$

12. $3(2u - w) = 5u - w + 1$
$6u + 7w + 4 = 4(u + 2w)$

13. $\frac{3}{4}(4x + y) = 4$
$2x = \frac{3}{5}(2x - 3y)$

14. $\dfrac{3}{a} - \dfrac{2}{m} = -1$

$\dfrac{9}{a} - \dfrac{8}{m} = 0$

15. $5(3x - 2y) = 2(5x - 4y) + 3$
$3(2x + 3y) - 5 = 4(x + 2y) - 2y$

Example 6 *Solve the equations $x - 2y = 4$, $x^2 + y^2 = 5$.*

$$x - 2y = 4 \qquad \text{(i)}$$
$$x^2 + y^2 = 5 \qquad \text{(ii)}$$

From (i) $\qquad x = 2y + 4$
Substituting for x in (ii),
$$(2y + 4)^2 + y^2 = 5$$
$$\therefore \ 4y^2 + 16y + 16 + y^2 = 5$$
$$\therefore \ 5y^2 + 16y + 11 = 0$$
$$\therefore \ (y + 1)(5y + 11) = 0$$
$$\therefore \ y = -1 \text{ or } -\tfrac{11}{5}$$

Substituting in (i),
when $y = -1$, $\ x + 2 = 4$
$$\therefore \ x = 2$$
and when $y = -\tfrac{11}{5}$, $x + \tfrac{22}{5} = 4$
$$\therefore \ x = 4 - 4\tfrac{2}{5} = -\tfrac{2}{5}$$

Ans. $(2, -1), (-\tfrac{2}{5}, -2\tfrac{1}{5})$.

Check in (ii) $\quad 2^2 + (-1)^2 = 4 + 1 = 5$
$$(-\tfrac{2}{5})^2 + (-\tfrac{11}{5})^2 = \tfrac{4}{25} + \tfrac{121}{25} = 5.$$

Notice that when the values of y have been found, the corresponding values of x are found by substituting back in the *linear* equation.

Example 7 *If* $A = \{x, y : 3x - 4y = 2\}$ *and* $B = \{x, y : xy = 2\}$ *find* $A \cap B$.

$$3x - 4y = 2 \qquad \text{(i)}$$
$$xy = 2 \qquad \text{(ii)}$$

From (ii) $y = \dfrac{2}{x}$

Substituting for y in (i),

$$3x - 4 \times \frac{2}{x} = 2$$

$\therefore\ 3x^2 - 2x - 8 = 0$
$\therefore\ (x - 2)(3x + 4) = 0$
$\qquad\qquad \therefore\ x = 2 \text{ or } -\frac{4}{3}$
When $x = 2,\quad y = \frac{2}{2} = 1$

and when $x = -\frac{4}{3}$, $y = \dfrac{2}{-\frac{4}{3}} = -\frac{3}{2}$

Ans. $(2, 1), (-1\frac{1}{3}, -1\frac{1}{2})$.

Check in (i) $3 \times 2 - 4 \times 1 = 6 - 4 = 2$
$\qquad\qquad 3 \times (-\frac{4}{3}) - 4 \times (-\frac{3}{2}) = -4 + 6 = 2.$

Example 8   *Solve the equations* $2x - y = 5, 4x^2 - y^2 = 15$.

$$2x - y = 5 \qquad \text{(i)}$$
$$4x^2 - y^2 = 15 \qquad \text{(ii)}$$
From (ii), $(2x - y)(2x + y) = 15$
$\qquad \therefore\ 5(2x + y) = 15 \text{ since } 2x - y = 5$
$\qquad \therefore\ 2x + y = 3 \qquad \text{(iii)}$
But $\qquad\qquad 2x - y = 5 \qquad \text{(i)}$
Adding, $\qquad\qquad 4x \quad\ = 8 \quad \therefore\ x = 2$
Subtracting, $\qquad\qquad 2y = -2 \quad \therefore\ y = -1$
Ans. $(2, -1)$.

Check in (i) $2 \times 2 - (-1) = 4 + 1 = 5$
and   in (ii) $4 \times 2^2 - (-1)^2 = 16 - 1 = 15.$

This method is clearly limited to those occasions when the second degree equation can be expressed in factors, one of which occurs in the linear equation.

Exercise 30c

Solve the following pairs of equations:

1. $2x + y = 5$
   $x^2 + y^2 = 25$

2. $4x - y = 7$
   $xy = 15$

3. $x + y = 3$
   $x^2 - y^2 = -3$

4. $4x^2 + y^2 = 61$
   $2x + y = 1$

5. $3x + 2y = 6$
   $xy = -12$

6. $2x^2 - y^2 = -2$
   $3x + y = 1$

7. $2x + 3y = 1$
   $4x^2 - 9y^2 = -17$

8. $x + 2y = 2$
   $x^2 + 2xy = 8$

9. $x^2 + 2y^2 = 3$
   $x - 3y = 2$

10. $xy = 30$
    $3x + y = 21$

11. $25x^2 - 4y^2 = 36$
    $5x - 2y = 2$

12. $2x - 5y = 1$
    $4x^2 + 25y^2 = 41$

13. $x - 3y = 1$
    $x^2 - 2xy - y^2 = 7$

14. $3xy - y^2 = 2$
    $2x - 3y = -4$

15. $\dfrac{x}{2} + \dfrac{y}{3} = 1$
    $2xy + 9 = 0$

16. $9x^2 + 16y^2 = 52$
    $3x - 4y = 2$

17. $25x^2 - 7y^2 = 29$
    $5x + 7y + 1 = 0$

18. $2x + y = 3$
    $\dfrac{1}{x} + \dfrac{1}{y} + \dfrac{1}{2} = 0$

19. $2x^2 + 3xy + 2y^2 = 9$
    $2x + y = 3$

20. $x + 3y = 1$
    $2x^2 + 5xy - 3y^2 = 9$

Chapter 31

Inequalities. Linear programming

Inequalities

$5 > 3$, but $-5 < -3$ (i)   (See Fig. 78)
If $-x > -1$, then $x < 1$ (ii)
    $-x < 2$,   then $x > -2$ (iii)
$x \leqslant 3$ and $x \ngtr 3$ are equivalent statements, $\leqslant$ meaning 'is less than or equal to', $\ngtr$ meaning 'is not greater than'.
(iv) represents $x \geqslant 3$ or $x \nless 3$
 (v) represents $x \leqslant -1$ or $x \ngtr -1$.

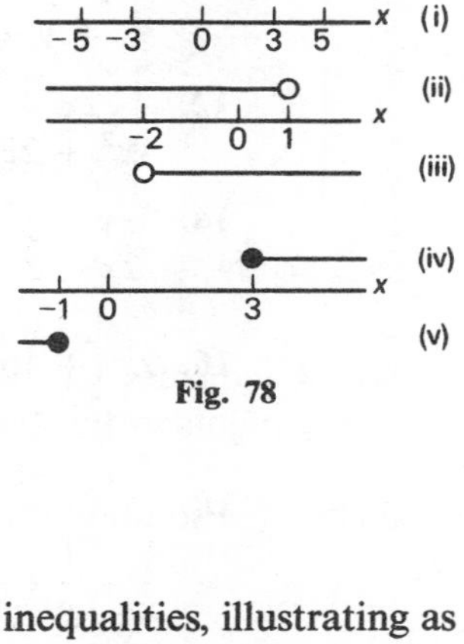

Fig. 78

Exercise 31a

Solve the following inequalities, illustrating as in Fig. 78.

1. $x + 2 \geqslant 3$ **2.** $x - 3 < 1$ **3.** $3 - x \nless 1$
4. $3x < 12$ **5.** $3x + 12 \geqslant 0$ **6.** $5 - 2x \leqslant x - 1$
7. $2(x + 4) > 3(x - 1)$ **8.** $\frac{1}{2}(3x - 2) \nless x - 6$

9. $\dfrac{x}{2} + \dfrac{3}{4} \leqslant \dfrac{5x}{6} - \dfrac{7}{12}$

Example 1 *Show on a graph the area which gives the solution-set of the inequalities* $y - x \leqslant 1$, $2x < 5$, $5y > -4x$.

In Fig. 79 the boundary-line $y - x = 1$ is shown solid (P) to emphasise that the set of points conforming to $y - x \leqslant 1$ is the whole area below that line together with all the points on the line.

Q is the line $5y = -4x$, and all points in the area above it are given by $5y > -4x$. Points *on* the line are *not* included, so the line is shown dotted.

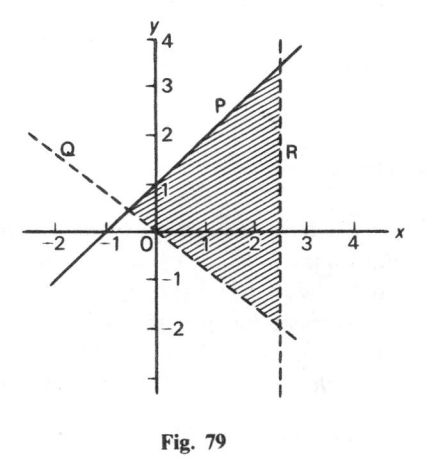

Fig. 79

Similarly the dotted line R indicates the boundary of the area $2x < 5$, which includes all the points to the left of R, but not those on it.

Hence the shaded area gives the solution-set for all points which satisfy all three inequalities.

Exercise 31b

Draw diagrams as in Fig. 79, using solid and broken lines where appropriate, and shade in the areas which give solution-sets for the following inequalities.

1. $x - y > -2$, $x + y < 4$, $x \geqslant 1$, $y \geqslant 0$

2. $x - y \geqslant 1, 2x + 3y < 6, y \leqslant 0, x < 4$

3. $-4 \leqslant y - x \leqslant 2, x > 1, y < 4$

4. $1 < x < 4, y - 2x \leqslant 2, 2 < y < 4$

5. $3x + 4y \leqslant 12, y - x \leqslant 2, y > 1, x \geqslant 0$

6. $2y - 3x \leqslant 6, y + 2x < 8, y > x$

7. $4y - x < 4, x - y < 3, x + 2 \geqslant 0, y \leqslant 1$

8. $6 \leqslant 2x + 3y \leqslant 12, 2x - 3y < 8, y < 3$

Linear programming

Example 2 *A boy is given 50p to spend on his model farm, and decides to divide the money between cows at 5p each and sheep at 2p each, getting at least five of each; what he spends on cows must be more than what he spends on sheep by more than 10p.*

If he wants to get as many animals as possible, how should he lay out his money, and how much change will there be from the 50p?

He buys x cows at 5p, costing $5x$ p
He buys y sheep at 2p, costing $2y$ p
$$5x + 2y \leqslant 50$$
$$x \geqslant 5$$
$$y \geqslant 5$$
$$5x - 2y > 10$$

These inequalities are shown in Fig. 80 and twelve possible arrangements are marked.

Also $x + y$ must be as great as possible. In Fig. 80 the lines $x + y = 10$, $x + y = 12$, $x + y = 14$ are lightly drawn in. To get the largest possible total for $x + y$ the line must be drawn as far to the right as possible. This is $x + y = 15$.

∴ the correct distribution is 6 cows and 9 sheep, and there will be 2p change.

188

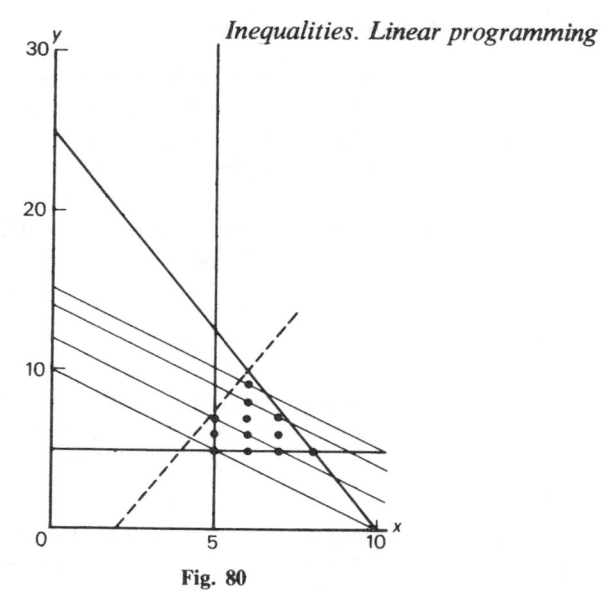

Exercise 31c   Fig. 80

1. Draw Fig. 80 to as large a scale as possible and mark in the nineteen points in a shaded area. Add the lines $x + y = 10$, etc. and also the line $x + y = 15$.

2. A man running a 'Do It Yourself' shop is going to order a supply of fastening gadgets which come in two sizes: large at 9p each and small at 4p. He is prepared to spend up to £2 altogether and needs at least twice as many small ones as large, with minimum quantities of ten large and twenty small. What is the maximum number that he can buy? If the profit is 1p on each large one sold and $\frac{1}{2}$p on each small one, what arrangement produces the largest profit, and how much is it?

3. £2·40 has been collected to buy prizes for a form party. At the shop only ten bars of chocolate (12p each) and fifteen bags of toffees (9p each) are available. There are 22 children and each must get at least one prize. Which distribution provides the largest number of prizes and at the same time comes nearest to spending all the money available? How much is left unspent?

4. A small-holder plans to plant out an area of 15 m² with strawberries and raspberries. Strawberries cost 9p per plant and need

a quarter of a square metre each; raspberries 4p and half a square metre. He reckons to spend up to £3·60 on plants and decides to have at least twice as many strawberries as raspberries, though not less than 12 of the latter. Which arrangement uses the largest number of plants? How much does he spend this way?

If he wants to use all the ground available, which arrangement uses the largest number of plants?

5. A manufacturer is prepared to spend at least £5 000 in tooling up a new workshop. The shop has a floor-area of 120 square metres, and two sorts of machine are to be installed: type A occupies 6 m² of space and costs £200; type B 4 m² and £250. More of type A than of type B are needed. Which possible arrangement uses all the space available, and which is the most expensive?

6. A building speculator has 8 Ha of land to develop, and plans to put up two types of house: the larger costs £8 000 to build and occupies a quarter of a hectare; the smaller £5 000 and one-tenth of a hectare. There must be at least 16 large houses and 30 small ones. He is prepared to spend up to £320 000 in building. What is the largest number of the bigger houses that he can build, and what distribution gives him the largest number of houses altogether? What distributions use up all the land available?

Inequalities with fractions

$5 > 4$ but $-5 < -4$.

An inequality is reversed when it is multiplied by a negative number. If therefore both sides of an inequality are multiplied by x, the cases of x positive and x negative must be carefully distinguished.

Example 3 $\dfrac{6}{x} > 2$.

(i) If $x > 0$ then $6 > 2x$

$$\left. \begin{array}{l} \therefore \quad x < 3 \\ \text{but } x > 0 \end{array} \right\} \quad \therefore \quad 0 < x < 3$$

(ii) If $x < 0$ then $6 < 2x$
$$\left.\begin{array}{l} \therefore \ x > 3 \\ \text{but } x < 0 \end{array}\right\} \quad \therefore \ \text{no negative solution}$$
The complete solution is $0 < x < 3$.

N.B. The situation arising when $x = 0$ cannot be considered since the meaning of $\dfrac{0}{0}$ has not yet been defined.

Example 4 $\left\{x : \dfrac{6}{x} \leqslant -2\right\}.$

(i) If $x > 0$ then $6 \leqslant -2x$
$$\left.\begin{array}{l} \therefore \ x \leqslant -3 \\ \text{but } x > 0 \end{array}\right\} \quad \therefore \ \text{no positive solution}$$
(ii) If $x < 0$ then $6 \geqslant -2x$
$$\left.\begin{array}{l} \therefore \ x \geqslant -3 \\ \text{but } x < 0 \end{array}\right\} \quad \therefore \ -3 \leqslant x < 0$$
The complete solution is $\{x : -3 \leqslant x < 0\}$.

Exercise 31d

Solve the following inequalities.

1. $\dfrac{15}{x} < 5$
2. $\dfrac{15}{x} > -5$
3. $\left\{x : \dfrac{15}{x} \geqslant 3\right\}$

4. $\left\{x : \dfrac{18}{x} < -6\right\}$
5. $20 \leqslant \dfrac{4}{x}$
6. $\left\{x : \dfrac{4}{x} - 24 > 0\right\}$

7. $\dfrac{20}{x} + 5 \leqslant 0$
8. $\left\{x : \dfrac{3}{x} < \dfrac{6}{x} + 2\right\}$
9. $\dfrac{5}{2x} + \dfrac{2}{3} \geqslant \dfrac{7}{12}$

Quadratic inequalities

If the product $ab > 0$, then a and b must both be positive or both negative.

If the product $ab < 0$, then either $a > 0$ and $b < 0$ or $a < 0$ and $b > 0$.

New General Mathematics Revision

Example 5   *Solve* $(x - 2)(x - 3) > 0.$

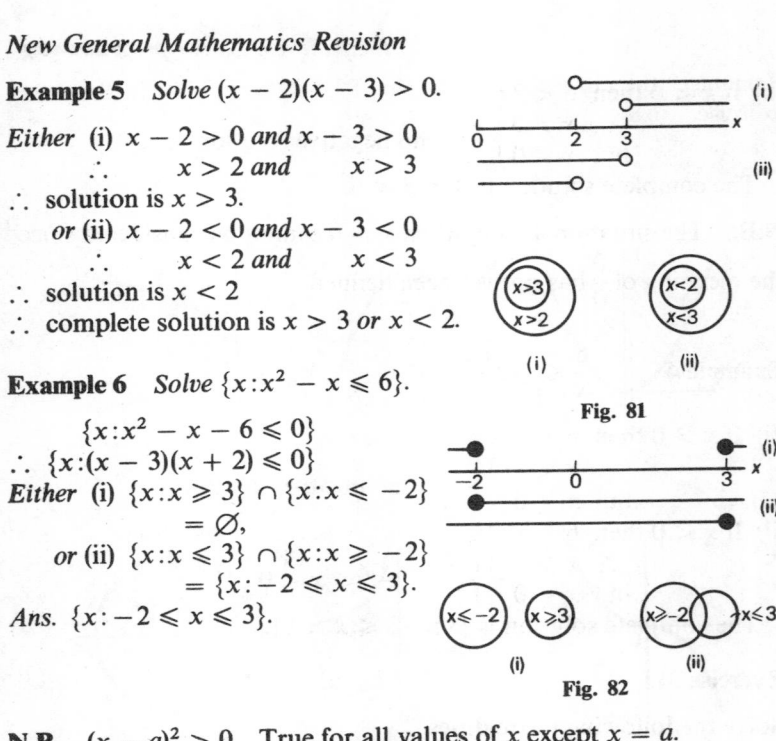

Either (i) $x - 2 > 0$ *and* $x - 3 > 0$
∴ $x > 2$ *and* $x > 3$
∴ solution is $x > 3.$
   or (ii) $x - 2 < 0$ *and* $x - 3 < 0$
∴ $x < 2$ *and* $x < 3$
∴ solution is $x < 2$
∴ complete solution is $x > 3$ *or* $x < 2.$

(i)   (ii)

Example 6   *Solve* $\{x : x^2 - x \leqslant 6\}.$

Fig. 81

$\{x : x^2 - x - 6 \leqslant 0\}$
∴ $\{x : (x - 3)(x + 2) \leqslant 0\}$
Either (i) $\{x : x \geqslant 3\} \cap \{x : x \leqslant -2\}$
      $= \varnothing,$
   or (ii) $\{x : x \leqslant 3\} \cap \{x : x \geqslant -2\}$
      $= \{x : -2 \leqslant x \leqslant 3\}.$
Ans. $\{x : -2 \leqslant x \leqslant 3\}.$

(i)   (ii)

Fig. 82

N.B. $(x - a)^2 > 0$ True for all values of x except $x = a.$
      $(x - a)^2 \geqslant 0$ True for all values of $x.$
      $(x - a)^2 < 0$ Impossible for real values of $x.$
      $(x - a)^2 \leqslant 0$ True only for $x = a.$

Exercise 31e

Solve the following inequalities:

1. $(x - 4)(x - 6) > 0$

2. $\{x : (x - 4)(x - 6) < 0\}$

3. $(x - 2)(x + 1) < 0$

4. $\{x : (x - 2)(x + 1) > 0\}$

5. $x^2 - 25 \geqslant 0$

6. $\{x : x^2 < 64\}$

7. $\{x : x^2 - x \geqslant 20\}$

8. $2x^2 - 3 < x$

9. $2x^2 + 3x \leqslant 0$

10. $\dfrac{8}{x} > x + 2$

192

Reminder: the curves shown in Fig. 83 will be needed in the next exercise.

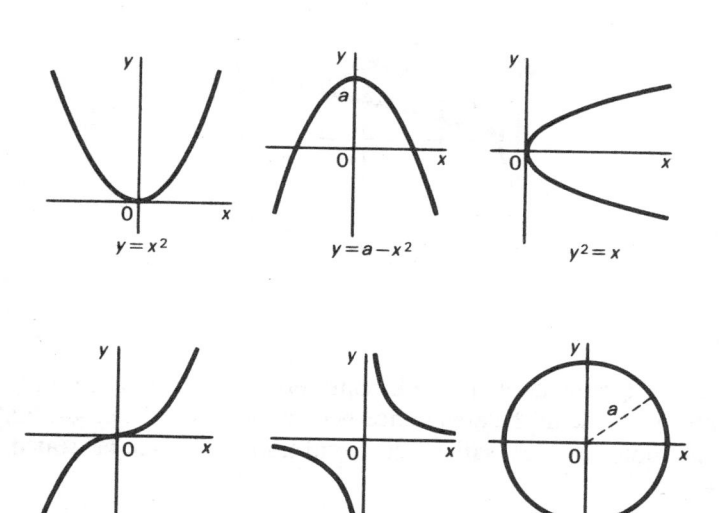

Fig. 83

Example 7 *Show on a diagram the area bounded by $y^2 \leqslant 4x$, $y > 2x - 4$, $4y \geqslant x + 4$, $x > 1$ for positive values only of x and y. Write down the co-ordinates of all points included in the area which are integral.*

The required area is shown in Fig. 84. As before, broken lines denote $>$ or $<$ boundaries, solid lines $\geqslant$ or $\leqslant$ boundaries.

The points are $(2, 2)$, $(3, 3)$.

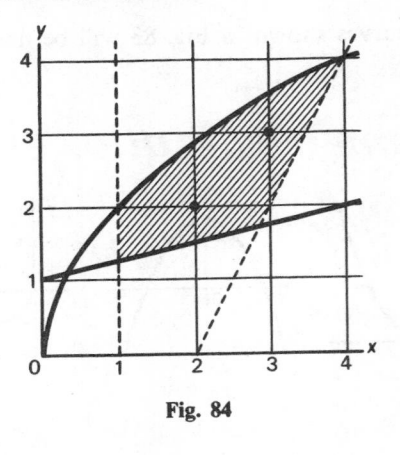

Fig. 84

Exercise 31f

Draw diagrams as in Fig. 84, considering positive values only of x and y: shade in the area concerned: write down the co-ordinates of all points which satisfy the conditions and can be stated in integers.

1. $x^2 + y^2 \leqslant 49, 2y < 3x, x + y \geqslant 6, x < 5$

2. $xy > 12, y \leqslant 10, 2y \geqslant x + 12, x + y < 10$

3. $y \leqslant 5 - x^2, 5y + 4x \geqslant 10, y < 4x$

4. $x^2 + y^2 < 64, 5 \leqslant 5y - 3x \leqslant 15, x > 4$

5. $2y \geqslant x^3, y^2 \leqslant 100x, x > 2$

6. $4y > x^2, x^2 + y^2 \leqslant 13, 4x + 3y \geqslant 12$
(The point $(3, 2)$ lies on the circle $x^2 + y^2 = 13$.)

7. $xy \geqslant 16, y^2 \leqslant x, x > 10, x + y < 16$

8. $y \geqslant \frac{1}{8}x^3, 20 < x^2 + y^2 < 64, 2 \leqslant y - x \leqslant 5, x > 1$

Chapter 32

Trigonometrical ratios of an obtuse angle

sin (180° − θ) = sin θ
cos (180° − θ) = − cos θ
tan (180° − θ) = − tan θ
 For example,
sin 155° = sin (180° − 25°) =   sin 25° = 0·422 6
cos 155° = cos (180° − 25°) = − cos 25° = − 0·906 3
tan 155° = tan (180° − 25°) = − tan 25° = − 0·466 3

Exercise 32a

Write down in decimal form the values of the following:

1. sin 114°	**2.** cos 114°	**3.** tan 114°
4. sin 162°	**5.** sin 100°	**6.** cos 97°
7. cos 151°	**8.** tan 171°	**9.** tan 96°
10. cos 129°	**11.** sin 148° 30′	**12.** tan 169° 48′
13. cos 172° 12′	**14.** tan 132° 54′	**15.** sin 95° 6′
16. sin 136° 49′	**17.** cos 102° 17′	**18.** tan 98° 45′
19. cos 158° 21′	**20.** tan 163° 53′	

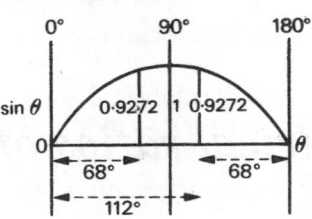

Fig. 85

If θ lies between 0° and 180° and $\sin \theta$ is given, there are **two possible values** for θ.

For example, if $\sin \theta = 0.927\,2$, then from the tables, $\theta = 68°$.

But $\sin 68° = \sin(180° - 68°) = \sin 112°$.

Hence if $\sin \theta = 0.927\,2$, then θ could be either 68° or 112°.

The sketch-graph in Fig. 85 should make this clear.

If $\sin \theta = -0.927\,2$, then θ does not lie between 0° and 180°.

If $\cos \theta$ is given, then there is **only one** value for θ lying between 0° and 180°.

For example, if $\cos \theta = 0.325\,6$, then from the tables, $\theta = 71°$.

If $\cos \theta = -0.325\,6$, then $\theta = 180° - 71°$
$$= 109°.$$

This is easily seen from the sketch-graph in Fig. 86.

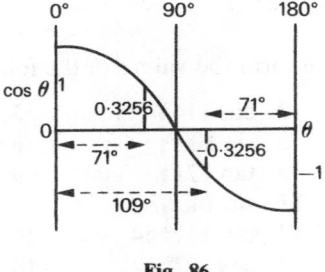

Fig. 86

Similarly if tan θ is given, there is **only one** value for θ lying between
0° and 180°.
If tan θ = 2·246 0, then from the tables, θ = 66°.
If tan θ = −2·246 0, then θ = 180° − 66°
$$= 114°.$$
This is illustrated in the sketch-graph in Fig. 87.

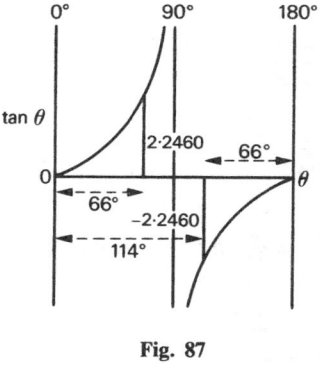

Fig. 87

Exercise 32b

In the following examples, find the values of θ lying between 0°
and 180°.

1. cos θ = 0·974 4
2. cos θ = −0·974 4
3. tan θ = 2·050 3
4. tan θ = −2·050 3
5. sin θ = 0·241 9
6. tan θ = −1·234 9
7. cos θ = −0·156 4
8. sin θ = 0·882 9
9. cos θ = −0·669 1
10. tan θ = −0·230 9
11. cos θ = 0·592 5
12. sin θ = 0·577 1
13. tan θ = 0·703 7
14. sin θ = 0·983 9
15. cos θ = −0·413 9
16. tan θ = −1·776 0
17. sin θ = 0·065 4
18. sin θ = 0·651 2
19. tan θ = −13·46
20. cos θ = −0·970 5

197

Chapter 33

Connections between the trigonometrical ratios

$$\sin^2 \theta + \cos^2 \theta = 1$$

$$\tan \theta = \frac{\sin \theta}{\cos \theta}$$

$$\cot \theta = \frac{\cos \theta}{\sin \theta}$$

Example 1 *If $\sin \theta = \frac{8}{17}$, find the value of $\cos \theta$.*

$\sin^2 \theta + \cos^2 \theta = 1$
$\therefore \cos^2 \theta = 1 - \sin^2 \theta$
$\qquad\qquad = 1 - \frac{64}{289}$
$\qquad\qquad = \frac{225}{289}$
$\therefore \cos \theta = \pm\frac{15}{17}$.
  If θ is acute, then $\cos \theta = \frac{15}{17}$.
  If θ is obtuse, then $\cos \theta = -\frac{15}{17}$.

Alternatively, draw a triangle PQR right-angled at R, with RP = 8 units and QP = 17 units.

The PQ̂R is θ, since $\sin \theta = \frac{8}{17}$.
  $QR^2 = 17^2 - 8^2 = 289 - 64 = 225$
$\therefore$ QR = 15 units

$$\therefore \cos \theta = \frac{QR}{QP} = \frac{15}{17}.$$

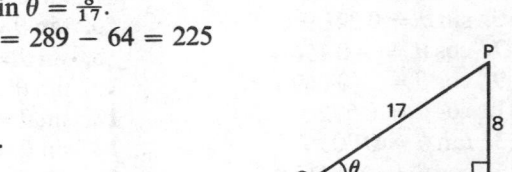

This result is true only if θ is acute.
  If θ is obtuse, then $\cos \theta = -\frac{15}{17}$.

Fig. 88

198

Example 2   *If* $\tan \theta = 1 \cdot 3$, *find the values of* $\sin \theta$ *and* $\cos \theta$.

Since $\tan \theta$ is positive, θ cannot be obtuse.
Draw $\triangle$ LMN right-angled at N, with MN = 10 units and
NL = 13 units.
Then L$\hat{\text{M}}$N is θ, since $\tan \theta = 1 \cdot 3 = \frac{13}{10}$.

$$\text{ML}^2 = 13^2 + 10^2 = 169 + 100 = 269$$
$$\therefore \ \text{ML} = \sqrt{269} \text{ units} \fallingdotseq 16 \cdot 40 \text{ units}$$

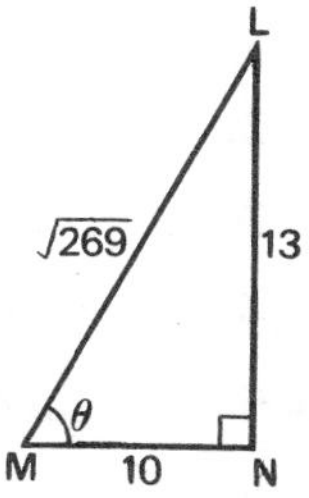

$$\therefore \ \sin \theta = \frac{13}{16 \cdot 4} = 0 \cdot 792 \, 7$$

and $\cos \theta = \dfrac{10}{16 \cdot 4} = 0 \cdot 609 \, 8.$

Fig. 89

Example 3   *If* θ *is acute and* $\cos \theta = c$, *find* $\sin \theta$ *and* $\tan \theta$ *in terms of* c.

Draw a right-angled triangle as in Fig. 90, so that $\cos \theta = \dfrac{c}{1}$.

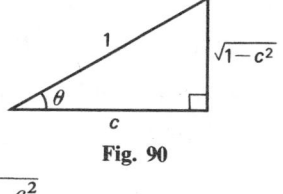

Fig. 90

Then $\sin \theta = \dfrac{\sqrt{1 - c^2}}{1} = \sqrt{1 - c^2}$

and $\tan \theta = \dfrac{\sqrt{1 - c^2}}{c}$.

Example 4   *Find the value of* $\dfrac{\sin^2 47°}{\cos 47°} \times \cot 47°$.

$$\frac{\sin^2 47°}{\cos 47°} \times \cot 47° = \frac{\sin^2 47°}{\cos 47°} \times \frac{\cos 47°}{\sin 47°}$$

$$= \sin 47°$$
$$= 0 \cdot 731 \, 4.$$

Exercise 33

Trigonometrical tables should not be used in nos. 1–10.
In nos. 1–12 the angle θ may be assumed to be acute.

1. If $\sin \theta = \frac{5}{13}$, find $\cos \theta$ and $\tan \theta$.

2. „ $\cos \theta = \frac{24}{25}$,   „ $\sin \theta$ „ $\tan \theta$.

3. „ $\tan \theta = \frac{21}{20}$,   „ $\sin \theta$ „ $\cos \theta$.

4. „ $\cos \theta = \frac{9}{41}$,   „ $\sin \theta$ „ $\tan \theta$.

5. „ $\sin \theta = \frac{12}{37}$,   „ $\sec \theta$ „ $\cot \theta$.

6. „ $\tan \theta = \frac{4}{5}$,   „ $\sin \theta$ „ $\cos \theta$, to 3 sig. fig.

7. „ $\cot \theta = 1{\cdot}7$,   „ $\sin \theta$ „ $\cos \theta$, „ „ „   „

8. „ $\cos \theta = \frac{2}{7}$,   „ $\sin \theta$ „ $\tan \theta$, „ „ „   „

9. „ $\operatorname{cosec} \theta = 2$,   „ $\cos \theta$ „ $\tan \theta$, „ „ „   „

10. „ $\sin \theta = 0{\cdot}9$,   „ $\cos \theta$ „ $\tan \theta$, „ „ „   „

11. „ $\sin \theta = s$,   „ $\cos \theta$ „ $\tan \theta$, in terms of s.

12. „ $\sec \theta = x$,   „ $\sin \theta$ „ $\cot \theta$, „   „   „ x.

With as little working as possible, find the value of

13. $\cos 29° \tan 29°$

14. $\cot 57° \sec 57°$

15. $\dfrac{\tan 42°}{\sin 42°}$

16. $\tan 63° \times \dfrac{\cos^2 63°}{\sin 63°}$

17. $\tan^2 34° \operatorname{cosec} 34° \cos 34°$

Chapter 34

Monetary systems and exchange

Country	Local unit	Units to £1
Australia	dollar ($)	1·80
Belgium	franc (f)	84·50
Denmark	kroner (k)	13·20
France	franc (F)	10·23
W. Germany	deutschmark (DM)	5·65
Greece	drachma (dr)	72·20
Italy	lira (lr)	1 525·00
Japan	yen (yn)	712·00
Holland	guilder (gld)	5·72
Portugal	escudo (esc)	58·64
Spain	peseta (pes)	135·20
Switzerland	franc (f)	6·05
U.S.A.	dollar ($)	2·42

The table shown above gives the rates at which various currencies can be exchanged for pounds sterling. These rates are not fixed, but are liable to fluctuate, and the examples and questions which follow can be taken to illustrate only general principles and must not be taken to be the rates in actual operation on any particular day.

Example 1   *If a tourist presents a £50 traveller's cheque in France, how many francs should he get?*

$$£1 = 10·23F$$
$$\therefore £50 = 50 \times 10·23F$$
$$= 511·5F.$$

New General Mathematics Revision

Example 2 *What is the value of an American $10 note to the nearest penny?*

$2·42 = £1

$$\therefore \quad \$10 \quad = £1 \times \frac{10}{2·42}$$

$$\simeq £4·13.$$

Example 3 *How many West German deutschmarks can be bought for 10 000 Italian lire?*

£1 = 1 525 lr = 5·65 DM

$$\therefore \quad 10\,000\,\text{lr} = 5·65 \times \frac{10\,000}{1\,525}\,\text{DM}$$

$$= \frac{56\,500}{1\,525}\,\text{DM}$$

$$\simeq 37·05\,\text{DM}.$$

Exercise 34

1. How many (i) American dollars, (ii) Swiss francs, (iii) Dutch guilders, (iv) Spanish pesetas, (v) Japanese yen can be bought for £20?

2. Evaluate in £ to the nearest penny
   (i) 1 000 Belgian francs
   (ii) 25 Australian dollars
   (iii) 500 Greek drachmae
   (iv) 320 Danish kroner
   (v) 20 000 Spanish pesetas.

3. By how much does the value of an American $5 bill rise or fall if the rate of exchange alters from 2·41 to 2·38?

4. What is a Dutch guilder worth, to the nearest halfpenny?

5. How many Spanish pesetas can be bought for 1 500 Swiss francs?

In nos. 6–10 find the equivalent costs to the nearest penny.

6. A Sydney haircut at $1.

7. A silver dish bought in Holland for 50 guilders.

8. A bottle of Spanish brandy at 210 pesetas.

9. A week in Florence which cost 98 000 lire.

10. An ivory carving which cost 4 800 yen in Tokyo.

11. The same brand of whisky costs £2·75 a bottle in England and $6·80 in America. Which is the more expensive, and by how much, to the nearest penny?

12. How much is a $10 American Express card worth in Portugal (in escudo)?

13. A traveller bought a camera in Japan for 47 000 yn and later sold it in France for 620 F. How much did he gain or lose on the transaction? (Answer in sterling to the nearest penny.)

14. An Australian touring western Europe brought with him $2 000. He changed all of these into £ sterling and spent £474 in the United Kingdom. He then changed what was left into French francs; spent 5 028 F in France and finally changed what he had left into Australian dollars at the rate of 100 F to $17·5. How many dollars did he receive (nearest whole number)?

15. A traveller bought £100 worth of deutschmarks from his bank. He did not spend any money in Germany, but changed it all into Belgian francs at 14·96 f to the deutschmark. He spent 5 800 f in Brussels and changed the rest back into sterling at 84·68 f to the £. How much did he bring back with him (nearest penny)?

Chapter 35

The sine formula

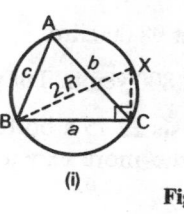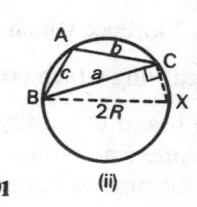

Fig. 91

$$\frac{a}{\sin A} = \frac{b}{\sin B} = \frac{c}{\sin C} = 2R$$

Example 1 *In* $\triangle ABC$, $B = 33°$, $C = 79°$, $a = 8.27\ cm$. *Find b.*

$$A = 180° - (33° + 79°) = 68°$$

$$\frac{b}{\sin B} = \frac{a}{\sin A}$$

$$\therefore \frac{b}{\sin 33°} = \frac{8.27}{\sin 68°}$$

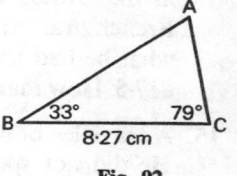

$$\therefore b = 8.27 \sin 33° \operatorname{cosec} 68°$$

$$\simeq 4.86\ cm.$$

Fig. 92

No.	Log.
8.27	0·917 5
sin 33°	$\bar{1}$·736 1
cosec 68°	0·032 8
4·857	0·686 4

N.B. The working is simplified by using cosec instead of $\frac{1}{\sin}$.

204

In Examples 2 and 3, which follow, notice the fact that $\sin \theta = \sin(180° - \theta)$ is always taken into consideration. In some cases it will be found that both the acute and obtuse values of θ give possible solutions.

Example 2 *Find the remaining angles of the* $\triangle ABC$ *in which* $a = 11\cdot2\ cm$, $b = 21\cdot5\ cm$, $B = 113°$.

$$\frac{\sin A}{11\cdot2} = \frac{\sin 113°}{21\cdot5}$$

$$\therefore \ \sin A = \frac{11\cdot2 \sin 113°}{21\cdot5}$$

$$= \frac{11\cdot2 \sin 67°}{21\cdot5}$$

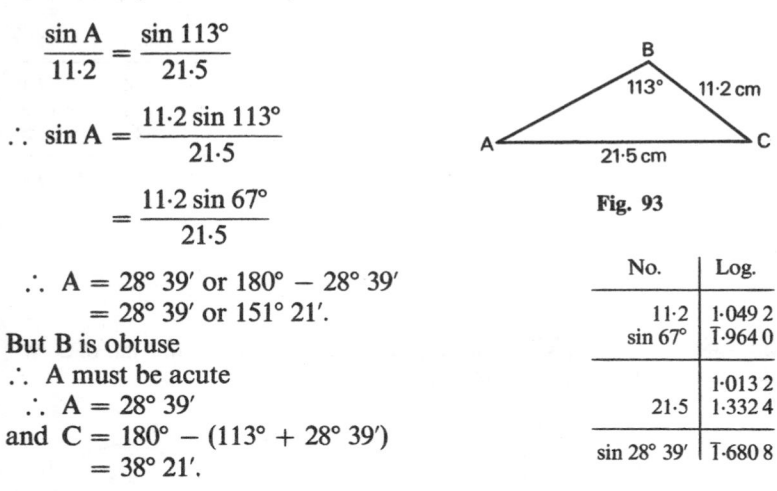

Fig. 93

$$\therefore \ A = 28° \ 39' \text{ or } 180° - 28° \ 39'$$
$$= 28° \ 39' \text{ or } 151° \ 21'.$$
But B is obtuse
$$\therefore \ A \text{ must be acute}$$
$$\therefore \ A = 28° \ 39'$$
and $C = 180° - (113° + 28° \ 39')$
$$= 38° \ 21'.$$

No.	Log.
$11\cdot2$	$1\cdot049\ 2$
$\sin 67°$	$\bar{1}\cdot964\ 0$
	$1\cdot013\ 2$
$21\cdot5$	$1\cdot332\ 4$
$\sin 28° \ 39'$	$\bar{1}\cdot680\ 8$

Example 3 *Solve completely the* $\triangle ABC$ *in which* $a = 12\cdot4\ cm$, $c = 14\cdot7\ cm$, $C = 72° \ 4'$.

$$\frac{\sin A}{12\cdot4} = \frac{\sin 72° \ 4'}{14\cdot7}$$

$$\therefore \ \sin A = \frac{12\cdot4 \sin 72° \ 4'}{14\cdot7}$$

$$\therefore \ A = 53° \ 23' \ or \ 126° \ 37'.$$

But $a < c$
$$\therefore \ A < C$$
$$\therefore \ A = 53° \ 23'$$
$$\therefore \ B = 54° \ 33'$$

Fig. 94

$$\frac{b}{\sin 54° 33'} = \frac{14 \cdot 7}{\sin 72° 4'}$$

$$\therefore b = 14 \cdot 7 \sin 54° 33' \operatorname{cosec} 72° 4'$$

$$\fallingdotseq 12 \cdot 6 \text{ cm}$$

$$\therefore A = 53° 23', B = 54° 33', b = 12 \cdot 6 \text{ cm.}$$

No.	Log.
12·4	1·093 4
sin 72° 4'	$\bar{1}$·978 4
	1·071 8
14·7	1·167 3
sin 53° 23'	$\bar{1}$·904 5

No.	Log.
14·7	1·167 3
sin 54° 33'	$\bar{1}$·911 0
cosec 72° 4'	0·021 6
12·59	1·099 9

Example 4 *Find the radius of the circumcircle of the* $\triangle ABC$ *in which* $B = 69°$ *and* $b = 8 \cdot 34$ *cm.*

$$2R = \frac{b}{\sin B} = \frac{8 \cdot 34}{\sin 69°}$$

$$\therefore R = 4 \cdot 17 \operatorname{cosec} 69°$$

$$\fallingdotseq 4 \cdot 47 \text{ cm.}$$

Fig. 95

No.	Log.
4·17	0·620 1
cosec 69°	0·029 8
4·466	0·649 9

N.B. The two dimensions B and b determine R uniquely, but there is an infinite number of possible triangles, all of them inscribed in the same circle.

Exercise 35a

1. In $\triangle$ABC, B = 38°, C = 48°, c = 15·8 cm. Find b.

2. In $\triangle$ABC, A = 98°, C = 36°, a = 34·4 cm. Find c.

3. „ „ B = 29°, b = 8·6 cm, c = 3·1 cm. Find C.

4. „ „ A = 96° 13', a = 39·4 cm, b = 11·2 cm. Find B.

   Solve completely the triangles ABC in which

5. a = 14·7 cm, b = 16·3 cm, B = 52°.

6. a = 6·4 cm, c = 8·7 cm, C = 72°.

7. a = 4·9 cm, b = 10·6 cm, B = 123°.

8. Bembury is 8 km from Applewick on a bearing of 052°: Cordale is due east of Applewick and on a bearing of 170° from Bembury. How far is Cordale from Applewick?

9. A, B and C are buoys marking the turning-points on a triangular course for a yacht race. B is 7·8 km from A on a bearing of 055°. BC is 10·3 km and the bearing of C from A is 122°. Find the bearing of B from C and also the distance AC.

10. In a circle of diameter 8·3 cm a chord of length 6·1 cm is drawn. What angle is subtended at the circumference by this chord?

11. The beams of two searchlights placed 3·5 km apart on level ground converge on an aircraft between the lights and in the vertical plane containing them. If the beams are angled at 42° and 61° to the horizontal, how far is the aircraft from the nearer one, and at what height is it flying (nearest 100 m)?

12. A golfer drives a ball 240 m from the tee but is 32° off the direct line to the hole and is short of the hole. If his ball lies 135 m from the hole, how far short would it have been if he had driven it dead straight?

13. A scout trying to reach a special target spots it on a bearing S 75° W, but there is a deep bog between him and it. He therefore crawls for 200 m on a bearing of N 43° W, and then straight to his target on a bearing of S 56° W. How far from the target was he when he first spotted it?

14. Two ships, *Oyster* and *Whelk*, leave their home port at the same time, *Oyster* sailing at 8 knots on a bearing of 058°. *Whelk* sails on a bearing of 123° and, after one hour, finds *Oyster* bearing 336° from her. What is *Whelk's* speed?

15. The shorter sides of a parallelogram are 6·4 cm in length and the shorter diagonal is 8·5 cm long. If the smaller angles of the parallelogram are 51° what are the lengths of the longer sides?

The ambiguous case

Example 5 *Solve completely the* $\triangle ABC$ *in which* $b = 9.2\,cm$, $c = 8.5\,cm$, $C = 63°$.

$$\frac{\sin B}{9.2} = \frac{\sin 63°}{8.5}$$

$$\therefore \quad \sin B = \frac{9.2 \sin 63°}{8.5}$$

$$\therefore \quad B = 74° \, 42' \ or \ 105° \, 18'$$

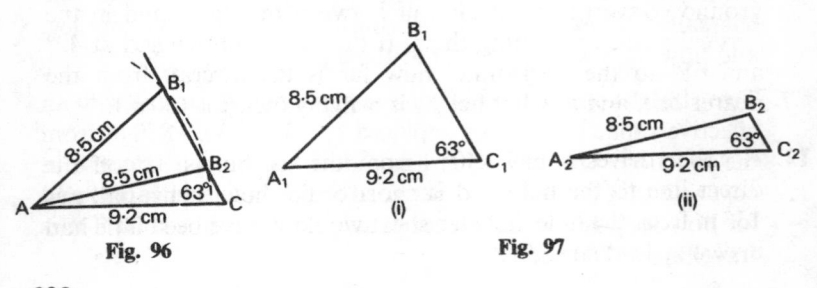

Fig. 96   Fig. 97

There are two possible $\triangle$s (Fig. 96).

These $\triangle$s are solved separately (Fig. 97 (i) and (ii)).

(i) $B_1 = 74° 42'$

∴ $A_1 = 42° 18'$

$$\frac{a_1}{\sin 42° 18'} = \frac{8·5}{\sin 63°}$$

∴ $a_1 = 8·5 \sin 42° 18' \operatorname{cosec} 63°$

$≃ 6·42$ cm

(ii) $B_2 = 105° 18'$

∴ $A_2 = 11° 42'$

∴ $a_2 = 8·5 \sin 11° 42' \operatorname{cosec} 63°$

$≃ 1·93$ cm

Ans. $\begin{cases} A = 42° 18', B = 74° 42', a = 6·42 \text{ cm} \\ A = 11° 42', B = 105° 18', a = 1·93 \text{ cm}. \end{cases}$

Exercise 35b

Solve completely the triangles in which

1. $BC = 12·5$ cm, $CA = 9·6$ cm, $B = 42°$.

2. $AB = 1\,600$ m, $BC = 2\,000$ m, $C = 51°$.

3. $CA = 5·3$ km, $AB = 7·2$ km, $B = 46°$.

4. $BC = 28·5$ cm, $CA = 23·6$ cm, $A = 72°$.

5. $AB = 6·8$ cm, $BC = 3·5$ cm, $A = 22°$.

6. A vessel sails 12 km due east from port on a triangular course; the next leg of the course finds her due S.E. from port after she has sailed 9 km. On what bearing does she sail on this leg, and how far is she from port at the end of it?

7. Two straight roads diverge at an angle of 56°. A mortar with an effective range of 2 500 m is placed on one road 2 850 m from the junction. Through what angle does the mortar traverse in covering that part of the other road which is within range, and for how long is a truck in the danger zone on this road if it is travelling at 70 km h^{-1}?

8. An observation balloon is in the same vertical plane as two observation posts on level ground below it. The balloon is 1 500 m from one post and at an angle of elevation of 53° from it, and is 1 400 m from the other post. How far apart are the two posts, and what is the elevation of the balloon from the second one?

9. Two ships *Antelope* and *Badger* are 4·2 km apart, the bearing of the second from the first being 074°. *Antelope* locates a floating object on a bearing of 112°, and estimates that it is 3·4 km from *Badger*. In what direction should *Badger* steam in order to reach the object?

10. Distress signals are picked up by a naval station from a point somewhere due west of it. A destroyer located on a bearing of 229° from the station is instructed to steam at 30 knots directly towards the sound, while at the same time a motor-boat is sent straight from the station towards it, travelling at 40 knots. If both vessels reach the source of the signals 40 minutes after starting towards it how far was the destroyer from the station at the time the signal was received?

Chapter 36

The cosine formula

In $\triangle ABC$ $a^2 = b^2 + c^2 - 2bc \cos A$
 $b^2 = c^2 + a^2 - 2ca \cos B$
 $c^2 = a^2 + b^2 - 2ab \cos C$

These formulae are used for solving triangles in which two sides and the included angle are given, and they apply whether the angles are acute or obtuse.

Example 1   *Find x in Fig.* 98.

$x^2 = 8^2 + 5^2 - 2 \times 8 \times 5 \times \cos 46°$
$ = 64 + 25 - 80 \times 0 \cdot 694\ 7$
$ = 89 - 55 \cdot 576$
$ = 33 \cdot 424$
$\therefore\ x = 5 \cdot 781 \simeq 5 \cdot 78$

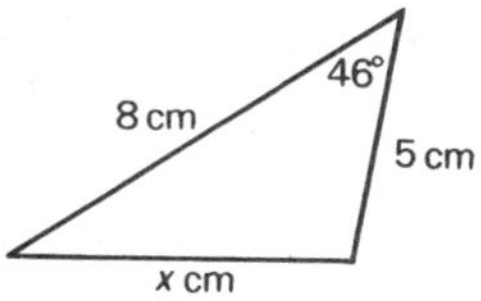

Fig. 98

Example 2   *Find y in Fig.* 99.

$y^2 = 6^2 + 15^2 - 2 \times 6 \times 15 \times \cos 112°$
$ = 36 + 225 - 180 \times (-\cos 68°)$
$ = 261 + 180 \times 0 \cdot 374\ 6$
$ = 261 + 67 \cdot 428$
$ = 328 \cdot 428$
$\therefore\ y = 18 \cdot 12 \simeq 18 \cdot 1$

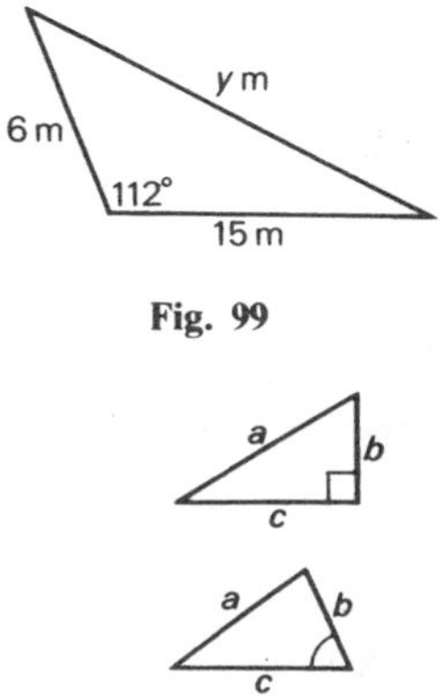

Fig. 99

N.B.   in Fig. 100

if a is opposite a right angle,　$a^2 = b^2 + c^2$
„ a „　　„　an acute angle,　$a^2 < b^2 + c^2$
„ a „　　„　an obtuse angle, $a^2 > b^2 + c^2$.
Hence in Example 1 above $x^2 < 8^2 + 5^2$
 i.e. $x^2 < 89$
 and in Example 2 $y^2 > 6^2 + 15^2$
 i.e. $y^2 > 261$.

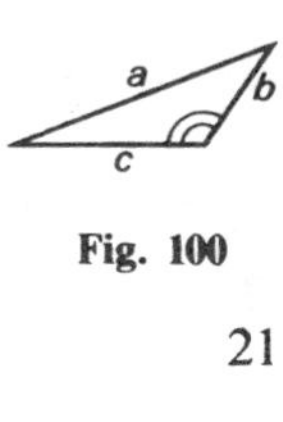

Fig. 100

Exercise 36a

Calculate the side opposite the given angle for each of the △s ABC given.

1. $A = 60°$, $b = 5$ cm, $c = 3$ cm.

2. $B = 22°$, $a = 4$ cm, $c = 5$ cm.

3. $C = 123°$, $a = 3$ m, $b = 2$ m.

4. $B = 143°$, $a = 25$ cm, $c = 40$ cm.

5. $A = 67° \ 16'$, $b = 15$ cm, $c = 10$ cm.

6. $C = 121°$, $a = 70$ cm, $b = 50$ cm.

When all three sides of a triangle are known, the angles can be found by rearranging the three basic formulae as follows:

$$\cos A = \frac{b^2 + c^2 - a^2}{2bc},$$

$$\cos B = \frac{c^2 + a^2 - b^2}{2ca},$$

$$\cos C = \frac{a^2 + b^2 - c^2}{2ab}.$$

Example 3 *Find the angles of a triangle having sides 5 cm, 8 cm, 11 cm.*

Lettering the angles of the △ as in Fig. 101,

$$\cos \alpha = \frac{8^2 + 11^2 - 5^2}{2 \times 8 \times 11} = \frac{160}{16 \times 11} = \frac{10}{11} = 0.909 \ 1$$

$\therefore \ \alpha = 24° \ 37'$

$$\cos \beta = \frac{5^2 + 11^2 - 8^2}{2 \times 5 \times 11} = \frac{82}{110} = 0.745 \ 5$$

$\therefore \ \beta = 41° \ 48'$

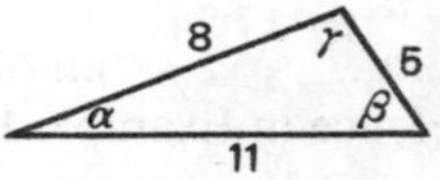

Fig. 101

$$\cos \gamma = \frac{8^2 + 5^2 - 11^2}{2 \times 8 \times 5} = -\frac{32}{80} = -0.4$$

$$\therefore \ \gamma = 180° - 66° 25' = 113° 35'.$$

Check. $\alpha + \beta + \gamma = 180°.$

In questions of this type all three angles should be worked out and the results checked by adding, as above.

Example 4 *Find the angles of triangles having sides* (i) 500 *m,* 800 *m,* 1 100 *m* (ii) 6·3 *cm,* 8·1 *cm,* 9·9 *cm.*

In both these cases the working becomes much simpler if similar and equiangular triangles are found which have less awkward numbers as their sides.

e.g. in (i) $500:800:1\,100 = 5:8:11$
∴ solve the triangle with sides 5, 8 and 11 units,
   in (ii) $6·3:8·1:9·9 = 7:9:11$
∴ solve the triangle with sides 7, 9 and 11 units.

Exercise 36b

In the following questions the sides a, b, c of a triangle ABC are given in cm. Find the corresponding angles A, B, C.

1. 5, 6, 7   **2.** 15, 21, 24   **3.** 5, 6, 10

4. 8, 14, 18   **5.** 20, 25, 16   **6.** 9, 6, 4·8

Example 5 *Solve completely the triangle* ABC *in which* $a = 3·4$ *cm,* $c = 6·2$ *cm,* B = 39°.

$$b^2 = 3·4^2 + 6·2^2 - 2 \times 3·4 \times 6·2 \times \cos 39°$$
$$= 11·56 + 38·44 - 32·76$$
$$= 17·24$$
$$\therefore \ b = 4·152$$

$$\frac{\sin A}{3·4} = \frac{\sin 39°}{4·152}$$

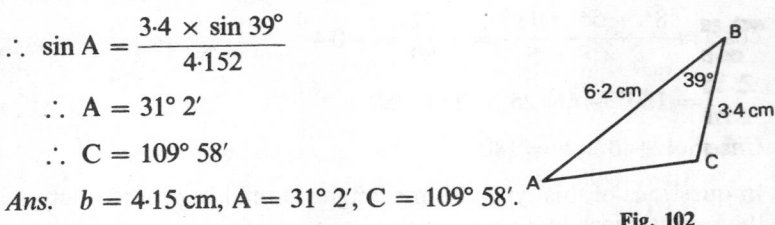

$$\therefore \ \sin A = \frac{3 \cdot 4 \times \sin 39°}{4 \cdot 152}$$

$$\therefore \ A = 31° \ 2'$$

$$\therefore \ C = 109° \ 58'$$

Ans. $b = 4 \cdot 15$ cm, $A = 31° \ 2'$, $C = 109° \ 58'$.

Fig. 102

Notice the correct procedure:
 (i) Use cosine formula to find side opposite given angle.
(ii) Use sine formula to find the smaller of the other two angles.
The smaller angle must be acute, therefore no ambiguity.

Exercise 36c

1. In $\triangle ABC$ $a = 8$ cm, $b = 7$ cm, $c = 9$ cm, and M is the mid-point of $\overline{BC}$. Find cos C, but do not work out the angle C itself. Hence, in $\triangle ACM$ find AM.

2. As in no. 1 write down expressions for cos B

    (i) in $\triangle ABM$ (Fig. 103),
   (ii) in $\triangle ABC$.

   Deduce the **Theorem of Apollonius**

   $$(b^2 + c^2 = 2x^2 + 2y^2)$$

Fig. 103

3. In $\triangle ABC$ $A = 103°$, $b = 8$ cm, $c = 5$ cm. Find a and hence the radius of the circumcircle of the triangle.

4. In $\triangle ABC$ $a = 10$ cm, $b = 7$ cm, $c = 9$ cm. P is a point in $\overline{AB}$, and AP $= 6$ cm. Find cos A and hence CP, without looking out the angle A.

5. The sides of a parallelogram are 9 cm and 10 cm, and the longer diagonal is 15 cm. Find the angles of the parallelogram and the length of the other diagonal.

6. Solve completely the △s ABC in which
   (i) A = 86°, b = 6 m, c = 5 m.
   (ii) C = 105°, a = 8 cm, b = 5 cm.
   (iii) B = 85° 14′, a = 5·27 cm, c = 8·34 cm.

7. In Fig. 104 find x and θ (lengths in cm).

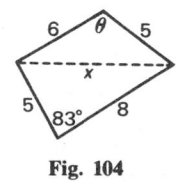

Fig. 104

8. Two ships leave port at the same time, one steaming at 10 knots on a bearing of 053°; the other at 15 knots on a bearing of 279°. How far apart are the ships after one hour, and what is then the bearing of the second from the first?

9. Straight roads connect three villages, Acton, Beldown and Parby. Two cyclists leave Acton simultaneously, one going straight to Beldown at 10 km h⁻¹, the other to Beldown via Parby at 12 km h⁻¹. If Parby is 5 km from Acton and 4 km from Beldown, and the angle APB is 116°, which cyclist reaches Beldown first, and by how many seconds?

10. A, B, C are three buoys marking out the course for a yacht race. The first leg $\overline{AB}$ is 20 km long and bears N 39° E from A. At B the yachts turn right-handed through 44° and sail 30 km to C; then from C straight back to A. What is the length of the last leg of the course, and on what bearing from C should the yachts sail?

Chapter 37

Ratio

In the following worked examples the first line of the working is a statement of what is given, arranged so that **whatever is to be found comes last.**

Example 1 *If £73·35 is the cost of 9 identical tyres, find the cost of 5 of them.*

Since the number of tyres to be bought is $\frac{5}{9}$ of the original number, the cost will be $\frac{5}{9}$ of the original cost,

    i.e. since the number of tyres is **decreased** in the ratio 5:9, the cost will also be **decreased** in the ratio 5:9.

    Money is to be found,

∴ in the first line of the working, money comes last.

    9 tyres cost £73·35

∴ 5 tyres cost £73·35 × $\frac{5}{9}$

           = £8·15 × 5

           = £40·75.

This example illustrates **direct ratio.**

Example 2 *If 9 men paint a building in 21 days, how long would 7 men take?*

Seven men take longer than 9 men.

The number of men is **decreased** in the ratio 7:9,

∴ the time taken is **increased** in the ratio 9:7.

Time is to be found,

∴ in the first line of the working, time comes last.

    9 men take 21 days

∴ 7 men take 21 × $\frac{9}{7}$ days

            = 27 days.

This example illustrates **inverse ratio.**

Example 3 *If* 9 *copies of a book cost* £12·15, *how many can be bought for* £17·55?

£12·15 is the cost of 9 books

∴ £17·55 is the cost of $9 \times \dfrac{17 \cdot 55}{12 \cdot 15}$ books

$$= \frac{1\,755}{135} \text{ books}$$

$$= 13 \text{ books.}$$

Example 4 *A heating system uses up a tankful of oil in* 15 *weeks when* 3 *litres a day are used. How long would the tankful last if* 10 *litres a day are used?*

The supply would last for a **shorter** time at 10 litres a day.

At   3 litres a day the oil lasts for 15 weeks

∴ at 10 litres a day the oil lasts for $15 \times \frac{3}{10}$ weeks

$$= 4\tfrac{1}{2} \text{ weeks.}$$

Exercise 37a

1. If 14 tins of meat cost £13·02, how much would 12 tins cost?

2. If 15 packets of biscuits cost £1·95, how many packets can be bought for £2·34?

3. A load of hay would last 16 horses for 33 days. How long would it last 11 horses?

4. A bricklayer working for 8 hours a day builds a wall in 12 days. How long would he take if he works for 6 hours a day?

5. A salesman's commission on sales of £187 is £11·22. Find his commission on sales of £255.

6. If the salesman in no. 5 receives commission of £13·92, what is the value of his sales?

7. A cyclist averaging 14 km h^{-1} completes a journey in 2 h 56 min. How long would he have taken at 16 km h^{-1}?

8. A motorist reaches his destination in 3 h 15 min by driving at an average speed of 60 km h^{-1}. At what average speed would he have arrived in 3 hours?

9. A bonus shared between 18 workmen gives each man £3·60. How much would each have received if there had been 20 workmen?

10. If $9\frac{1}{2}$ litres of paint cost £7·79, find the cost of $11\frac{1}{2}$ litres.

11. Find how much paint can be bought for £9·66 if $7\frac{1}{2}$ litres cost £6·90.

12. A ball of string can be cut into 28 pieces each 1·55 m long. How many 1·40 m lengths could be cut?

13. A train travels 154 km in 1 h 50 min. At the same average speed, how far would it travel in 2 h 10 min?

14. A bookshelf holds 72 textbooks each 2·1 cm thick. How many textbooks 1·8 cm thick would it hold?

15. A certain sum of money will buy 17·6 m of material at £1·80 per metre. Find the price of material at which 19·2 m can be bought.

If three numbers a, b, c are in the ratio $5:9:6$,
i.e. if $a:b:c = 5:9:6$,

$$\text{then } \frac{a}{5} = \frac{b}{9} = \frac{c}{6}.$$

$$\text{Also } \frac{a}{b} = \frac{5}{9}, \ \frac{b}{c} = \frac{9}{6} = \frac{3}{2}, \ \frac{c}{a} = \frac{6}{5}.$$

Example 5 *Three members d, m, n are in the ratio $3:6:4$. Find the value of* $\dfrac{4d - m}{m + 2n}$.

If $d:m:n = 3:6:4$, then $\dfrac{d}{3} = \dfrac{m}{6} = \dfrac{n}{4}$.

Let $\dfrac{d}{3} = \dfrac{m}{6} = \dfrac{n}{4} = k$.

Then $d = 3k, m = 6k, n = 4k$

$\therefore \dfrac{4d - m}{m + 2n} = \dfrac{12k - 6k}{6k + 8k} = \dfrac{6k}{14k} = \dfrac{3}{7}$.

Example 6 *Divide x litres into two parts in the ratio a:b.*

Let the parts be *ma* litres and *mb* litres.
Then $ma + mb = x$

$\therefore m(a + b) = x$

$\therefore m = \dfrac{x}{a + b}$

$\therefore$ the parts are $\dfrac{xa}{a + b}$ litres and $\dfrac{xb}{a + b}$ litres.

Example 7 *If $u:v = 5:4$ and $v:w = 6:7$, find $u:v:w$.*

$\dfrac{u}{5} = \dfrac{v}{4}$ and $\dfrac{v}{6} = \dfrac{w}{7}$

v occurs in both statements.

$\therefore$ make the fraction containing v the same each time.

Then $\dfrac{u}{15} = \dfrac{v}{12}$ and $\dfrac{v}{12} = \dfrac{w}{14}$ [12 is the L.C.M. of 4 and 6]

$\therefore \dfrac{u}{15} = \dfrac{v}{12} = \dfrac{w}{14}$

$\therefore u:v:w = 15:12:14$.

Example 8 *Find the ratio $m:n$ if $6m^2 - 11mn + 3n^2 = 0$.*

$6m^2 - 11mn + 3n^2 = 0$

$\therefore (2m - 3n)(3m - n) = 0$

$\therefore 2m = 3n$ or $3m = n$

$\therefore \dfrac{m}{n} = \dfrac{3}{2}$ or $\dfrac{m}{n} = \dfrac{1}{3}$

i.e. $m:n = 3:2$ or $1:3$.

Alternatively $6m^2 - 11mn + 3n^2 = 0$

$\therefore$ dividing both sides by n^2,

$$6\frac{m^2}{n^2} - 11\frac{m}{n} + 3 = 0$$

$$\therefore 6\left(\frac{m}{n}\right)^2 - 11\left(\frac{m}{n}\right) + 3 = 0$$

$$\therefore \left[2\left(\frac{m}{n}\right) - 3\right]\left[3\left(\frac{m}{n}\right) - 1\right] = 0$$

$$\therefore 2\left(\frac{m}{n}\right) = 3 \text{ or } 3\left(\frac{m}{n}\right) = 1$$

$$\therefore \frac{m}{n} = \frac{3}{2} \text{ or } \frac{1}{3}$$

i.e. $m:n = 3:2$ or $1:3$.

Example 9 *If $a:b = 5:3$, $c:d = 4:7$, and $a + 2c:b + d = 3:2$, find the ratio $a - 2c:2b - d$.*

Since $a:b = 5:3$, let $a = 5m$ and $b = 3m$.
Since $c:d = 4:7$, let $c = 4n$ and $d = 7n$.

Then $\dfrac{a + 2c}{b + d} = \dfrac{3}{2}$

$\therefore \dfrac{5m + 8n}{3m + 7n} = \dfrac{3}{2}$

$\therefore 2(5m + 8n) = 3(3m + 7n)$

$\therefore 10m + 16n = 9m + 21n$

$\therefore m = 5n$

Hence $\dfrac{a - 2c}{2b - d} = \dfrac{5m - 8n}{6m - 7n}$

$$= \frac{25n - 8n}{30n - 7n}$$

$$= \frac{17n}{23n}$$

$$= \frac{17}{23}$$

$\therefore \ a - 2c:2b - d = 17:23.$

Exercise 37b

If $\dfrac{m}{n} = \dfrac{3}{4}$, evaluate

1. $\dfrac{2m}{3n}$ **2.** $\dfrac{n^2}{2m^2}$ **3.** $\dfrac{2m - n}{3m - 2n}$

If $a:b:c = 5:2:3$, evaluate

4. $a - 2b:3b - c$ **5.** $a + b + c:5a$ **6.** $a - b:b + c$

7. If $u:v = 2:3$ and $v:w = 4:5$, find $u:v:w$.

8. If $a:b = 5:6$ and $b:c = 4:3$, find $a:b:c$.

Find the value of the ratio $m:n$ if

9. $4m = 7n$ **10.** $5m - n = 2m + 5n$

11. $2m^2 - 7mn + 6n^2 = 0$ **12.** $3m^2 - 10mn + 8n^2 = 0$

13. The ages of a mother and daughter are in the ratio $8:3$. If the daughter's age now is 12, what will be the ratio of their ages in 4 years' time?

14. A man's income is increased in the ratio $47:40$. Find the increase per cent.

15. The price of a car is increased from £x to £y. Find the ratio of the increase in price to the original price.

16. The price, £m, of a car is reduced by £n. Find the ratio in which the price is reduced.

17. In a school the number of girls exceeds the number of boys by 15%. Find the ratio of the numbers of boys to girls.

18. If a motorist increases his average speed in the ratio $m:n$, how is the time for a given journey affected?

19. If the cost of cement is decreased in the ratio $h:k$, what effect does this have on the quantity of cement that can be bought for a given sum of money?

20. The profit on sales to the value of £a is £b. At the same rate, find the profit on sales to the value of £c.

21. Two numbers are in the ratio $u:v$, and the second one is d. Find the first number.

22. The prices per kg of sugar and tea are in the ratio $u:v$. If the price of sugar increases by 10% and that of tea by 5%, find the new ratio of their costs.

23. If the radius of a sphere is increased in the ratio 3:2, find the ratio in which the volume is increased.

24. Two prisms stand on square bases, and the ratio of the lengths of the sides of the squares is $c:d$. If $h:k$ is the ratio of the heights of the prisms, find the ratio of their volumes.

25. Two triangles of equal area have altitudes in the ratio $h:k$. Find the ratio of the lengths of their bases.

26. Two circular cones have the same volume, and the radii of their bases are in the ratio $m:n$. Find the ratio of their altitudes.

27. If $h:k = 2:5$, $x:y = 3:4$, and $2h + x:k + 2y = 1:2$, find the ratio $h - x:k - y$.

28. If $u:v = 3:1$, $m:n = 4:3$, and $u - m:3v + n = 2:3$, find the ratio $u - 2m:v - n$.

29. The masses of two buckets are in the ratio 4:3. The masses of the amounts of sand that they can contain are in the ratio

5:3. When both buckets are full of sand their masses are in the ratio 3:2. Find the ratio of the mass of the larger bucket half full to that of the smaller bucket completely full.

30. Two housewives go shopping with sums of money which are in the ratio 3:5. The amounts that they spend are in the ratio 4:7, and the amounts that they have left are in the ratio 2:3. Find the ratio of the sum of their original amounts of money to the sum of the amounts that they spend.

Chapter 38

Similar triangles

If the **three angles** of one triangle are respectively equal to the three angles of another, the two triangles are said to be **similar**. They are of the same **shape**, but may be of different **size** as in Fig. 105.

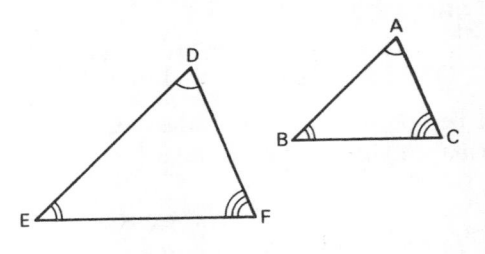

Fig. 105

The corresponding sides are not equal but in proportion. For example if equiangular triangles are drawn as in Fig. 105 with AB equal to $\frac{2}{3}$ of DE then BC will be found to be $\frac{2}{3}$ of EF and CA will be $\frac{2}{3}$ of FD. Hence AB and DE, BC and EF, CA and FD are all in the ratio $2:3$.

i.e. $\dfrac{AB}{DE} = \dfrac{BC}{EF} = \dfrac{CA}{FD} = \dfrac{2}{3}$.

Since $\dfrac{AB}{DE} = \dfrac{BC}{EF}$

$AB \times EF = BC \times DE$ (multiplying by $DE \times EF$)

$\therefore \dfrac{AB}{BC} = \dfrac{DE}{EF}$ (dividing by $BC \times EF$)

Similarly $\dfrac{BC}{CA} = \dfrac{EF}{FD}$ and $\dfrac{CA}{AB} = \dfrac{FD}{DE}$.

224

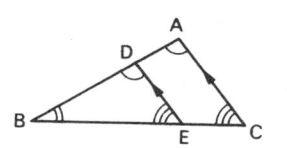

Fig. 106

If a line is drawn parallel to the side $\overline{AC}$ of $\triangle ABC$ to meet $\overline{AB}$ in D and $\overline{BC}$ in E,
then in $\triangle$s ABC, DBE, $B\hat{A}C = B\hat{D}E$ *corr.* $\angle$s
                $\hat{B}$ is common
$\therefore$ $\triangle$s ABC, DBE are equiangular and similar.

$\triangle ABC$ can be considered as the **enlargement** of $\triangle DBE$. $\triangle DBE$ is said to be mapped into $\triangle ABC$ by an enlargement of ratio BA : BD with centre B.

Example 1   *In Fig. 107 calculate YZ and ZN.*

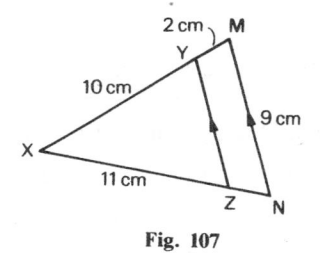

Fig. 107

$\triangle$s XYZ, XMN are equiangular and similar.
$\triangle XMN$ is the enlargement of $\triangle XYZ$ in the ratio XM : XY with centre X.

$$\therefore \frac{XY}{XM} = \frac{XZ}{XN} = \frac{YZ}{MN}$$

$$\therefore \frac{10}{12} = \frac{11}{XN} = \frac{YZ}{9}$$

225

∴10XN = 132 and 90 = 12YZ
∴ XN = 13·2 cm and YZ = 7·5 cm
∴ ZN = 2·2 cm and YZ = 7·5 cm.

Exercise 38a

1. In Fig. 108 state why △s ABC, ADE are similar. If AB = 6 cm, AC = 5 cm, AE = 7 cm and BC = 4 cm calculate AD and DE.

2. In Fig 108 if AB = 4 m, BD = 1 m, AC = 3·6 m and DE = 3·5 m calculate BC and CE.

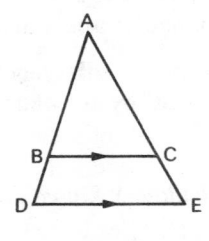

Fig. 108

3. In Fig. 109 which triangle is similar to △XOP and why? If OP = 9 cm, OX = 7 cm, PX = 8 cm and YQ = 12 cm calculate OY and OQ. Describe the mapping.

4. In Fig. 109 if OX = 3 m, PX = 4 m, OY = 4·2 m and OQ = 4·9 m calculate OP and YQ.

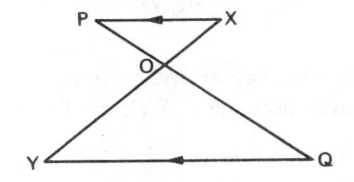

Fig. 109

5. Fig. 110 represents a roof $\overline{RF}$, leaning against a wall $\overline{WR}$ and supported by $\overline{SP}$. If the support is 2·4 m high, the wall is 5·4 m

Similar triangles

high and the bottom of the roof is 2 m from the support, find
how far the support is from the wall.

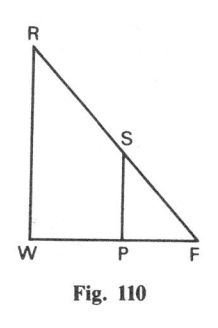

Fig. 110

6. A man wants to find the width of a canal (see Fig. 111). There
is a post on the far side at A. He puts posts at C and D 20 m
apart, one at B directly opposite A so that BC = 40 m, and one
at E so that DE is at right angles to the bank, and A, C and E
are in line with each other. He measures DE and finds it to be
11·3 m. How wide is the canal?

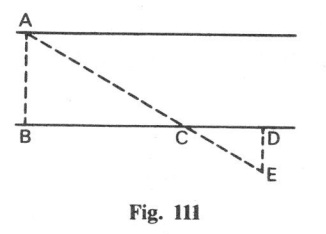

Fig. 111

7. Find the height of a tree whose shadow is 42 m long when the
shadow of a man 1·8 m tall is 2·4 m long.

8. In Fig. 112 name the triangle which is similar to △OHK and
describe the mapping. If OH = 12 cm, OK = 15 cm, OB = 20
cm and AB = 19 cm calculate OA and HK.

227

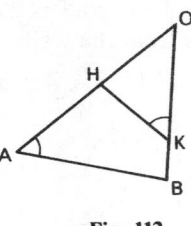

Fig. 112

9. Fig. 113 represents a pair of steps. The vertical height is 2·05 m when the feet are 1·23 m apart as shown. Find the length of the bar CD if it is 72 cm from the ground.

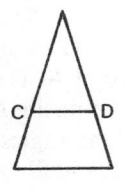

Fig. 113

10. A lampshade is in the form of part of the curved surface of a cone as in Fig. 114. If AP = 37 cm, AB = 46 cm and PQ = 69 cm find XP.

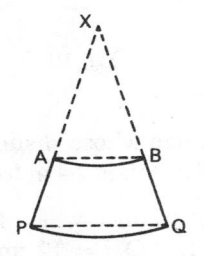

Fig. 114

Theorem

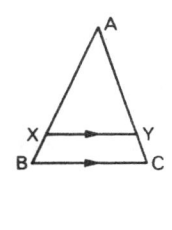 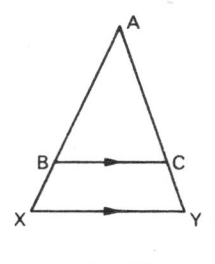 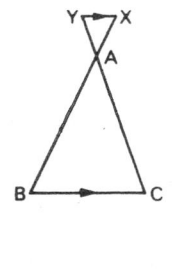

Fig. 115

In $\triangle ABC$, if $\overline{XY}/\!/\overline{BC}$ then $AX:XB = AY:YC$.

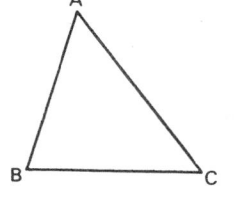 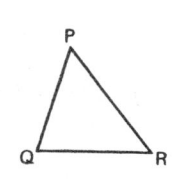

Fig. 116

Theorem

If $\triangle$s ABC, PQR are equiangular then

$$\frac{AB}{PQ} = \frac{BC}{QR} = \frac{CA}{RP}$$

Theorem

In $\triangle$s ABC, PQR, if $\dfrac{AB}{PQ} = \dfrac{BC}{QR} = \dfrac{CA}{RP}$

then the triangles are similar.

229

Theorem

In $\triangle$s ABC, PQR, if $\hat{A} = \hat{P}$ and $\dfrac{AB}{PQ} = \dfrac{AC}{PR}$

then the triangles are similar.

Example 2 ABCD *is a parallelogram,* P *is any point on* $\overline{AD}$ *and* $\overline{BP}$ *cuts* $\overline{AC}$ *at* Q. *Prove that* AP:AD = AQ:QC.

$\overline{AD}/\!/\overline{BC}$ *opp. sides of* $/\!/$ *gm*

$\therefore$ $x_1 = x_2$ *alt.* $\angle s$

$\quad y_1 = y_2$ *vert. opp.* $\angle s$

$\therefore$ $\triangle$s APQ, CBQ are similar   *2* $\angle s$ *of one* $\triangle$ = *2* $\angle s$ *of the other* $\triangle$

$\therefore$ $\dfrac{AP}{CB} = \dfrac{PQ}{BQ} = \dfrac{QA}{QC}$ *corr. sides are in proportion*

But BC = AD   *opp. sides of* $/\!/$ *gm*

$\therefore$ $\dfrac{AP}{AD} = \dfrac{QA}{QC}$

$\therefore$ AP:AD = AQ:QC

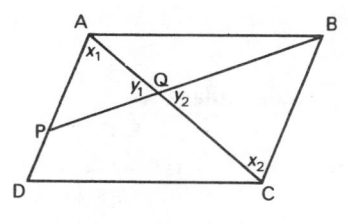

Fig. 117

Exercise 38b

1. ABC is a triangle with $\overline{BC}$ produced to N. L is a point in $\overline{AB}$; $\overline{AC}$ and $\overline{LN}$ meet at M and $A\hat{B}C = A\hat{M}L$.
   Prove that NM $\times$ NL = NB $\times$ NC.

2. ABC is a triangle, D is a point in $\overline{BC}$ such that $\overline{AD}$ bisects $B\hat{A}C$ and X is a point in $\overline{AD}$ such that CD = CX.
Prove that AB:AC = BD:DC.

3. Two circles intersect at A and B. $\overline{PQ}$ is a tangent to one circle at P and to the other at Q. $\overline{PA}$ is produced to a point R on the circle QAB and $\overline{QA}$ is produced to a point S on the circle PAB.
Prove that $PQ^2 = PS \times QR$.

4. A triangle ABC is inscribed in a circle. D is the mid-point of the arc BC and $\overline{AD}$ meets $\overline{BC}$ at E.
Prove that $AB \times CD = AD \times BE$.

5. Two circles PAR, SAQ touch externally at A and $\overline{PAQ}$, $\overline{SAR}$ are straight lines. Prove that $AP \times AS = AQ \times AR$.

6. ABC is any triangle, a line drawn through C cuts $\overline{AB}$ (produced if necessary) at P, and $A\hat{C}P = \hat{B}$.
Prove that $AC \times BC = AB \times PC$.

7. The circles ABCE and ACD intersect at A and C. The tangent at A to the circle ACD meets the other circle at B, $\overline{BC}$ is produced to D and $\overline{DA}$ meets the circle ABCE at E. Prove that $CA \times CE = CB \times CD$.

8. $\overline{TP}$ is a tangent to the circle APB at P. The line from T to the centre O of the circle meets the circle at A and is produced to B. The bisector of $B\hat{T}P$ meets $\overline{AP}$ at Q and $\overline{BP}$ at R. Prove that $\triangle$s QTP and RTB are similar and that PQ = PR.

9. $\overline{AB}$ is the tangent at A to the circle ACPD. $\overline{DC}/\!/\overline{AB}$ and $\overline{BCP}$ is a straight line. Prove that $\triangle$s DAP and ABP are similar and that $PA^2 = PB \times PD$.

10. The circles ABC and ADE touch internally at A. $\overline{TA}$ is the common tangent and $\overline{TD}$ is a tangent to the smaller circle at D. $\overline{TD}$ cuts the larger circle at B and is produced to C. $\overline{AB}$ cuts the smaller circle at E. Prove (i) $B\hat{A}D = C\hat{A}D$ (ii) $\triangle$s DAE, CAD are similar (iii) $DA^2 = EA \times CA$.

11. ABC is a triangle inscribed in a circle. The bisector of $\hat{A}$ cuts $\overline{BC}$ at P and the circle at Q. Prove that AB:AP = AQ:AC.

12. The circles ABZYX and ABPQR intersect at A and B. $\overline{XAP}$, $\overline{YAQ}$ and $\overline{ZAR}$ are straight lines. Prove that △s XYZ, PQR are similar.

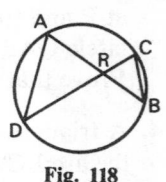

Theorem

RA × RB = RC × RD

Fig. 118

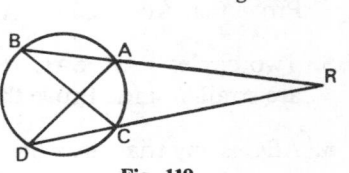

Theorem

RA × RB = RC × RD

Fig. 119

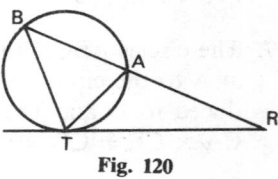

Theorem

RA × RB = RT²

Fig. 120

Example 3 Find a, b and c in Fig. 121.

From Theorem $\quad 6a = 5 \times 4$

$$\therefore a = \frac{20}{6} = 3\tfrac{1}{3}$$

From Theorem $\quad b^2 = 3 \times 12$
$$\therefore b = 6$$

From Theorem $4(4 + c) = b^2$
$$\therefore 16 + 4c = 36$$
$$\therefore 4c = 20$$
$$\therefore c = 5$$

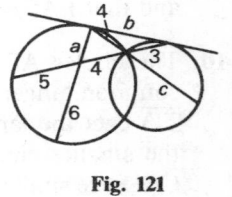

Fig. 121

Exercise 38c

Find $a, b, \ldots, u$ in Fig. 122.

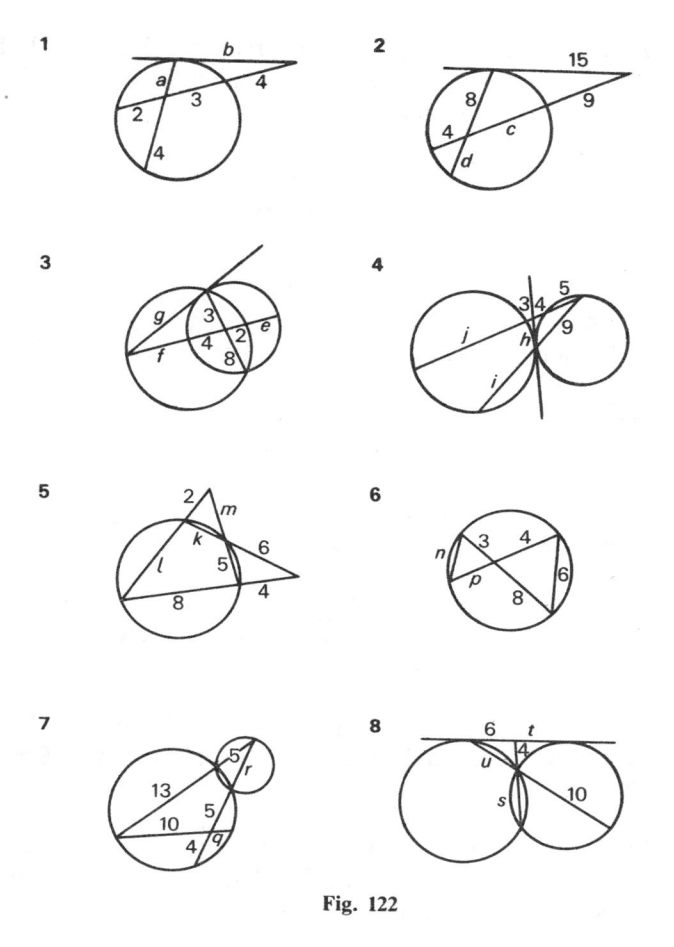

Fig. 122

9. A tunnel-mouth is in the form of a segment of a circle 5 m high in the middle and 4 m wide at the ground. What is the radius of the circle?

10. A bridge is in the form of an arc of a circle 10 m high in the middle and 50 m wide horizontally. What is the radius of the circle?

11. ABCD is a parallelogram. The circumcircle of $\triangle$ACD bisects $\overline{AB}$. $\overline{BC}$ produced cuts the circle again at X. If AD = 8 cm and DC = 12 cm calculate CX.

12. ABCD is a parallelogram. The circumcircle of $\triangle$ACD cuts $\overline{DB}$ at E and the diagonals intersect at F. If EF = 4 cm and AC = 12 cm calculate BE.

13. $\overline{AB}$ is a tangent to the circle BCD at B. $\overline{ADC}$ is a straight line and E is a point in $\overline{BC}$ such that $\overline{DE}/\!/\overline{AB}$. Prove (i) the triangles BDE and BCD are similar and (ii) $\overline{BD}$ touches the circle CDE.

14. $\overline{PQR}$ is a secant of a circle TQR and $\overline{PT}$ is a tangent to the circle. If 4QR = 5PQ prove that 2PT = 3PQ.

15. $\overline{PAB}$ and $\overline{PCD}$ are secants of the circle ABDC. If PC = 2PA prove that AB − 2CD = 3PA.

16. The circles TAB and TCD touch internally at T. $\overline{TP}$ is the common tangent and $\overline{PACDB}$ is a straight line. If PA = AC = CD prove that DB = 3CD.

17. The circles ABDC and ABFE intersect at A and B. P is a point on $\overline{BA}$ produced and $\overline{PCD}$, $\overline{PEF}$ are straight lines. Prove that D, C, E, F are concyclic.

18. The circles ACBF and ADBG intersect at A and B. E is a point in $\overline{AB}$ and a line through it cuts one circle in C and F and the other circle in D and G. If DE = EF prove that CD = FG.

19. $\overline{AB}$ is a diameter of the circle ABC and $\overline{AT}$ is a tangent to the circle at A. $\overline{TB}$ cuts the circle at C. If AB = 3 cm and AT = 4 cm prove that BC : CT = 9 : 16.

20. The tangent $\overline{\text{AT}}$ to the circle ABC touches it at A and $\overline{\text{TBC}}$ is a straight line. If TA = 15 cm and BC = 16 cm calculate TB and find the ratio AB:AC.

Theorem
The areas of similar triangles are in the ratio of the squares of corresponding sides.

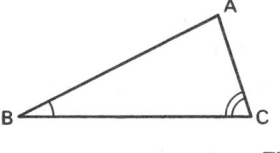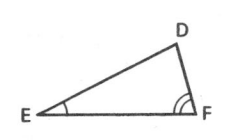

Fig. 123

$$\frac{\triangle\text{ABC}}{\triangle\text{DEF}} = \frac{\text{AB}^2}{\text{DE}^2} = \frac{\text{AC}^2}{\text{DF}^2} = \frac{\text{BC}^2}{\text{EF}^2}$$

An enlargement in the ratio $r:1$ with centre the origin can be performed by the matrix operator $\begin{pmatrix} r & 0 \\ 0 & r \end{pmatrix}$. The determinant of this matrix is r^2 which is the multiple by which the area of the object is increased by this transformation.

Example 4 *Find the co-ordinates of the vertices of the similar triangle whose area is 4 times the area of the triangle whose vertices are at*

$\begin{pmatrix} 1 \\ 2 \end{pmatrix}, \begin{pmatrix} 3 \\ 1 \end{pmatrix}, \begin{pmatrix} 5 \\ -1 \end{pmatrix}$, the centre of the enlargement being $\begin{pmatrix} 1 \\ 2 \end{pmatrix}$.

The ratio of the areas is $4:1$
$\therefore$ the ratio of the lengths is $2:1$.

The operator is $\begin{pmatrix} 2 & 0 \\ 0 & 2 \end{pmatrix}$ if the centre of the enlargement is $\begin{pmatrix} 0 \\ 0 \end{pmatrix}$.

235

Translating the triangle through $\begin{pmatrix} -1 \\ -2 \end{pmatrix}$,

$\begin{pmatrix} 1 \\ 2 \end{pmatrix}$ is mapped into $\begin{pmatrix} 1 \\ 2 \end{pmatrix} - \begin{pmatrix} 1 \\ 2 \end{pmatrix} = \begin{pmatrix} 0 \\ 0 \end{pmatrix}$,

$\begin{pmatrix} 3 \\ 1 \end{pmatrix}$ is mapped into $\begin{pmatrix} 3 \\ 1 \end{pmatrix} - \begin{pmatrix} 1 \\ 2 \end{pmatrix} = \begin{pmatrix} 2 \\ -1 \end{pmatrix}$

and $\begin{pmatrix} 5 \\ -1 \end{pmatrix}$ is mapped into $\begin{pmatrix} 5 \\ -1 \end{pmatrix} - \begin{pmatrix} 1 \\ 2 \end{pmatrix} = \begin{pmatrix} 4 \\ -3 \end{pmatrix}$.

Enlarging, $\begin{pmatrix} 0 \\ 0 \end{pmatrix}$ is mapped into $\begin{pmatrix} 0 \\ 0 \end{pmatrix}$,

$\begin{pmatrix} 2 \\ -1 \end{pmatrix}$ is mapped into $\begin{pmatrix} 2 & 0 \\ 0 & 2 \end{pmatrix}\begin{pmatrix} 2 \\ -1 \end{pmatrix} = \begin{pmatrix} 4 \\ -2 \end{pmatrix}$

and $\begin{pmatrix} 4 \\ -3 \end{pmatrix}$ is mapped into $\begin{pmatrix} 2 & 0 \\ 0 & 2 \end{pmatrix}\begin{pmatrix} 4 \\ -3 \end{pmatrix} = \begin{pmatrix} 8 \\ -6 \end{pmatrix}$.

Translating through $\begin{pmatrix} 1 \\ 2 \end{pmatrix}$,

$\begin{pmatrix} 0 \\ 0 \end{pmatrix}$ is mapped into $\begin{pmatrix} 0 \\ 0 \end{pmatrix} + \begin{pmatrix} 1 \\ 2 \end{pmatrix} = \begin{pmatrix} 1 \\ 2 \end{pmatrix}$,

$\begin{pmatrix} 4 \\ -2 \end{pmatrix}$ is mapped into $\begin{pmatrix} 4 \\ -2 \end{pmatrix} + \begin{pmatrix} 1 \\ 2 \end{pmatrix} = \begin{pmatrix} 5 \\ 0 \end{pmatrix}$

and $\begin{pmatrix} 8 \\ -6 \end{pmatrix}$ is mapped into $\begin{pmatrix} 8 \\ -6 \end{pmatrix} + \begin{pmatrix} 1 \\ 2 \end{pmatrix} = \begin{pmatrix} 9 \\ -4 \end{pmatrix}$.

The required co-ordinates are $\begin{pmatrix} 1 \\ 2 \end{pmatrix}$, $\begin{pmatrix} 5 \\ 0 \end{pmatrix}$ and $\begin{pmatrix} 9 \\ -4 \end{pmatrix}$.

Exercise 38d

1. P and Q are points in the sides $\overline{AB}$ and $\overline{AC}$ of a triangle ABC such that $\overline{PQ}/\!/\overline{BC}$ and AP:PB = 3:5.

   Write down the ratios
   (i) PQ:BC
   (ii) $\triangle$APQ:$\triangle$ABC
   (iii) $\triangle$APQ:trapezium PQCB.

2. In Fig. 124 (i) find the ratio of the areas A:B:C.

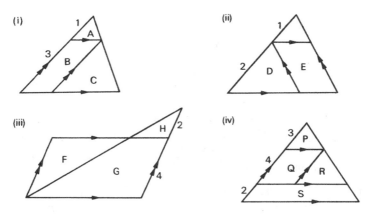

Fig. 124

3. In Fig. 124 (ii) find the ratio of the areas D:E.

4. In Fig. 124 (iii) find the ratio of the areas F:G:H.

5. In Fig. 124 (iv) find the ratio of the areas P:Q:R:S.

6. In a circle ABCD chords $\overline{AC}$, $\overline{BD}$ cut at E inside the circle. AE = 4 cm, EC = 9 cm, DE = 5 cm. Find the ratio of the areas (i) $\triangle$AED:$\triangle$BEC (ii) $\triangle$AFB:$\triangle$CED.

7. A line parallel to one side of a triangle divides it into a triangle and a quadrilateral with areas in the ratio 25:24. In what ratio does the line divide the other two sides of the triangle?

8. In a parallelogram ABCD, AD = 8 cm and the side $\overline{CB}$ is produced to E so that BE = 4 cm. Prove that $\overline{DE}$ divides the parallelogram into a triangle and a trapezium with areas in the ratio 1:2.

9. In Fig. 125 find the ratio of the areas A, B, C, D and deduce the ratio of the three parts into which $\overline{PQ}$ is divided.

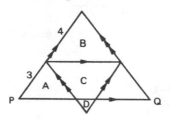

Fig. 125

10. In a triangle ABC, BA = BC = 12 cm. D is a point on $\overline{AB}$ such that AD = 4 cm and $\overline{DE}$, drawn parallel to $\overline{BC}$, cuts $\overline{AC}$ in E. M is the mid-point of $\overline{BC}$.
Find the ratio $\triangle DEM : \triangle ABC$. (*Hint.* Join $\overline{AM}$.)

11. PQRS is a parallelogram and A, B are the mid-points of $\overline{PQ}$, $\overline{PS}$ respectively. Prove that $\triangle ABR = \frac{3}{8}$ of the parallelogram.

12. ABCD is a quadrilateral in which $\overline{AC}$ bisects $\hat{A}$ and $\hat{C}$. If $\hat{A} = 60°$ and $\hat{C} = 120°$ prove that $\triangle ABD = 3 \triangle BCD$.

13. $\overline{ABE}$ and $\overline{CDE}$ are secants of the circle ABDC meeting at E. Prove that $\triangle ADE : \triangle CBE = AD^2 : CB^2$.

14. ABCD is a parallelogram and a straight line through A cuts $\overline{BC}$ at E and $\overline{DC}$ produced at F.
Prove that $\triangle ABE : \triangle CEF = DC^2 : CF^2$.

15. $\overline{AB}$ is a diameter of the circle ABC, centre O. $\overline{AC}$ is produced to E and a line through E perpendicular to $\overline{AB}$ produced meets it in F. Prove that $\triangle AEF : \triangle ABC = AE^2 : 4\,OC^2$.

16. Use the operator $\begin{pmatrix} 3 & 0 \\ 0 & 3 \end{pmatrix}$ to enlarge the triangle whose vertices are $\begin{pmatrix} 2 \\ 1 \end{pmatrix}$, $\begin{pmatrix} 6 \\ -3 \end{pmatrix}$ and $\begin{pmatrix} 8 \\ -1 \end{pmatrix}$. What is the ratio of the areas of the two triangles?

17. What matrix has the effect of enlarging in the ratio $5:1$ with centre the origin? What is its determinant?

18. Enlarge the triangle whose vertices are $\begin{pmatrix} -2 \\ 1 \end{pmatrix}$, $\begin{pmatrix} 1 \\ -3 \end{pmatrix}$ and $\begin{pmatrix} 3 \\ 2 \end{pmatrix}$ in the ratio $3:2$ with centre $\begin{pmatrix} 2 \\ -1 \end{pmatrix}$. What is the ratio of the areas of the triangles?

19. Two similar triangles are such that one has an area 16 times the other and has vertices $\begin{pmatrix} 8 \\ 2 \end{pmatrix}$, $\begin{pmatrix} 0 \\ -4 \end{pmatrix}$ and $\begin{pmatrix} 6 \\ 12 \end{pmatrix}$. Find the set of co-ordinates of the vertices of the smaller triangle. (Centre of enlargement at the origin.)

20. A triangle has vertices $\begin{pmatrix} -1 \\ 3 \end{pmatrix}$, $\begin{pmatrix} 1 \\ 9 \end{pmatrix}$ and $\begin{pmatrix} 5 \\ -2 \end{pmatrix}$. A similar triangle has 9 times the area. Find the co-ordinates of its vertices, the centre of enlargement being $\begin{pmatrix} 0 \\ 2 \end{pmatrix}$.

Chapter 39

Functional notation. Remainder theorem

Relations

An algebraic equation implies a **relation** between the variables involved. There are four types of relation between two variables as shown by the following examples

(i) $y = 3x - 2$ is a **one-to-one** relation as for any value of x there is only one value of y, and for any value of y there is only one value of x,

(ii) $y = 9x^2$ is a **many-to-one** relation as there are several values of x (two in this case) for any one value of y,

(iii) $y^2 = 4x$ is a **one-to-many** relation as there are several values of y for any value of x,

(iv) $y^4 = 4x^2$ is a **many-to-many** relation as there is more than one value of y for any value of x, and more than one value of x for any value of y.

Functional notation

A many-to-one relation is called a **function.** As a one-to-one relation, often called a **one-to-one correspondence,** is a special case of a many-to-one relation it is also a function. Any algebraic expression which involves the variable x (and no other variable) is a **function of x**, and its value depends on the value of x. The symbol used is $f(x)$ which is read as 'function of x'; $f(2)$ means 'the same expression with 2 written instead of x'; $f(-1)$ means 'the same expression with -1 written instead of x', and so on.

Thus if

$$f(x) \equiv x^3 + 3x^2 - 2x - 1,$$

then

$$f(2) = 2^3 + 3 \times 2^2 - 2 \times 2 - 1 = 15$$
$$f(y) = y^3 + 3y^2 - 2y - 1$$
$$f(x - 1) = (x - 1)^3 + 3(x - 1)^2 - 2(x - 1) - 1$$
$$= x^3 - 3x^2 + 3x - 1 + 3x^2 - 6x + 3 - 2x + 2 - 1$$
$$= x^3 - 5x + 3$$

Example 1 If $f(x) \equiv \dfrac{2(x - 1)}{x^2 + 2}$, find $f(0), f(1), f(-2)$.

$$f(0) = \frac{2(-1)}{2} = -1$$

$$f(1) = \frac{2(1 - 1)}{1 + 2} = 0$$

$$f(-2) = \frac{2(-2 - 1)}{4 + 2} = \frac{2(-3)}{6} = -1$$

Exercise 39a

1. State which type of relation is expressed by the following equations:

(i) $y = 4x$ (ii) $y = 2x^2 - 1$
(iii) $y^2 = 3x$ (iv) $y^2 = 2x^2 + 5x$
(v) $3y = 7x^2$ (vi) $2y + y^2 = 3x$
(vii) $y - 2y^2 = x + 3x^2$ (viii) $y^6 = 2x^2 + x$
(ix) $y = x^3 - x^2 + 2x$ (x) $2y + y^2 = 3x - 1$

2. If $f(x) \equiv x^2 - 2x$ find the values of

(i) $f(0)$ (ii) $f(1)$ (iii) $f(2)$
(iv) $f(-3)$ (v) $f(-5)$ (vi) $f(y)$
(vii) $f(x - 1)$ (viii) $f(3x)$ (ix) $f(x + h)$

241

3. If $f(x) \equiv 3^x$ find the values of

(i) $f(1)$ (ii) $f(2)$ (iii) $f(-1)$ (iv) $f(0)$ (v) $f(4)$
(vi) $f(-3)$

4. If $f(x) \equiv \dfrac{x^2 - 7x + 12}{3x - 4}$ find the values of

(i) $f(0)$ (ii) $f(1)$ (iii) $f(3)$ (iv) $f(4)$ (v) $f(-2)$

5. Evaluate $\dfrac{f(x) - f(x - h)}{h}$ for each of the following functions:

(i) $f(x) \equiv 2x$ (ii) $f(x) \equiv 3x^2$ (iii) $f(x) \equiv -x^3$

(iv) $f(x) \equiv -\dfrac{1}{x}$ (v) $f(x) \equiv 3x + x^2$

Remainder theorem

When $f(x)$ is divided by $x - a$ the remainder is $f(a)$.

Example 2 *Find the remainder when* $3x^3 + 4x^2 - 7x - 12$ *is divided by* $2x - 3$.

Let the quotient be Q and the remainder R.
Then $3x^3 + 4x^2 - 7x - 12 \equiv (2x - 3)Q + R$.
Put $x = \frac{3}{2}$ (so that $2x - 3 = 0$).
Then $3(\frac{3}{2})^3 + 4(\frac{3}{2})^2 - 7(\frac{3}{2}) - 12 = 0 \times Q + R$

$\therefore \dfrac{81}{8} + 9 - \dfrac{21}{2} - 12 = R$

$\therefore R = -3\frac{3}{8}$

$\therefore$ the remainder is $-3\frac{3}{8}$.

Example 3 *Find the remainder when* $2x^2 + 5x + 1$ *is divided by* $x + 3$.

If $x = -3$, $2x^2 + 5x + 1 = 2 \times 9 + 5 \times (-3) + 1$
$\qquad\qquad\qquad\qquad\qquad = 4$

$\therefore$ the remainder is 4.

Alternatively, using the functional notation,

$$\text{let } f(x) \equiv 2x^2 + 5x + 1$$
$$\text{Then } f(-3) = 2 \times 9 + 5 \times (-3) + 1$$
$$= 4$$

∴ the remainder is 4.

Exercise 39b

1. Find the remainder when $x^2 - 3x + 5$ is divided by
   (i) $x - 1$ (ii) $x + 1$ (iii) $x + 2$ Check by division.

2. Find the remainder when $2x^2 + 4x - 7$ is divided by
   (i) $x - 1$ (ii) $x - 3$ (iii) $x + 2$ Check by division.

3. Find the remainder when $3x^2 + 5x - 11$ is divided by
   (i) $x + 1$ (ii) $x - 2$ (iii) $x - 5$ Check by division.

4. Find the remainder when $4x^3 + 2x^2 - 6x + 9$ is divided by
   (i) $x - 2$ (ii) $2x - 1$ (iii) $2x + 1$

5. Find the remainder when $9x^3 + 3x^2 - 2x + 1$ is divided by
   (i) $x + 3$ (ii) $3x - 1$ (iii) $3x + 2$

Factorisation

Example 4 *Verify that $x - 2$ is a factor of $2x^3 - x^2 - 15x + 18$.*

If $x - 2$ is a factor, then when $2x^3 - x^2 - 15x + 18$ is divided by $x - 2$ the remainder is 0.
Let $2x^3 - x^2 - 15x + 18 \equiv f(x)$.
Then $f(2) = 2 \times 8 - 4 - 15 \times 2 + 18$
$= 0$

∴ $x - 2$ is a factor.

Example 5 *Factorise the expression $6x^3 + 5x^2 - 12x + 4$.*

If $x = 1$, $6x^3 + 5x^2 - 12x + 4 = 6 + 5 - 12 + 4 = 3$
∴ $x - 1$ is not a factor.

243

If $x = -1$, $6x^3 + 5x^2 - 12x + 4 = -6 + 5 + 12 + 4 = 15$

$\therefore$ $x + 1$ is not a factor

If $x = 2$, $6x^3 + 5x^2 - 12x + 4 = 48 + 20 - 24 + 4 = 48$

$\therefore$ $x - 2$ is not a factor

If $x = -2$, $6x^3 + 5x^2 - 12x + 4 = -48 + 20 + 24 + 4 = 0$

$\therefore$ $x + 2$ is a factor

$\therefore$ $6x^3 + 5x^2 - 12x + 4 = (x + 2)(6x^2 - 7x + 2)$
$$= (x + 2)(2x - 1)(3x - 2)$$

Notice that when $x + 2$ has been established as a factor, the other factors can be found by inspection.

Example 6   *Factorise the expression* $2x^4 + 7x^3 - 15x^2 + x + 5$.

Since the absolute term is 5 there is no point in trying the values $x = 2$ or -2, 3 or -3, 4 or -4 as the absolute term of the factor must always be a factor of the absolute term of the expression.

Let $2x^4 + 7x^3 - 15x^2 + x + 5 \equiv f(x)$

then $f(1) = 0$ $\therefore$ $x - 1$ is a factor

$f(-1) = -16$ $\therefore$ $x + 1$ is not a factor

$f(5) = 1\,760$ $\therefore$ $x - 5$ is not a factor

$f(-5) = 0$ $\therefore$ $x + 5$ is a factor

$\therefore$ $2x^4 + 7x^3 - 15x^2 + x + 5 = (x - 1)(2x^3 + 9x^2 - 6x - 5)$
$$= (x - 1)(x + 5)(2x^2 - x - 1)$$
$$= (x - 1)(x + 5)(x - 1)(2x + 1)$$
$$= (x - 1)^2(x + 5)(2x + 1)$$

Exercise 39c

Factorise the following expressions:

1. $x^3 - 21x - 20$

2. $x^3 - 3x - 2$

3. $x^3 - 5x^2 - 22x + 56$

4. $6x^3 - 17x^2 - 5x + 6$

5. $2a^3 + 5a^2 - 4a - 12$

6. $3b^3 + 7b^2 - 8b - 20$

7. $2b^3 - 3b^2 - 72b - 35$

8. $6y^3 - 11y^2 - 4y + 4$

9. $2p^3 - 9p^2 - 6p + 40$

10. $4q^3 - 13q + 6$

11. $4x^4 - 20x^3 + 29x^2 - 16x + 3$

12. $4x^4 + 8x^3 - 17x^2 - 12x + 9$

13. $6x^4 + 7x^3 - 104x^2 + 67x + 60$

14. $6x^4 - 5x^3 - 48x^2 + 33x + 70$

15. $8x^4 - 4x^3 - 34x^2 + 21x + 18$

Example 7 *If* $x - 3$ *and* $3x + 1$ *are factors of* $3x^3 + ax^2 + bx + 12$ *find a, b and the other factor.*

Let $3x^3 + ax^2 + bx + 12 \equiv f(x)$
$x - 3$ is a factor
$\therefore \ f(3) = 0$

$\therefore \ 81 + 9a + 3b + 12 = 0$
$\qquad \therefore \ 9a + 3b + 93 = 0$ i.e. $3a + b + 31 = 0$ (i)
$3x + 1$ is a factor
$\therefore \qquad f(-\frac{1}{3}) = 0$
$\therefore \ -\frac{1}{9} + \frac{1}{9}a - \frac{1}{3}b + 12 = 0$

$\therefore \ -1 + a - 3b + 108 = 0$ i.e. $a - 3b + 107 = 0$ (ii)

(i) $\times 3$ $9a + 3b + \ 93 = 0$
(ii) $a - 3b + 107 = 0$
Add $10a \qquad + 200 = 0$
$\qquad\qquad \therefore \ a = -20$
Subst. in (i) $-60 + b + 31 = 0$
$\qquad\qquad\qquad \therefore \ b = 29$
$3x^3 + ax^2 + bx + 12 \equiv 3x^3 - 20x^2 + 29x + 12$
$\qquad\qquad\qquad \equiv (x - 3)(3x + 1)(x - 4)$

The final factor is easily found by inspection, since the product of the three 'x terms' is $3x^3$ and the product of the three absolute terms is $+12$.

Exercise 39d

1. Given that $x + 2$ is a factor of $6x^3 + x^2 + ax + 8$ find a and the other two factors.

2. When $x^4 + bx^3 - 2x^2 - 5$ is divided by $x + 3$ the remainder is 4. Find b and the remainder when the expression is divided by $x - 2$.

3. Given that $x^4 - x^3 - ax - b$ is exactly divisible by $x + 1$ and by $x - 2$, find a and b and the other factor.

4. If $ax^3 - 8x^2 - x + b$ is exactly divisible by $x - 2$ and by $x + 1$, find a and b and the other factor.

5. Given that $6x^3 - ax^2 - 44x + 3a$ is exactly divisible by $x - 3$, find a and the other factors.

6. The factors of $ax^3 + bx^2 + cx + 6$ are $x + 3$, $2x - 1$, $3x - 2$. Find a, b and c.

7. Two factors of $ax^3 + bx^2 + cx - 30$ are $x + 3$ and $3x + 2$. The remainder when the expression is divided by $x - 2$ is -40. What is the third factor?

8. A factor of $ax^3 + bx + c$ is $x + 3$. When the expression is divided by $x - 2$ the remainder is -120, and when it is divided by $x + 2$ the remainder is 276. Find the other two factors of the expression.

Chapter 40

Vector applications

In Fig. 126 the displacement $\overrightarrow{AC}$ is the vector sum of the displacements $\overrightarrow{AB}$ and $\overrightarrow{BC}$, i.e. $\overrightarrow{AC} = \overrightarrow{AB} + \overrightarrow{BC}$. Displacement is one example of a vector, others being velocity, acceleration and force. All vectors can be added by the triangle rule; in Fig. 126 *AC* represents the vector sum of *AB* and *BC*, i.e. *AC* = *AB* + *BC*. Note that the two Bs are consecutive and that in the vector triangle arrows are drawn to indicate the directions of the vectors, a double arrow indicating the direction of the resultant.

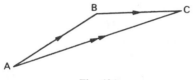

Fig. 126

In velocity examples the symbol $_AV_B$ for the velocity of A relative to B is often useful. $_OV_A$ is the velocity of O relative to A, and $_OV_B$ is the velocity of O relative to B. By examining the positions of the letters O, A and B it can be seen that the only way of forming the vector equation is $_OV_B = {_OV_A} + {_AV_B}$.

Reminder on bearings. It is usual to give a bearing by means of a three digit number, which states the numbers of degrees of rotation clockwise from due north.

Thus S 25° E is given by 155°,
  N 25° E is given by 042°,
  N 60° W is given by 300°.

Example 1 *A boat is heading in a direction 060° at a speed which in still water would be 15 km h⁻¹. It is carried off course by a current of 6 km h⁻¹ in a direction 150°. Find the boat's actual speed and direction.*

Let $_BV_W$ represent the velocity of the boat in still water, $_WV_E$ represent the velocity of the water relative to the earth and $_BV_E$ represent the velocity of the boat relative to the earth. $_BV_E = {_BV_W} + {_WV_E}$, from which a rough sketch is drawn, estimating angles and lengths. $\overline{\text{NBS}}$ and $\overline{\text{XWY}}$ are north–south lines. $N\hat{B}W = 60°$ and $X\hat{W}E = 150°$. The $\triangle BWE$ is the triangle of velocities.

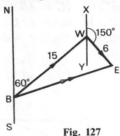

Fig. 127

(i) *By drawing and measurement*

Use a scale of 1 cm to 1 km h⁻¹.

Draw $\triangle BWE$ as in Fig. 127, with BW = 15 cm, WE = 6 cm and the angles as shown.

By measurement, BE = 16·2 cm and $N\hat{B}E = 82°$.

∴ the boat is moving at 16·2 km h⁻¹ on a bearing of 082°.

(ii) *By calculation*

$\triangle BWE$ is right-angled at W.

By Pythagoras, $BE^2 = 15^2 + 6^2$

$$= 225 + 36$$
$$= 261$$
$$\therefore \quad BE = 16·16$$
$$\tan E\hat{B}W = \frac{6}{15}$$
$$= 0·4$$
$$\therefore \quad E\hat{B}W = 21° \, 48'$$
$$\therefore \quad N\hat{B}E = 60° + 21° \, 48' = 81° \, 48'$$

∴ the speed of the boat is $16\cdot2$ km h^{-1} on a bearing of $082°$ to the nearest degree.

Example 2 *A man wants to swim to a point on the opposite bank of a river. If he can swim at $3\cdot5$ km h^{-1} in still water and the current flows at 2 km h^{-1}, find the angle to the bank at which he must head.*

Let $_sV_W$ represent the velocity of the swimmer in still water, $_wV_E$ represent the velocity of the current and $_sV_E$ represent the velocity of the swimmer relative to the earth.

$_sV_E = {_sV_W} + {_wV_E}$, from which a rough sketch is drawn.

(i) *By drawing and measurement*

Use a scale of 2 cm to 1 m s^{-1}.

Draw $\overline{SE}$ at right angles to the bank, and a line $\overline{PR}/\!/\overline{SE}$ and 4 cm from it. With centre S and radius 7 cm draw an arc to cut $\overline{PR}$ at W. Then $\triangle$ SWE is the triangle of velocities.

By measurement $T\hat{S}W = 55°$.

∴ the swimmer must head upstream at $55°$ to the bank.

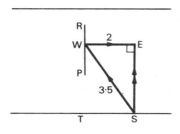

Fig. 128

(ii) *By calculation*

$$\sec T\hat{S}W = \sec S\hat{W}E$$
$$= \frac{3\cdot5}{2}$$
$$= 1\cdot75$$
$$\therefore T\hat{S}W = 55°\,9'$$

∴ the swimmer must head upstream at approximately $55°$ to the bank.

Example 3 *In Fig.* 129 *two strings are holding up a particle of weight 5 newtons. The string* $\overline{AC}$ *is at 45° to the vertical and* $\overline{CB}$ *is at 55° to the vertical. What is the tension in each string?*

Let *OP* represent the force in $\overline{CA}$ and *PQ* the force in $\overline{CB}$. The resultant force *OQ* given by *OQ* = *OP* + *PQ* must be 5 newtons vertically upwards, as it is equal and opposite to the force in $\overline{CD}$ if equilibrium is maintained. To draw the triangle of forces first draw $\overline{OQ}$, then $\overline{OP}$ and $\overline{PQ}$ in the appropriate directions.

(i) *By drawing and measurement*

Use a scale of 2 cm to 1 newton.

Draw $\overline{OQ}$ of length 10 cm. Then draw $\overline{OY}$ with $Q\hat{O}Y = 45°$ and $\overline{QX}$ with $O\hat{Q}X = 55°$.

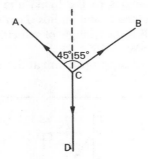

Fig. 129

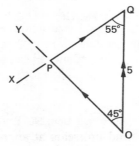

Fig. 130

These lines meet at P.

By measurement $\overline{OP}$ = 8·3 cm and PQ = 7·2 cm.

∴ the tension in $\overline{CA}$ is 4·15 newtons and the tension in $\overline{CB}$ is 3·6 newtons.

(ii) *By calculation*

$O\hat{P}Q = 180° - 45° - 55°$

$= 80°$

Using the sine formula,

$$\frac{OP}{\sin 55°} = \frac{PQ}{\sin 45°} = \frac{5}{\sin 80°}$$

$$\therefore \ OP = \frac{5 \sin 55°}{\sin 80°}$$

$$= 4·16$$

$$PQ = \frac{5 \sin 45°}{\sin 80°}$$

$$= 3·59$$

No.	Log.
5	0·699 0
sin 55°	$\bar{1}$·913 4
-	0·612 4
sin 80°	$\bar{1}$·993 4
4·159	0·619 0
5	0·699 0
sin 45°	$\bar{1}$·849 5
	0·548 5
sin 80°	$\bar{1}$·993 4
3·590	0·555 1

∴ the tension in $\overline{CA}$ = 4·16 newtons and the tension in $\overline{CB}$ = 3·59 newtons.

Course, track and drift

The speed which an aircraft would have if the air were still is called its **air-speed** (i.e. speed relative to the air).

The speed of an aircraft over the ground is called its **ground-speed** (i.e. speed relative to the ground).

The direction in which an aircraft is heading is called its **course**.

The direction in which it is actually moving relative to the ground is called its **track**.

The angle between the track and the course is called the **drift**.

Angles are usually given to the nearest degree.

Notice that although the aircraft is travelling along its **track**, it is pointing in the direction of its **course** (see Fig. 131).

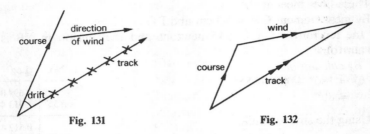

Fig. 131   Fig. 132

When putting the arrows on the triangle of velocities for an aircraft it is usual to use a single arrow for the course, a double arrow for the wind, and a triple arrow for the track. Thus a vector marked with one arrow and a vector marked with two arrows add up to a vector marked with three arrows.

Remember that the **direction of the wind** is usually given as the direction **from** which it is blowing, e.g. a north wind blows **from** the north. Hence if, for example, the direction of the wind is given as 240° it is as in Fig. 133.

This is in contrast to the way in which the direction of a **current of water** is given. If a current is flowing as in Fig. 133 its direction is given as 060°. A north-easterly current flows **towards** the north-east, and is said to 'set north-east'.

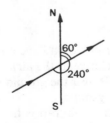

Fig. 133

Example 4   *An aircraft is flying on a course of 279° with an air-speed of 1 200 km h⁻¹. The wind is blowing from 027° at 90 km h⁻¹. Find the ground speed of the aircraft, its track and drift.*

Let $_A V_W$ represent the air-speed, $_W V_E$ represent the wind-speed and $_A V_E$ represent the ground-speed.

$_A V_E = _A V_W + _W V_E$, from which a rough sketch is drawn. $\overline{NAS}$ is the north-south line, $B\hat{A}W = 81°$ (reflex $B\hat{A}W = 279°$) and $A\hat{B}W = 27°$.

$A\hat{W}E = A\hat{B}W + B\hat{A}W = 81° + 27° = 108°$.

Then $\triangle AWE$ is the triangle of velocities.

In $\triangle AWE$, using the cosine formula,

$AE^2 = 1\ 200^2 + 90^2 - 2 \times 1\ 200 \times 90 \cos 108°$
$= 1\ 440\ 000 + 8\ 100 + 216\ 000 \cos 72°$
$= 1\ 440\ 000 + 8\ 100 + 66\ 800$
$= 1\ 514\ 900$

$\therefore AE = 1\ 231$

Using the sine formula,

$$\frac{\sin E\hat{A}W}{90} = \frac{\sin 108°}{1\ 231}$$

$$\therefore \sin E\hat{A}W = \frac{90 \sin 72°}{1\ 231}$$

$$\therefore E\hat{A}W = 3° 59'$$

$$\therefore E\hat{A}B = 84° 59'$$

i.e. reflex $E\hat{A}B = 360° - 84° 59'$

$= 275° 1'$

$\therefore$ the ground-speed is $1\ 230\ \text{km h}^{-1}$, the track is $275°$ and the drift is $4°$.

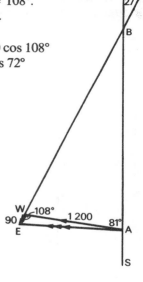

Fig. 134

No.	Log.
216 000	5·334 5
cos 72°	$\bar{1}$·490 0
66 760	4·824 5
90	1·954 2
sin 72°	$\bar{1}$·978 2
	1·932 4
1 231	3·090 2
sin 3° 59'	$\bar{2}$·842 2

Example 5   *An aircraft is flying at an air-speed of 960 km h⁻¹ on a course of 242°. Its track is 235° and the ground-speed is 1 050 km h⁻¹. Find the speed and direction of the wind.*

Let $_AV_W$ represent the air-speed and $_AV_E$ the ground-speed. $_WV_E$ represents the wind-speed and $_AV_W + {_WV_E} = {_AV_E}$, from which a rough sketch is drawn.

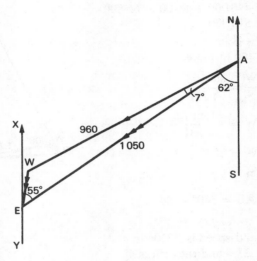

Fig. 135

$\overline{NAS}$ is the north–south line, $S\hat{A}W = 62°$ and $S\hat{A}E = 55°$.
Then $\triangle AWE$ is the triangle of velocities.
In $\triangle AWE$, using the cosine formula,
$WE^2 = 1\,050^2 + 960^2 - 2 \times 1\,050 \times 960 \cos 7°$
$\quad\quad\; = 23\,600$
$\therefore\; WE = 153{\cdot}6.$

Using the sine formula,

$$\frac{\sin \text{A}\hat{\text{E}}\text{W}}{960} = \frac{\sin 7°}{153 \cdot 6}$$

$\therefore$ A$\hat{\text{E}}$W $= 49° \, 37'$

$\therefore$ X$\hat{\text{E}}$W $= 55° - 49° \, 37' = 5° \, 23'$

$\therefore$ wind-speed is $154 \, \text{km h}^{-1}$ from $005°$.

Example 6 *An aircraft is to have a ground speed of* $750 \, \text{km h}^{-1}$ *on a track of* $192°$. *If the speed of the wind is* $94 \, \text{km h}^{-1}$ *from a direction* $107°$ *find the air-speed and course.*

Let $_A V_W$ represent the air-speed, $_A V_E$ represent the ground-speed and $_W V_E$ represent the wind-speed.

$_A V_W + {_W V_E} = {_A V_E}$ from which a rough sketch is drawn.

NAS is the north south line, B$\hat{\text{A}}$E $= 12°$ and A$\hat{\text{B}}$C $= 107°$. Hence A$\hat{\text{E}}$W $= 95°$. Then $\triangle$AEW is the triangle of velocities.

In $\triangle$AEW, using the cosine formula,

$$\begin{aligned}
\text{AW}^2 &= 750^2 + 94^2 - 2 \times 750 \times 94 \cos 95° \\
&= 750^2 + 94^2 + 1\,500 \times 94 \cos 85° \\
&= 583\,600
\end{aligned}$$

$\therefore$ AW $= 763 \cdot 9$

Using the sine formula,

$$\frac{\sin \text{W}\hat{\text{A}}\text{E}}{94} = \frac{\sin 95°}{763 \cdot 9}$$

$\therefore$ W$\hat{\text{A}}$E $= 7° \, 3'$
$\therefore$ W$\hat{\text{A}}$B $= 12° - 7° \, 3' = 4° \, 57'$
$\therefore$ N$\hat{\text{A}}$W $= 184° \, 57'$

$\therefore$ the air-speed is $764 \, \text{km h}^{-1}$ on a course $185°$.

Fig. 136

255

Example 7   *An aircraft is to have a track 357° and the wind is blowing at 80 km h⁻¹ from a direction 260°. If the air-speed is 920 km h⁻¹ find the course which must be set.*

Let $_AV_W$ represent the air-speed, $_AV_E$ represent the ground-speed and $_WV_E$ represent the wind-speed.

$_AV_W + {_W}V_E = {_A}V_E$, from which a rough sketch is drawn.

NAS is the north–south line, $\hat{NAE} = 3°$ and $\hat{ABE} = 80°$. Hence $\hat{AEW} = 83°$.

Then $\triangle AEW$ is the triangle of velocities.

In $\triangle AEW$, using the sine formula,

$$\frac{\sin E\hat{A}W}{80} = \frac{\sin 83°}{920}$$

$$\therefore \ \sin E\hat{A}W = \frac{80 \sin 83°}{920}$$

$\therefore \ \ E\hat{A}W = 4° \ 57'$
$\therefore \ \ N\hat{A}W = 4° \ 57' + 3° = 7° \ 57'$

$\therefore$ the course required is 352°.

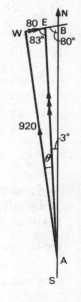

Fig. 137

Examples 4–7 can also be solved by means of scale drawing.

Exercise 40

In this exercise solve each problem by means of a scale drawing and check by calculation.

1. A yacht which is heading due east at $12\,\text{km h}^{-1}$ is carried off course by a current of $5\,\text{km h}^{-1}$ which sets north-east. Find the resultant speed and direction of the yacht.

2. A liner which is heading due south with a speed in still water of $35\,\text{km h}^{-1}$ is actually moving at $38\,\text{km h}^{-1}$ on a bearing 169°. Find the speed and direction of the current.

3. A ferry which is scheduled to steam due west at $25\,\text{km h}^{-1}$ is affected by a current of $6\cdot5\,\text{km h}^{-1}$ flowing in a direction 185°. Find the speed and course on which the ferry must set.

4. A boat whose speed in still water would be $4\,\text{m s}^{-1}$ heads straight across a river, but because of the current it actually travels at an angle of 75° to the bank. Find the speed of the current and the boat's speed relative to the ground. If the river is 84 m wide how long will it take to cross it?

5. A yacht wants to go due east. If its speed in still water is $16\,\text{km h}^{-1}$ and there is a current of $6\,\text{km h}^{-1}$ which sets SE, find the direction in which the yacht must set and the time it takes to go 2 km east.

6. A man can row a boat on a river at a speed which is four times that of the current. If he wishes to go straight across find the direction in which he must keep the boat pointing. In what direction must it point if he wishes to cross in the shortest possible time?

New General Mathematics Revision

7. A motor boat has an acceleration of 0·6 m s^{-2}. The current, at right angles to the direction in which the boat is headed, gives it an acceleration of 0·2 m s^{-2}. What is the magnitude and direction of the resultant acceleration?

8. Horizontal forces of 6·3 N and 7·5 N at 42° to each other are applied to a mass which is lying on a smooth horizontal table. In what direction will it move?

9. A particle of weight 9 N is held by two strings each inclined at 45° to the vertical. What is the tension in each string?

10. A particle is accelerating at 8 m s^{-2} when it is subjected to a force inclined at 60° to the original line of motion which gives it an acceleration of 3 m s^{-2}. What is the magnitude and direction of the resultant acceleration?

In each of the following find the ground-speed and track.

11. Course 189°, air-speed 820 km h^{-1}, wind 85 km h^{-1} from 036°.

12. Course 110°, air-speed 760 km h^{-1}, wind 70 km h^{-1} from 095°.

13. Course 304°, air-speed 950 km h^{-1}, wind 110 km h^{-1} from 020°.

In each of the following find the speed and direction of the wind.

14. Course 065°, air-speed 840 km h^{-1}, track 072°, ground speed 890 km h^{-1}.

15. Course 123°, air-speed 970 km h^{-1}, track 127°, ground-speed 1 000 km h^{-1}.

16. Course 241°, air-speed 1 100 km h^{-1}, track 238°, ground-speed 1 050 km h^{-1}.

In each of the following find the air-speed and course.

17. Track 320°, ground-speed 980 km h^{-1}, wind 80 km h^{-1} from 195°.

18. Track 058°, ground-speed 960 km h^{-1}, wind 75 km h^{-1} from 125°.

19. Track 230°, ground-speed 1 200 km h^{-1}, wind 130 km h^{-1} from 152°.

In each of the following find the course.

20. Track 030°, air-speed 1 100 km h^{-1}, wind 95 km h^{-1} from 235°.

21. Track 234°, air-speed 1 250 km h^{-1}, wind 105 km h^{-1} from 261°.

22. Track 358°, air-speed 1 220 km h^{-1}, wind 125 km h^{-1} from 107°.

Chapter 41
Probability

If n events are equally probable the probability of any one of x of them occurring is $\frac{x}{n}$ and the probability of its not occurring is $1 - \frac{x}{n}$.

Example 1 *On average 1 in 30 apples in a certain consignment is rotten. What is the probability that an apple taken at random is good.*

From the given experimental data the probability of a bad apple is $\frac{1}{30}$.
∴ the probability of a good apple is $1 - \frac{1}{30} = \frac{29}{30}$.
   Alternatively, if 1 in 30 of the apples is bad, 29 in 30 are good.
∴ the probability of a good apple is $\frac{29}{30}$.

Example 2 *Four coins are thrown. What is the probability of 3 heads and 1 tail?*

There are sixteen possible results as follows:

HHHH
HHHT HHTH HTHH THHH
HHTT HTTH TTHH HTHT THTH THHT
HTTT THTT TTHT TTTH
TTTT

Of these, four consist of 3 heads and 1 tail.
∴ the probability of 3 heads and 1 tail is $\frac{4}{16} = \frac{1}{4}$.

Addition law, mutually exclusive events

Probabilities can be added provided that the events are **mutually exclusive,** that is to say that one event excludes the possibility of the other.

Example 3 *If two dice are thrown, what is the probability of a total score which is prime?*

There are 36 possible scores as follows:

$1 + 1 = 2,$ $\quad 1 + 2 = 3,$ $\quad 2 + 1 = 3,$ $\quad 2 + 2 = 4,$
$1 + 3 = 4,$ $\quad 3 + 1 = 4,$ $\quad 2 + 3 = 5,$ $\quad 3 + 2 = 5,$
$1 + 4 = 5,$ $\quad 4 + 1 = 5,$ $\quad 3 + 3 = 6,$ $\quad 2 + 4 = 6,$
$4 + 2 = 6,$ $\quad 1 + 5 = 6,$ $\quad 5 + 1 = 6,$ $\quad 3 + 4 = 7,$
$4 + 3 = 7,$ $\quad 2 + 5 = 7,$ $\quad 5 + 2 = 7,$ $\quad 1 + 6 = 7,$
$6 + 1 = 7,$ $\quad 4 + 4 = 8,$ $\quad 3 + 5 = 8,$ $\quad 5 + 3 = 8,$
$2 + 6 = 8,$ $\quad 6 + 2 = 8,$ $\quad 4 + 5 = 9,$ $\quad 5 + 4 = 9,$
$3 + 6 = 9,$ $\quad 6 + 3 = 9,$ $\quad 5 + 5 = 10,$ $\quad 4 + 6 = 10,$
$6 + 4 = 10,$ $\quad 5 + 6 = 11,$ $\quad 6 + 5 = 11,$ $\quad 6 + 6 = 12.$

$\therefore$ the probability of a score of $2 = \frac{1}{36}$,
the probability of a score of $3 = \frac{2}{36}$,
the probability of a score of $5 = \frac{4}{36}$,
the probability of a score of $7 = \frac{6}{36}$,
and the probability of a score of $11 = \frac{2}{36}$.

These events are mutually exclusive.

$\therefore$ the probability of a prime score is
$\frac{1}{36} + \frac{2}{36} + \frac{4}{36} + \frac{6}{36} + \frac{2}{36} = \frac{15}{36} = \frac{5}{12}.$

Multiplication law, statistically independent events

Probabilities can be multiplied if the one event has no effect on the other; the events are said to be **statistically independent**.

Example 4 *A bag contains 7 black balls and 5 white balls. A ball is drawn from the bag and replaced, then a second one is drawn. What is the probability that (i) one is black and one is white (ii) at least one is black?*

There are 12 balls of which 7 are black.

$\therefore$ the probability of drawing a black ball is $\frac{7}{12}$ and the probability of drawing a white ball is $\frac{5}{12}$.

The colour drawn second is independent of the colour drawn first.

$\therefore$ the probability of drawing first a black ball then a white ball is

$\frac{7}{12} \times \frac{5}{12} = \frac{35}{144}$, and the probability of drawing first a white ball and then a black ball is $\frac{5}{12} \times \frac{7}{12} = \frac{35}{144}$.

These are mutually exclusive, so that the probability of drawing a black ball and a white ball when the order does not matter is $\frac{35}{144} + \frac{35}{144} = \frac{70}{144} = \frac{35}{72}$.

The probability of at least one black ball = 1—probability of no black ball = $1 - \frac{5}{12} \times \frac{5}{12} = \frac{119}{144}$.

Exercise 41a

1. When two dice are thrown what is the probability of (i) an odd score (ii) a score more than 7?

2. A bag contains 4 red marbles and 5 blue marbles. If one marble is drawn and replaced and then another drawn, what is the probability of (i) both being red (ii) one of each colour?

3. A card is drawn from a pack of 52 and then replaced. A second card is drawn. What is the probability that (i) they are both spades (ii) at least one is a spade (iii) at least one is an ace?

4. When 4 coins are thrown what is the probability of (i) 4 heads (ii) 2 heads and 2 tails (iii) at least one head?

5. If the probability of one darts player hitting the board is $\frac{7}{9}$ and the probability of another hitting it is $\frac{9}{10}$ for each throw, what is the probability that they both hit it if they each throw one dart? What is the probability that at least one hits it?

6. The probability of a seed germinating is $\frac{4}{5}$. If 4 seeds are planted what is the probability that (i) at least one will germinate (ii) exactly three will germinate?

7. If the probability of one pupil solving a problem is $\frac{6}{7}$ and of a second solving it is $\frac{7}{8}$ and of a third solving it is $\frac{8}{9}$, what is the probability that (i) they will all solve it (ii) at least one will solve it?

8. When three dice are thrown what is the probability of a score of 6?

9. The ratio of red to yellow to green marbles in a large bag is 5:4:6. Two marbles are drawn at random. What is the probability that (i) they are both green (ii) they are of different colours?

10. In a particular town 3 out of 5 houses have a washing machine. If three houses are visited at random what is the probability that (i) they all have washing machines (ii) only one has a washing machine?

11. Out of every 1 000 boxes produced by a machine 30 contain more than fifty sweets. What is the probability that if two boxes are chosen at random (i) both contain more than fifty sweets (ii) one contains more than fifty and the other fifty or less?

12. The ratio of flavours in a box of chocolates of coffee, strawberry, caramel and nut is 2:3:1:4. If two chocolates are drawn at random what is the probability that (i) they are both nuts (ii) one is coffee and one is strawberry?

13. If it is assumed that one in five of the cars on the road is blue and one in four is red, what is the probability that out of the first three cars one sees on the road one is red and one is blue?

14. If it is assumed that the ratio of Conservative to Labour to Liberal support in a particular town is 2:2:1, what is the probability that out of three people one meets there is one of each party?

15. Three integers are chosen at random from 0 to 9. What is the probability that their sum is (i) 6 (ii) 25 (iii) 28?

Dependent probability, probability trees

Example 5 *A bag contains 4 red marbles and 5 blue marbles. Two marbles are taken from the bag. What is the probability that (i) both are red (ii) one is red and one is blue?*

The various possibilities can be illustrated by a diagram called a **probability tree** as in Fig. 138. The branches represent the different possibilities at each step with the associated probabilities.

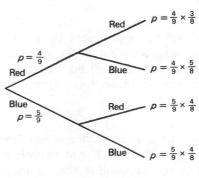

Fig. 138

p of two red $= \frac{4}{9} \times \frac{3}{8} = \frac{1}{6}$

p of one red and one blue $= \frac{4}{9} \times \frac{5}{8} + \frac{5}{9} \times \frac{4}{8}$

$\qquad\qquad\qquad\qquad\qquad = \frac{5}{18} + \frac{5}{18}$

$\qquad\qquad\qquad\qquad\qquad = \frac{5}{9}$

The first marble drawn can be either red or blue, and for each possibility there are then the possibilities of red or blue for the second marble. Hence the tree starts with 2 branches each of which has 2 further branches. The probability that the first marble is red is $\frac{4}{9}$ and this is independent of the second marble. There are 8 marbles left of which 3 are red. If the first marble is red the probability that the second one is blue is $\frac{5}{8}$ and the probability that the second one is

264

red is $\frac{3}{8}$. As the probability of the first being red is $\frac{4}{9}$, the probability of the first and second being red is $\frac{3}{8}$ of $\frac{4}{9}$, and the probability of the first being red and the second being blue is $\frac{5}{8}$ of $\frac{4}{9}$. Similarly the probability of a blue then a red is $\frac{4}{8}$ of $\frac{5}{9}$.

∴ the probability of 2 red is $\frac{4}{9} \times \frac{3}{8} = \frac{1}{6}$, and the probability of 1 red and 1 blue is $\frac{4}{9} \times \frac{5}{8} + \frac{5}{9} \times \frac{4}{8} = \frac{5}{9}$.

Example 6 *If three cards are drawn from a pack without replacement what is the probability of (i) 3 hearts (ii) 2 hearts?*

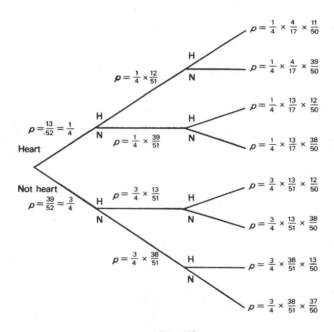

Fig. 139

p of 3 hearts $= \frac{1}{4} \times \frac{4}{17} \times \frac{11}{50} = \frac{11}{850}$.

p of 2 hearts $= \frac{1}{4} \times \frac{4}{17} \times \frac{39}{50} + \frac{1}{4} \times \frac{13}{17} \times \frac{12}{50} + \frac{3}{4} \times \frac{13}{51} \times \frac{12}{50} = \frac{117}{850}$.

Probability trees can be used for both dependent and independent probability.

Exercise 41b

In each of the following a probability tree is required.

1. If 3 cards are drawn from a pack without replacement what is the probability that (i) they are all red (ii) at least one is red?

2. If 2 cards are drawn from a pack without replacement what is the probability that (i) one is black and one is a diamond (ii) one is a diamond and one is a heart?

3. A coin is thrown 4 times. What is the probability of (i) 3 heads and 1 tail (ii) at least 1 tail?

4. A box of eggs contains 9 good ones and 3 cracked ones. What is the probability that out of 3 eggs taken from the box (i) they are all good (ii) one is good and 2 are cracked?

5. The probability that a tennis player can return a service is $\frac{2}{3}$ and the probability that he can return the ball in the ensuing rally is $\frac{3}{4}$ at each return. What is the probability that a rally will go to 4 returns?

6. A bag contains 4 red sweets, 6 green sweets and 10 yellow sweets. If 3 sweets are taken from the bag what is the probability of (i) one of each colour (ii) at least one red?

7. A box contains 20 light bulbs, 3 of which are faulty. If 4 bulbs are taken from the box what is the probability that (i) they are all good (ii) two are good and two are faulty (iii) at least one is good?

8. Eight women and 6 men are going on an outing in a 10-seater minibus and a four-seater car. What is the probability that the car will (i) take all women (ii) take 3 men and 1 woman?

9. A bag of mixed hyacinth bulbs contains 6 for red flowers, 9 for blue flowers and 3 for white flowers. Three are taken from the bag at random. What is the probability that (i) they are all for blue flowers (ii) they are all different?

10. If 5 pupils are chosen from a class of 30 what is the probability that they would all be above the median age of the class?

Chapter 42

Areas of triangles, parallelograms, trapeziums and polygons

Triangle

Area $= \frac{1}{2} \times b \times h$

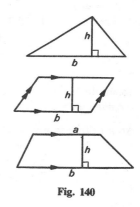

Parallelogram

Area $= b \times h$

Trapezium

Area $= \frac{1}{2}(a + b) \times h$

Fig. 140

Example 1 *Find the area of $\triangle ABC$ in which $AB = 8$ cm, $AC = 4$ cm and $B\hat{A}C = 58°$.*

Let the altitude CD be x cm.

Then $\dfrac{x}{4} = \sin 58°$

$\therefore\ x = 4 \sin 58°$

$\triangle ABC = \frac{1}{2}AB \times CD$

$\qquad = \frac{1}{2} \times 8 \times 4 \sin 58°\ \text{cm}^2$

$\qquad = 16 \times 0{\cdot}848\ \text{cm}^2$

$\qquad = 13{\cdot}6\ \text{cm}^2$

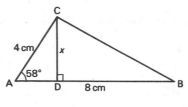

Fig. 141

Example 2 *Find the area of a parallelogram* PQRS *in which* PS = 5 *cm*, SR = 8 *cm*, $\widehat{S}$ = 117°.

Let the altitude PT be *h* cm.

$\widehat{PST}$ = 180° − 177° = 63°

Then $\dfrac{h}{5}$ = sin 63°

$\therefore$ *h* = 5 sin 63°

$\therefore$ area of //gm PQRS = SR × PT
$$= 8 \times 5 \sin 63° \text{ cm}^2$$
$$= 40 \times 0.891 \text{ cm}^2$$
$$= 35.6 \text{ cm}^2$$

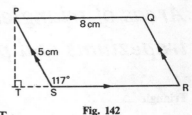

Fig. 142

Example 3 *If the area of the trapezium in Fig. 143 is* 32.6 cm² *find the value of x.*

Area of trapezium = $\frac{1}{2}(3 + 7)x$ cm²
$$= 5x \text{ cm}^2$$
$$\therefore \quad 5x = 32.6$$
$$\therefore \quad x = 6.52$$

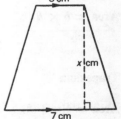

Fig. 143

Exercise 42a

Find the areas of the figures in Fig. 144, the dimensions being in centimetres.

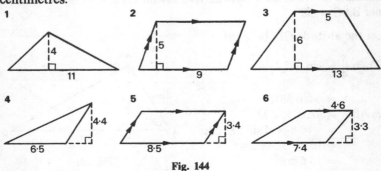

Fig. 144

In each of the figures in Fig. 145 find the value of *x*.

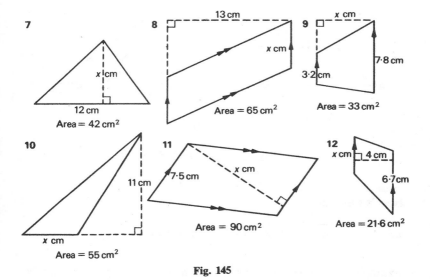

Fig. 145

Find the areas of the figures in Fig. 146, the dimensions being in centimetres (3 sig. fig.)

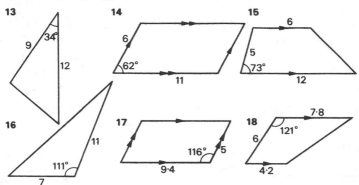

Fig. 146

Triangles

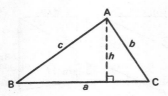 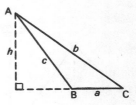

Fig. 147

$$\triangle = \tfrac{1}{2}ab \sin C \text{ or } \tfrac{1}{2}ac \sin B \text{ or } \tfrac{1}{2}bc \sin A$$

Hero's formula

$$\triangle = \sqrt{s(s-a)(s-b)(s-c)} \quad \text{where } s = \tfrac{1}{2}(a + b + c)$$

Example 4 *Use Hero's formula to find the area of a triangle having sides 16·1 cm, 18·2 cm, 9·4 cm.*

$s = \tfrac{1}{2}(16\cdot1 + 18\cdot2 + 9\cdot4) = 21\cdot85$
$s - a = 21\cdot85 - 16\cdot1 = 5\cdot75$
$s - b = 21\cdot85 - 18\cdot2 = 3\cdot65$
$s - c = 21\cdot85 - 9\cdot4 = 12\cdot45$
$\therefore \ \triangle = 75\cdot6 \text{ cm}^2$

No.	Log.
21·85	1·339 5
5·75	0·759 7
3·65	0·562 3
12·45	1·095 1
	3·756 6 ÷ 2
75·56 =	1·878 3

Example 5 *Find the area of the triangle shown in Fig. 148.*

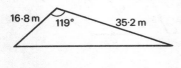

Fig. 148

No.	Log.
8·4	0·924 3
35·2	1·546 5
sin 61°	$\bar{1}$·941 8
258·6	2·412 6

Areas of triangles, parallelograms, trapeziums and polygons

$\triangle = \frac{1}{2} \times 16\cdot8 \times 35\cdot2 \sin 119° \ m^2$
$\quad = 8\cdot4 \times 35\cdot2 \sin 61° \ m^2$
$\quad = 259 \ m^2$

Exercise 42b

Use the method of Example 4 to find the areas of the $\triangle$s whose sides are given in centimetres in nos. 1 to 4.
1. $a = 9, b = 8, c = 3$
2. $a = 15, b = 12, c = 5$
3. $a = 15\cdot3, b = 21\cdot8, c = 30\cdot7$
4. $a = 4\cdot2, b = 3\cdot8, c = 2\cdot9$

Use the formulae $\triangle = \frac{1}{2}bc \sin A$, etc. to find the areas of the $\triangle$s in which

5.	$a = 4$ cm,	$b = 5$ cm,	$C = 85°$
6.	$b = 10$ cm,	$c = 6$ cm,	$A = 112°$
7.	$a = 15$ cm,	$c = 12$ cm,	$B = 107°$
8.	$a = 5\cdot2$ m,	$b = 7\cdot1$ m,	$C = 62° 12'$
9.	$b = 131$ mm,	$c = 46$ mm,	$A = 18° 21'$
10.	$a = 16\cdot5$ m,	$c = 24\cdot3$ m,	$B = 121° 7'$

Parallelograms

Area of ‖gm $= xy \sin \theta$
Area of ‖gm $= \frac{1}{2}pq \sin \alpha$

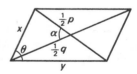

Trapeziums and quadrilaterals

Fig. 149

Example 6 *Find the area of the trapezium in Fig. 150, all the lengths given being in metres.*

Method (i)

Area of $\triangle = \sqrt{11 \times 2 \times 4 \times 5} \ m^2$
$\qquad\qquad = \sqrt{440} \ m^2$
$\qquad\qquad = 20\cdot98 \ m^2$

271

But area of $\triangle = \frac{1}{2} \times 6h$
$\therefore\ h = \frac{1}{3} \times 20 \cdot 98 = 6 \cdot 993$
$\therefore\ $ area of $/\!/$gm $= 8h = 55 \cdot 94\ \text{m}^2$
$\therefore\ $ area of trapezium $= 76 \cdot 92\ \text{m}^2$
$\qquad\qquad\qquad\ \simeq 76 \cdot 9\ \text{m}^2$

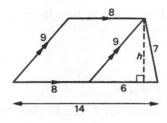

Fig. 150

Method (ii)

From the $\triangle$, $\cos\theta = \dfrac{9^2 + 6^2 - 7^2}{2 \times 9 \times 6}$

$$= \frac{68}{108} = 0 \cdot 629\ 6$$

$\qquad\qquad\ \therefore\ \theta = 50° \ 59'$
$\therefore\ $ area of $/\!/$gm $= 9 \times 8 \times \sin 50° \ 59'\ \text{m}^2$
$\qquad\qquad\qquad = 72 \sin 50° \ 59'\ \text{m}^2$
and area of $\triangle = \frac{1}{2} \times 9 \times 6 \sin 50° \ 59'\ \text{m}^2$
$\qquad\qquad\qquad = 27 \sin 50° \ 59'\ \text{m}^2$

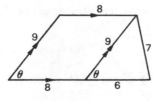

Fig. 151

Adding,

area of trapezium $= 99 \sin 50° 59' \, \text{m}^2$
$$= 99 \times 0{\cdot}776\,9 \, \text{m}^2$$
$$= 76{\cdot}91 \, \text{m}^2$$
$$\simeq 76{\cdot}9 \, \text{m}^2$$

Example 7 *Find the area of the quadrilateral* PQRS *shown in* Fig. 152.

In $\triangle$PQS,
$$QS^2 = 4^2 + 3^2 - 2 \times 3 \times 4 \cos 145°$$
$$= 16 + 9 + 24 \cos 35°$$
$$= 25 + 19{\cdot}66$$
$$= 44{\cdot}66$$

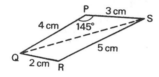

Fig. 152

In $\triangle$RQS,

$$\cos \widehat{R} = \frac{2^2 + 5^2 - QS^2}{2 \times 2 \times 5}$$

$$= \frac{4 + 25 - 44{\cdot}66}{20} = \frac{-15{\cdot}66}{20} = -0{\cdot}783$$

$\therefore \; \widehat{R} = 180° - 38° 28' = 141° 32'$

$\therefore \;$ area of $\triangle$RQS $= \frac{1}{2} \times 2 \times 5 \sin \widehat{R} \, \text{cm}^2$
$$= 5 \times 0{\cdot}622 = 3{\cdot}11 \, \text{cm}^2$$

Also area of $\triangle$PQS $= \frac{1}{2} \times 4 \times 3 \sin \widehat{P} \, \text{cm}^2$
$$= 6 \times 0{\cdot}573\,6 = 3{\cdot}441\,6 \, \text{cm}^2$$

$\therefore \;$ area of quad. PQRS $\simeq (3{\cdot}11 + 3{\cdot}44) \, \text{cm}^2 \simeq 6{\cdot}55 \, \text{cm}^2$

273

Regular polygons

To find the area of a **regular polygon**, join the vertices of the polygon to the centre and consider one of the isosceles $\triangle$s thus formed. The vertical angle of the $\triangle$ is 360° ÷ number of sides of polygon.

Example 8 *Find the area of a regular hexagon of side 4 cm.*

Let O be the centre of the hexagon, and $\overline{AB}$ one of the sides.

$A\hat{O}B = 360° \div 6 = 60°$

$\therefore \quad h = 2 \cot 30°$

Area of $\triangle OAB = \frac{1}{2} \times 4h = 2h$

$$\begin{aligned}\therefore \text{ area of hexagon} &= 6 \times \triangle AOB \\ &= 12h \\ &= 24 \cot 30° \text{ cm}^2 \\ &= 24 \times 1{\cdot}732\,1 \text{ cm}^2 \\ &\simeq 41{\cdot}6 \text{ cm}^2\end{aligned}$$

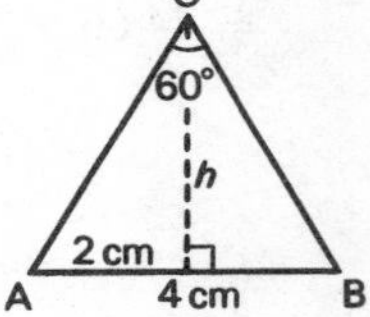

Fig. 153

Example 9 *Find the area of a regular decagon inscribed in a circle of radius* 3 *cm.*

$$A\hat{O}B = \frac{360°}{10} = 36° \text{ cm}^2$$

$$\begin{aligned}\therefore \text{ area of } \triangle AOB &= \tfrac{1}{2} \times 3 \times 3 \sin 36° \text{ cm}^2 \\ &= 4{\cdot}5 \sin 36° \text{ cm}^2\end{aligned}$$

$$\begin{aligned}\therefore \text{ area of polygon} &= 10 \times \triangle AOB \\ &= 45 \sin 36° \text{ cm}^2 \\ &\simeq 26{\cdot}5 \text{ cm}^2\end{aligned}$$

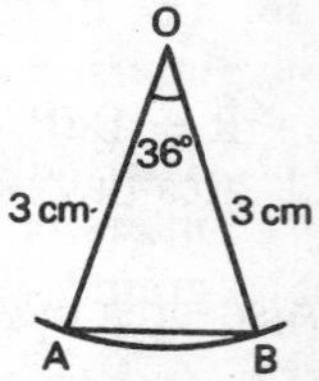

Fig. 154

Exercise 42c

Find the areas of the following figures, all dimensions given being in centimetres.

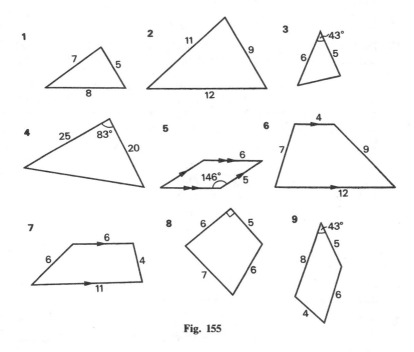

Fig. 155

10. The diagonals of a parallelogram are 4 cm and 5 cm long and intersect at an angle of 55°. What is the area of the parallelogram?

11. The diagonals of a parallelogram are 5 m and 6 m long and intersect at an angle of 132°. What is the area of the parallelogram?

12. Two sides of a triangular field are 138 m and 194 m, the angle between them being 73°. Find the area of the field in hectares.

13. Find the area of a regular pentagon inscribed in a circle of radius 20 cm.

14. Find the area of a regular octagon of side 2 m.

15. Find the area of a regular decagon of side 4 cm.

16. Find the area of a regular dodecagon of side 4 cm.

17. Find the area of a regular octagon inscribed in a circle of radius 25 mm. What percentage of the area of the circle is this?

18. A sand-box is of the shape shown in Fig. 156, each sloping face being a trapezium whose parallel sides are 10 cm and 15 cm long respectively. Each sloping edge is 12 cm long. Find the area of material required for the bottom and sides of the box, assuming it to be very thin.

Fig. 156

19. Find the volume of a prism whose length is 6 cm and whose cross section is a regular hexagon of side 1 cm.

20. A flower bed is in the shape of a trapezium ABCD. $\overline{AB}/\!/\overline{DC}$, AB = 4 m, CD = 6 m, AD = 5 m and BÂD = 73°. Find the area of the bed.

Chapter 43

Variation

Direct variation. $y \propto x$ means that $y = kx$, where k is a constant.

Example 1   *If* P $\propto$ R *and* P $= 10$ *when* R $= 6$, *find the law connecting* P *and* R *and also* R *when* P $= 12.5$.

Let P $= k$R
Then $10 = k6$
$\therefore\ k = \frac{10}{6} = \frac{5}{3}$
$\therefore\ $ P $= \frac{5}{3}$R, which is the required 'law'.
When P $= 12.5$
$\ \ \ 12.5 = \frac{5}{3}$R
$\therefore\ $ R $= \frac{3}{5} \times 12.5 = 7.5$

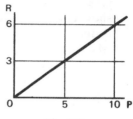

Fig. 157

Direct variation gives a straight-line relationship between the two variables, as in Fig. 157.

Exercise 43a

1. If $y \propto x$ and $y = 10$ when $x = \frac{1}{2}$ find the law of the variation. Find x if $y = 35$.

2. A $\propto$ M and A $= 8$ when M $= 20$. Find A when M $= 15$ and M when A $= 7$.

3. P $\propto$ Q and P $= 14$ when Q $= 8$. Find P when Q $= 6$ and Q when P $= 28$.

4. D $\propto$ V and D $= 108$ when V $= 3$. Find D when V $= 3.75$ and V when D $= 189$.

5. The number of Dutch florins (fl) obtainable for pounds sterling is shown in the following table. Show graphically that fl $\propto$ £.

Find the law and read off the values of £7·50 in florins and of 45fl in pounds.

£	2	5	8	11	14
fl	14·8	37·0	59·2	81·4	103·6

6. In an experiment to calibrate a spring-balance various masses (M g) are placed on the scale-pan and the corresponding compressions of the spring noted (d mm). by plotting d against M show that $d \propto M$. Draw a graph to represent the variation and deduce the law. Read off M when $d = 17$ and also d when M = 80.

M	50	100	120	150	180
d	5·6	10·9	13·3	16·5	19·7

7. Two variables x and y are found experimentally to have the comparative set of values given below:

x	10	20	30	40	50
y	3·4	7·1	10·5	13·9	17·6

Show that there is direct variation between x and y: find the law in the form $y = kx$: read off x when $y = 12$ and y when $x = 12$.

8. Show graphically that the following set of readings indicates direct variation between S and V.

V	15	20	25	30	35
S	169	225	283	338	396

Find the law in the form $S = kV$ and read off S when $V = 21.5$, V when $S = 320$.

If $x \propto \dfrac{1}{y}$ then x is said to **vary inversely** as y.

Note that, if $x \propto \dfrac{1}{y}$, then $y \propto \dfrac{1}{x}$.

Similarly, if $x \propto y^3$, then $y \propto \sqrt[3]{x}$, and so on.

Example 2 $R \propto \sqrt{M}$ *and* $R = 6$ *when* $M = 16$. *Find the law connecting R and M. Find R when* $M = 6\frac{1}{4}$ *and M when* $R = 15$.

Let $R = k\sqrt{M}$
Then $6 = k\sqrt{16} = 4k$
$\therefore\ k = \frac{3}{2}$
$\therefore\ R = \frac{3}{2}\sqrt{M}$, which is the required law.
When $M = 6\frac{1}{4}$, $R = \frac{3}{2}\sqrt{\frac{25}{4}} = \frac{3}{2} \times \frac{5}{2} = \frac{15}{4} = 3\frac{3}{4}$
" $R = 15$, $\sqrt{M} = \frac{2}{3}15 = 10$
$\therefore\ M = 100$

N.B.   If $R = \frac{3}{2}\sqrt{M}$, then $R^2 = \frac{9}{4}M$ or $M = \frac{4}{9}R^2$: it is often convenient to use an alternative form of the original law.

Example 3   *The number of spherical shot which can be cast from a given volume of lead varies inversely as the cube of the diameter of the shot. When the diameter is 3 mm the number of shot is 240. How many shot of diameter 2 mm can be cast from the same volume of lead?*

Let N = no. of shot, D = diameter in mm.

Then $N = \dfrac{k}{D^3}$

$\therefore\ 240 = \dfrac{k}{3^3}$

$\therefore\ k = 240 \times 27$

When D = 2, N = $\dfrac{240 \times 27}{2^3}$ = 810

∴ number of 2-mm shot is 810.

An alternative method of solution is given in Example 4. This method may be used if the value of k is not required.

Example 4 $y \propto x^2$. *How is the value of y affected if the value of x decreases by 20%?*

Let $y = kx^2$ (i)

  ,, y become y' when x decreases to $\frac{80}{100}x$.

Then $y' = k(\frac{80}{100}x)^2$ (ii)

Dividing (ii) by (i),

$$\dfrac{y'}{y} = \dfrac{k(\frac{80}{100}x)^2}{kx^2} = \left(\dfrac{80}{100}\right)^2 = \dfrac{64}{100}$$

$$y' = \dfrac{64}{100}y$$

y is decreased by 36%

Exercise 43b

1. $P \propto Q^2$. $P = 27$ when $Q = 6$. Find the law, P when $Q = 10$, Q when $P = 18\frac{3}{4}$.

2. $x \propto \dfrac{1}{y}$. $x = 7\frac{1}{2}$ when $y = 4$. Find the law, x when $y = 12$, y when $x = 20$.

3. $M \propto R^3$. $M = 40$ when $R = 4$. Find the law, M when $R = 10$, R when $M = 2\cdot56$.

4. $\sqrt{Y} \propto Z$. $Y = 4$ when $Z = 3$. Find the law, Y when $Z = 15$, Z when $Y = 16$.

5. $W \propto D^2$. How is W affected if D is (i) increased by 10%? (ii) decreased by 10%?

6. $p \propto \sqrt{q}$. How is p affected if q increases by 44%?

7. $V \propto R^3$. What is the percentage increase in V if R increases by 10%?

8. $M \propto L^3$. What is the percentage decrease in M if L decreases by 20%?

9. In an experiment the following values were found for the variables x and y:

x	2	4	6	8	10
y	3·1	12·9	28·8	51·3	79·9

By plotting y against x^2 show that there is a relationship connecting the variables of the form $y = kx^2$, and find the value of k.

10. Ball-bearings of various diameters are weighed and the following results obtained:

Diameter (d mm)	6	9	12	15	18
Mass (m g)	0·82	2·77	6·57	12·82	22·17

By plotting m against d^3 show that these results are consistent with the variation $m \propto d^3$. Find, as accurately as the graph allows (i) the mass of a ball of diameter 10 mm (ii) the diameter of a ball weighing exactly 10 g.

Joint variation involves three or more variables, the equations connecting them being of many forms, e.g.

$$M = kR^2T, \quad F = k\frac{MM'}{D^2}, \quad W = kDS, \quad t = k\frac{MV^2}{r}, \ldots$$

Partial variation. Here the relationships consist of two or more parts added together, such as

$$S = aT + bT^2, \quad T = a + bN^2, \quad E = a + bMH + cMV^2, \ldots$$

281

New General Mathematics Revision

Note that whereas in the forms of variation so far encountered there has been only one constant (generally k), in partial variation there may be several constants (as a, b, c above) and, in numerical work, these constants have to be found separately.

Example 5 *The mass of a solid metal ball varies jointly as its specific gravity and the cube of its diameter. When the diameter is 6 cm and the specific gravity 7·5 the mass is 850 g. Find the mass of a ball of specific gravity 10·5 and diameter 8 cm.*

Let M = mass in grams
　　D = diameter in cm
　　S = specific gravity
Then $M = kSD^3$
$\therefore$　$850 = k \times 7·5 \times 6^3$　　(i)
and $M = k \times 10·5 \times 8^3$　　(ii)
Dividing (ii) by (i),

$$\frac{M}{850} = \frac{10·5}{7·5} \times \left(\frac{8}{6}\right)^3 = \frac{7 \times 64}{5 \times 27}$$

$\diagup$ $\therefore$ $M = 850 \times \frac{7}{5} \times \frac{64}{27} \simeq 2\,821$

$\therefore$ mass is approximately $2\,821$ g.

Example 6 *The resistance to the motion of a car is partly constant and partly varies as the square of the speed. At 40 km h^{-1} the resistance is 530 N, and at 60 km h^{-1} it is 730 N. What will be the resistance at 70 km h^{-1}?*

Let R = resistance in newtons
　　V = speed in km h^{-1}
Then $R = a + bV^2$, where a and b are both constants.
$\therefore$　$530 = a + 1\,600b$
and $730 = a + 3\,600b$
Solving these equations, $b = \frac{1}{10}$ and $a = 370$.
$\therefore$ $R = 370 + \frac{1}{10}V^2$
When $V = 70$, $R = 370 + 490$
　　　　　　　$= 860$
$\therefore$ resistance is 860 N.

282

Exercise 43c

1. A $\propto$ BC. When B $= 6$ and C $= 3$, A $= 7\frac{1}{2}$. Find A when B $= 8$ and C $= 9$; also B if A $= 25$ and C $= 8$. What is the effect on A if B goes up by 10% and C down by 10%?

2. P $\propto \dfrac{Q}{R^2}$. When Q $= 5$ and R $= 3$, P $= 20$. Find P when Q $= 6$ and R $= 4$; also R when P $= 21 \cdot 6$ and Q $= 15$.

3. x is partly constant and partly varies as y. When $y = 5$, $x = 7$; and when $y = 7$, $x = 8$. Find the law of the variation and also x when $y = 11$.

4. x varies partly as y and partly as y^2. When $y = 4$, $x = 52 \cdot 8$; and when $y = 5$, $x = 81$. Find x when $y = 6$.

5. x varies partly as y^2 and partly inversely as z. When $y = 4$ and $z = 6$, $x = 19$; when $y = 5$ and $z = 12$, $x = 35$. Find x when $y = 6$ and $z = 10$.

6. $x \propto y$ and $y \propto z^2$. How does x vary with z?

7. $x \propto y^2$ and $y \propto \dfrac{1}{z}$. How does x vary with z?

8. $x \propto y^3 z$ and $z \propto y^2$. How does x vary with y?

9. The volume of a uniformly tapering tree trunk is sometimes taken as varying jointly as the square of the mean girth and as the length. If the length is increased by 20% and the girth by 10% what is the percentage increase in the volume?

10. The sag at the middle point of a girder with fixed ends under a uniformly distributed load varies jointly as the load and the cube of the length and inversely as its moment of inertia. If the load is increased by 10% and the moment of inertia by 5%, find the percentage change in the length of the girder if the sag is unchanged.

11. The illumination of a small object by a lamp vàries directly as the candle-power of the lamp and inversely as the square of

the distance between the lamp and the object. If a light-bulb of 8 candle-power, fixed 150 cm above a table, is replaced by a 5 candle-power bulb, how far must the new light be lowered to give the object the same illumination as before?

12. The resistance to the motion of a vehicle is partly constant and partly varies as the square of its speed. At 30 km h^{-1} the resistance is 496 N, and at 50 km h^{-1} it is 656 N. Find the resistance at 60 km h^{-1}.

13. The time taken for a committee meeting is partly constant and partly varies as the square of the number of members present. If there are twelve members present the meeting lasts only 56 minutes, but with twenty it takes exactly two hours. How long will it last if there are sixteen there?

14. The heat developed in a wire varies jointly as the time and the square of the voltage applied and inversely as the resistance of the wire. When the voltage is 100 and the resistance 50 ohms, the heat developed is 48 calories per second. What heat will be developed in one minute if 25 volts are applied to a wire of resistance 6 ohms?

15. The distance in which a car can pull up after the brakes have been applied varies partly as the speed of the car at the moment of application of the brakes and partly as the square of this speed. From 30 km h^{-1} it is possible to pull up in 9·5 m; from 60 km h^{-1} in 28 m. What is the braking-distance from 90 km h^{-1}?

Chapter 44

Right-angled triangle divided into similar triangles

In a right-angled triangle the perpendicular from the right angle to the hypotenuse divides the triangle into two triangles which are similar to the original triangle and to each other.

$\triangle s$ XYZ, MYX, MXZ are similar

$\therefore$ $YX^2 = YM \times YZ$ $\begin{cases} Y \text{ first} \\ Z \text{ first} \\ M \text{ first} \end{cases}$

     $ZX^2 = ZM \times ZY$ **N.B.**

     $MX^2 = MY \times MZ$

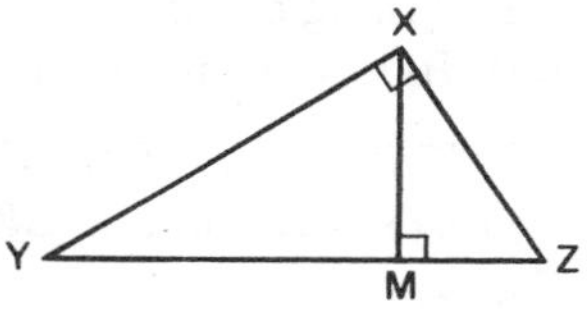

Fig. 158

N.B.   **MX is a mean proportional between MY and MZ.**

Example $\triangle$PQR *is such that* $\hat{P} = 90°$, PQ $= 24\,cm$, PR $= 7\,cm$ *and* $\overline{PS}$ *is an altitude. Calculate* PS, QS, RS.

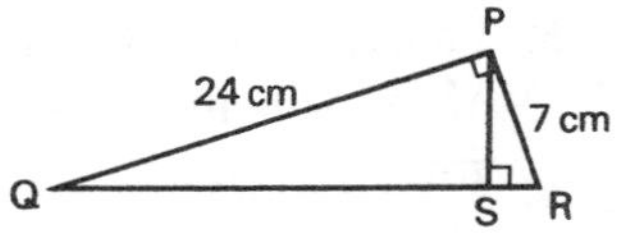

$$QR = \sqrt{24^2 + 7^2}\,\text{cm} = 25\,\text{cm}$$

$\triangle PQR = \frac{1}{2}PS \times QR = \frac{1}{2}PQ \times PR$

$\therefore$ PS $\times$ QR = PQ $\times$ PR

$\therefore$ PS $\times$ 25 = 24 $\times$ 7

Fig. 159

$$\therefore PS = \frac{24 \times 7}{25}\,\text{cm}$$

$$= 6\cdot72\,\text{cm}$$

$$QP^2 = QS \times QR$$

$$\therefore 24^2 = QS \times 25$$

$$\therefore QS = \frac{24^2}{25}\,\text{cm}$$

$$= 23\cdot04\,\text{cm}$$

$$RP^2 = RS \times RQ$$
$$\therefore 7^2 = RS \times 25$$

$$\therefore RS = \frac{7^2}{25} \, \text{cm}$$

$$= 1{\cdot}96 \, \text{cm}$$

$\therefore$ the lengths are 6·72 cm, 23·04 cm, 1·96 cm.

Check. QS + SR = 23·04 cm + 1·96 cm = 25 cm = QR.

Exercise 44

1. Triangle ABC is right-angled at A and $\overline{AD}$ is an altitude. If BD = 16 cm and DC = 4 cm calculate AD.

2. Triangle PQR is right-angled at P and $\overline{PS}$ is an altitude. If QS = 24 cm and SR = 3 cm calculate PR.

3. In the right-angled triangle XYZ, XY = 6 cm, YZ = 10 cm, ZX = 8 cm. Find the lengths of the two parts into which $\overline{YZ}$ is divided by the altitude $\overline{XV}$.

4. The altitude $\overline{PM}$ of a right-angled triangle meets the hypotenuse $\overline{QR}$ in M. If QM = 20 mm, MR = 5 mm calculate PM, $\hat{Q}$ and the area of $\triangle PQR$.

5. Triangle ABC is right-angled at B and $\overline{BD}$ is an altitude. If AB = 3BC prove that AD = 9DC.

6. $\overline{AB}$ is a diameter of a circle, centre O, and C is any point on the circumference of the circle. The foot of the perpendicular from C to $\overline{AB}$ is D. Prove that $CD^2 = OC^2 - OD^2$. (Do not use Pythagoras' theorem.)

7. Triangle LMN is such that $\hat{L} = 90°$, $\hat{M} = 45°$, LN = 2 cm and $\overline{LP}$ is an altitude. Using surds where necessary (*not* decimals) write down LM, MN, LP, MP, NP. Verify that $LP^2 = MP \times NP$, $LM^2 = MN \times MP$, $LN^2 = MN \times NP$.

8. In $\triangle DEF$, $\hat{D} = 90°$, $\hat{E} = 35°$, DE = 5 cm and $\overline{DH}$ is an altitude. Calculate DF, DH, EF, EH. Verify that $EF \times EH = DE^2$.

9. Triangle PQR is right-angled at P and $\overline{PS}$ is an altitude. If QR = 2PQ prove that SR = 3QS.

10. Construct a triangle ABC with $\hat{A} = 90°$, $\overline{DA}$ an altitude, BD = 4 cm, DC = 5 cm. Hence by measurement find $\sqrt{20}$. (*Hint.* $\overline{BC}$ is a diameter of circle ABC.)

11. Construct a triangle DEF, with $\hat{D} = 90°$, $\overline{DG}$ an altitude, EG = 3 cm, GF = 7 cm. Hence by measurement find $\sqrt{30}$.

12. In $\triangle ABC$, $\hat{A}$ is a right angle and $\overline{AD}$ is an altitude. If BD = 16DC prove that AD = 4DC.

13. In $\triangle DEF$ the perpendicular from D to $\overline{EF}$ meets $\overline{EF}$ in G. If $DG^2 = EG \times FG$ prove that $E\hat{D}F = 90°$.

14. Triangle ABC is right-angled at A and $\overline{AD}$ is an altitude. If 2AB = 3AC prove that 13AD = 6BC.

15. Triangle ABC is right-angled at A and AB = 5 m, AC = 12 m. If $\overline{AD}$, $\overline{DE}$, $\overline{DF}$ are the altitudes of $\triangle s$ ABC, ABD, ACD respectively, calculate the area of the rectangle AEDF in square metres correct to 3 sig. fig.

16. Triangle ABC is right-angled at C and AC = 7 cm, AB = 25 cm. If $\overline{CD}$ is an altitude of $\triangle ABC$ and $\overline{DE}$ is an altitude of $\triangle BCD$ calculate BE and EC.

Chapter 45

Bisectors of vertical angle of a triangle

The internal and external bisectors of an angle of a triangle divide the opposite side internally and externally respectively in the ratio of the sides which contain the angle.

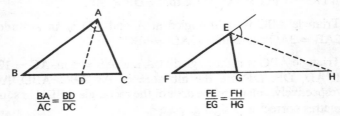

$$\frac{BA}{AC} = \frac{BD}{DC} \qquad\qquad \frac{FE}{EG} = \frac{FH}{HG}$$

Fig. 160

Example *PQR is a triangle in which the internal and external bisectors of* $Q\hat{P}R$ *meet* $\overline{QR}$ *and* $\overline{QR}$ *produced in S and T respectively. If* PQ = 6 *cm,* PR = 4 *cm,* QR = 9 *cm prove that* $\dfrac{QS}{QT} = \dfrac{RS}{RT} = \dfrac{1}{5}$.

$$\frac{QS}{SR} = \frac{QP}{PR} = \frac{6}{4} = \frac{3}{2}$$

$\therefore$ QS = $\frac{3}{5}$ of QR = $\frac{3}{5}$ of 9 cm = 5·4 cm

$\therefore$ SR = 9 cm − 5·4 cm = 3·6 cm

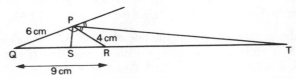

Fig. 161

288

$$\frac{QT}{RT} = \frac{QP}{PR} = \frac{6}{4} = \frac{3}{2}$$

$\therefore \ QR = \frac{1}{3}$ of QT

i.e. 9 cm $= \frac{1}{3}$ of QT

$\therefore \ QT = 27$ cm

$\therefore \ RT = 27$ cm $- \ 9$ cm $= 18$ cm

$\therefore \ \dfrac{QS}{QT} = \dfrac{5 \cdot 4}{27}$ and $\dfrac{RS}{RT} = \dfrac{3 \cdot 6}{18}$

i.e. $\dfrac{QS}{QT} = \dfrac{RS}{RT} = \dfrac{1}{5}$

Exercise 45

1. In $\triangle ABC$, $AB = 2$ cm, $BC = 4$ cm, $CA = 3$ cm and the bisector of $\hat{A}$ meets $\overline{BC}$ at D. Calculate BD, DC.

2. ABC is a triangle in which $AB = 15$ cm, $BC = 13$ cm, $CA = 11$ cm and D is a point on $\overline{BC}$ such that $BD = 7 \cdot 5$ cm. Prove that $\overline{AD}$ bisects $\hat{A}$.

3. P, X, Q, Y are four points on a straight line. X and Y divide $\overline{PQ}$ internally and externally in the same numerical ratio. If $XQ = 3$ cm, $QY = 5$ cm calculate PX.

4. PQR is a triangle in which $PQ = 18$ cm, $QR = 20$ cm, $RP = 12$ cm. The internal and external bisectors of $\hat{P}$ meet $\overline{QR}$ and $\overline{QR}$ produced at S and T, and the mid-point of $\overline{QR}$ is M. Calculate QS, SR, RT and show that $MS \times MT = MR^2$.

5. ABCD is a rhombus and M is the mid-point of $\overline{AB}$. The diagonal $\overline{AC}$ cuts $\overline{DM}$ at E. Prove that $DE = 2$ EM.

6. A straight line parallel to the side of $\overline{QR}$ of $\triangle PQR$ meets $\overline{PQ}$, $\overline{PR}$ in X, Y respectively and T is a point inside the triangle. Prove that if $\overline{XT}$ bisects $P\hat{T}Q$ and $\overline{YT}$ bisects $P\hat{T}R$ then $QT = RT$.

7. In △PQR, PQ = 26 cm, QR = 24 cm. $\hat{R}$ is a right angle and the bisector of $\hat{P}$ meets $\overline{QR}$ in S. Calculate PS. (3 sig. fig.)

8. In △LMN, LM = 10 cm, MN = 13 cm, NL = 7 cm and the internal and external bisectors of $\hat{L}$ meet $\overline{MN}$ and $\overline{MN}$ produced at P and Q. Calculate PQ in cm, correct to 2 dec. pl.

9. $\overline{AB}$ is a diameter of a circle and C is a point on the circumference. D and E are points on $\overline{AB}$, $\overline{AB}$ produced such that DB = 4 cm and $D\hat{C}B = B\hat{C}E$. Given that CD = 6 cm and CE = 9 cm calculate the radius of the circle.

10. The bisector of $\hat{P}$ of △PQR cuts $\overline{QR}$ in S and the median $\overline{QM}$ in T. If QS:SR = 5:2 find the value of QT:TM.

11. In △ABC the internal bisector of $\hat{A}$ meets $\overline{BC}$ in D. E is a point on $\overline{AC}$ such that $D\hat{E}C = A\hat{B}C$. Prove that BD = DE.

12. In △PQR, PQ = 6 cm, QR = 10 cm, PR = 13 cm. S is a point on $\overline{PR}$ such that $\overline{SQ}$ bisects $\hat{Q}$. T is a point on $\overline{PQ}$ such that $\overline{TS}/\!/\overline{QR}$. Calculate ST.

13. △PQR is right-angled at P, PQ = 21 cm, QR = 75 cm and the bisector of $\hat{Q}$ meets $\overline{PR}$ at S. Calculate the area of △QRS.

14. $\overline{ABCD}$ is a straight line and the circles on $\overline{AB}$ and $\overline{CD}$ as diameters intersect at E, F. If $\overline{EC}$ bisects $A\hat{E}B$ prove that AC:CB = AD:DB.

15. In △PQR the internal bisector of $Q\hat{P}R$ meets $\overline{QR}$ in S. Show that $QS = \dfrac{QP \times QR}{QP + PR}$.

Chapter 46

Circular measure

A **radian** is the angle subtended at the centre of a circle by an arc equal in length to the radius.

2π radians = 360°

1 radian (1ᶜ) = $\dfrac{180°}{\pi} \simeq 57° \, 17' \, 45''$

Summary (Fig. 162) **π radians   = 180°**
                    Length of arc = rθ
                    Area of sector = $\frac{1}{2}r^2\theta$

Fig. 162

Example 1   *Express in radians in terms of π (i) the angles 60°, 75°, 210° (ii) the supplement of $\dfrac{2\pi}{5}$ (iii) the complement of $\dfrac{2\pi}{9}$.*

(i) $60° = \dfrac{\pi}{3}$, $75° = \dfrac{5\pi}{12}$, $210° = \dfrac{7\pi}{6}$

(ii) the supplement of $\dfrac{2\pi}{5} = \pi - \dfrac{2\pi}{5} = \dfrac{3\pi}{5}$

(iii) the complement of $\dfrac{2\pi}{9} = \dfrac{\pi}{2} - \dfrac{2\pi}{9} = \dfrac{5\pi}{18}$

291

Example 2   *Express* 70° *in radians and* 1·28^c *in degrees and minutes, taking* π = 3·142 *(or log* π = 0·497 1*).*

$$70° = \frac{70}{180}\,\pi\,\text{rad} = \frac{7 \times 3·142}{18}\,\text{rad} \simeq 1·222^c$$

$$1·28^c = 1·28 \times \frac{180°}{\pi} = 73·35° = 73° 21'$$

Example 3   *A sector of a circle of radius* 5 cm *is bounded by two radii and an arc of length* 7 cm. *Find (i) the angle of the sector to the nearest minute (ii) the area of the sector.*

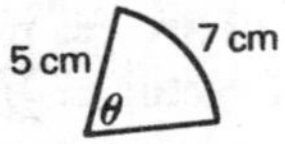

Fig. 163

(i) 7 = 5θ
∴ θ = 1·4^c = 80·22° = 80° 13'

(ii) Area of sector ($=\frac{1}{2}r^2\theta$) = $\frac{1}{2} \times 25 \times 1·4$ cm^2
     = 17·5 cm^2

Example 4   AXBO *is a* 105° *sector of a circle centre* O *and radius* 6 cm. *Calculate (i) the length of the minor arc* AXB *(ii) the area of the minor segment* AXB.

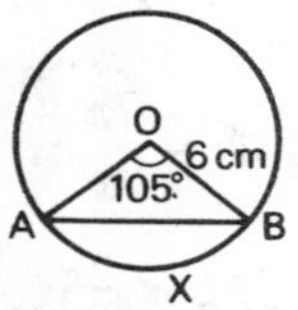

Fig. 164

(i) Arc AXB = $\dfrac{105\pi}{180} \times 6$ cm $\simeq 11·0$ cm

292

(ii) Sector AXBO $= \frac{1}{2} \times 36 \times \dfrac{105\pi}{180} \, \text{cm}^2$ $\qquad$ *sector* $= \frac{1}{2}r^2\theta$

$\qquad\qquad\quad = 32 \cdot 99 \, \text{cm}^2$

$\triangle \text{AOB} = \frac{1}{2} \times 36 \times \sin 105° \, \text{cm}^2$ $\qquad$ $\triangle = \frac{1}{2}bc \sin A$

$\qquad\qquad = 17 \cdot 39 \, \text{cm}^2$

$\therefore$ segment AXB $= 15 \cdot 6 \, \text{cm}^2$

Exercise 46

Take $\pi = 3 \cdot 142$ *or* $\log \pi = 0 \cdot 497\,1$

1. Express in radians as accurately as possible, checking results by the radian tables, (i) 36° (ii) 42° 24′ (iii) 86° 45′ (iv) 228° 16′.

2. Express the following angles, stated in radians, in degrees and minutes, checking from tables: (i) 1·8 (ii) 0·794 2 (iii) 3·210 6 (iv) 1·776 3.

3. Express in degrees (i) $\dfrac{\pi}{4}$ (ii) $\dfrac{2\pi}{5}$ (iii) $\dfrac{5\pi}{9}$ (iv) $\dfrac{9\pi}{8}$.

4. Express in radians, as fractions of π, (i) 80° (ii) 54° (iii) 135° (iv) 165°.

5. Write down the supplements of (i) $\dfrac{2\pi}{7}$ (ii) $\dfrac{5\pi}{8}$, and the complements of (iii) $\dfrac{3\pi}{8}$ (iv) $\dfrac{\pi}{6}$.

6. Write down the third angles of $\triangle$s of which two angles are (i) $\dfrac{\pi}{4}, \dfrac{2\pi}{3}$ (ii) $\dfrac{2\pi}{9}, \dfrac{\pi}{6}$ (iii) $\dfrac{4\pi}{15}, \dfrac{5\pi}{18}$ (iv) $\dfrac{5\pi}{12}, \dfrac{3\pi}{10}$.

7. The pendulum of a longcase clock is 50 cm long and swings through an arc of 8 cm. Through what angle does the pendulum swing?

8. Find the area of the sector of a circle of diameter 12 cm bounded by two radii and an arc of length 10 cm.

9. The mass of a circular brass disc is 280 g. The mass of a sector sheared out of it is 63 g. Find the angle of the sector.

10. AB is a chord of a circle of diameter 10 cm, and the chord subtends an angle of 96° at the centre. What is the length of the minor arc AB, and the area of the minor segment cut off by AB?

11. An electric motor runs at 1 500 rpm (revolutions per minute). What is the angular speed in radians per second?

12. A 20-cm diameter flywheel is rotating at 5 400 rpm. What is its angular speed and what is the linear speed of a point on its rim?

13. A car with 50-cm diameter wheels is travelling at $72 \, \text{km h}^{-1}$. What is the angular speed of rotation of the wheels and how many rpm does this represent?

14. The cross-section of a piece of corrugated plastic used for roofing consists of a series of circular arcs, each 8 cm across and 2 cm deep (Fig. 165). Each sheet is 80 cm wide. If the sheet could be flattened, how wide would it then be?

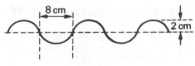

Fig. 165

15. A triangular wooden framework with sides 40 cm, 75 cm and 85 cm has grooved pulleys of diameter 4 cm centred at each vertex, and a string passes round the pulleys and is then pulled tight. How long is the string?

16. A garden railway track consists of two straights connected by a circular arc (Fig. 166) of radius 20 m. What is the total length of the track?

17. A child starts 10 m away from the nearest point of a circular pond of diameter 8 m, and runs round the pond and back to

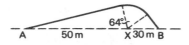

Fig. 166

the starting point by the shortest possible route. How long is this route?

18. A tramline AXYB (Fig. 167) consists of two straight portions AX and YB, each 500 m long, the angle between them being 132°, connected by a circular arc of radius 80 m. What is the total length of the line from A to B?

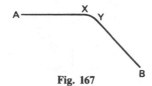

Fig. 167

19. The centres of two pulleys of diameters 20 cm and 8 cm respectively are 50 cm apart. What is the length of a belt tightly stretched over the pulleys without crossing?

20. If in no. 19 the belt was crossed between the pulleys, how long would it then be?

21. Fig. 168 shows the section of a concrete archway for a tractor shed, the curve being an arc of a circle of radius 9 m. If the archway itself is 50 cm thick, how many cubic metres of concrete will be needed for its construction?

Fig. 168

Chapter 47

Small circles and great circles.
Latitude and longitude

Fig. 169 represents the earth, centre O: N and S are the north and south poles.

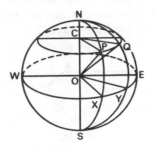

Fig. 169

All circles on the earth's surface centred at O are **great circles.**

All great circles passing through the poles are **meridians of longitude.**

All circles whose plane is at right angles to the line $\overline{NOS}$ are **parallels of latitude**: of these the **equator** is the only great circle.

The **longitude** of any point on the earth's surface is measured by its angular displacement east or west of the meridian which passes through Greenwich.

The **latitude** of any point is given by its angular displacement north or south of the plane of the equator.

In Fig. 169, if NPXS represents the meridian of Greenwich and NQYS another meridian, the circle centre C through P and Q a parallel of latitude, and the circle WXYE the equator, then the longitude of Q is the angle PCQ (or XOY), and the latitude of Q is the angle QOY ($= P\hat{O}X$).

If for example $\hat{PCQ} = 16°$ and $Q\hat{O}Y = 54°$, then the longitude of Q is 16° E and its latitude 54° N.

The **metre** was originally defined as one ten-millionth part of the quadrant of the meridian which passes through Paris. If R is the earth's radius, then

$\frac{1}{4}$ of $2\pi R = 10^7$ metres

$\therefore\ \ 2\pi R = 4 \times 10^7$ metres

$\therefore\ \ \mathbf{2\pi R = 4 \times 10^4}$ **kilometres**

If P is in latitude θ and r is the radius of the circle of latitude, then $r = R \cos \theta$.

This relationship, together with the formula for R given above, will be found very useful in many problems involving measurements on the earth's surface.

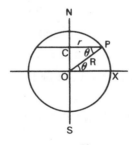

Fig. 170

Example 1 *Find the distance, measured along the parallel of latitude, between two places in latitude 42° N, whose longitudes are 23° W and 17° E.*

The difference in longitude between the two places (A and B)

$= A\hat{C}B$ or $X\hat{O}Y = 23° + 17° = 40°$

$$r = R \cos 42°$$

297

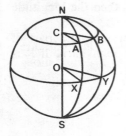 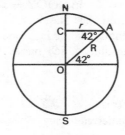 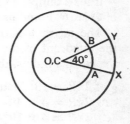

Fig. 171

$\therefore$ arc AB of circle of latitude $= \dfrac{40}{360}$ of $2\pi r$

$$= \tfrac{1}{9} \times 2\pi R \cos 42°$$

$$= \tfrac{1}{9} \times 4 \times 10^4 \cos 42° \text{ km}$$

$$= \tfrac{4}{9} \times 0.743\,1 \times 10^4 \text{ km}$$

$$\simeq 3\,300 \text{ km}$$

Exercise 47a

Take $2\pi R = 4 \times 10^4$ *km,* $\pi = 3.142$ *or* $\log \pi = 0.497\,1$. *Answers to* 3 *sig. fig.*

1. On a globe of radius 15 cm find the length of the parallel of latitude 62° S.

2. Two places on the same meridian have latitudes 23° S and 41° S. What is their distance apart, measured along the meridian?

3. As in no. 2, but the places in latitudes 23° S and 41° N.

4. Two places on the equator have longitudes 63° E and 132° E. How far apart are they, measured along the equator?.

5. As in no. 4, but the places having longitudes 132° E and 126° W.

6. Two places on the same meridian are 3 940 km apart. If one of them is in latitude 18° N and the other is in the southern hemisphere what is the latitude of the other?

7. What is the length of the Arctic Circle (latitude 66° 30′ N)? How far from the North Pole is any point on this circle?

8. Two places are both in latitude 37° S and their longitudes are 34° W and 29° E. What is their distance apart, measured along the parallel of latitude?

9. What is the length of the Tropic of Cancer (lat. 23° 30′ N)?

10. In what latitude does a difference of one degree in longitude represent a distance of 60 km along the parallel of latitude?

11. Derby and Ripon are both on longitude 1° 30′ W, and their latitudes are respectively 52° 56′ N and 54° 9′ N. How far apart are they?

12. Peking and Philadelphia are in the same latitude 39° 54′ N; their respective longitudes are 116° 34′ E and 75° 13′ W. What is their distance apart along their common parallel of latitude?

Longitude and time. The earth rotates on its axis once in 24 hours spinning from west to east. This means that a difference of one degree of longitude causes a difference of four minutes of time, and that places to the west reach noon later than places to the east.

Example 2 *The difference in longitude between London and New York is 74°. At what time should a TV set in London be switched on in order to receive a programme being broadcast in New York at 8 p.m. local time (i.e. New York's time)?*

Difference in longitude = 74°

∴ difference in time = 74 × 4 min = 296 min = 4 h 56 min

∴ switch on at 12.56 a.m..

The world is divided into various 'time-zones', local time being operative over the whole of one zone and jumping an hour backwards or forwards as one moves into the next zone. For instance the whole of Great Britain observes the same timing, which is that of the zero meridian (through Greenwich).

Example 3 *The longitudes of Harwich and Fishguard are respectively 1° 16′ E and 4° 56′ W. If sunset is at 20.48 hours at Harwich, what time will sunset be at Fishguard?*

Difference in longitude = 6° 12′ = 6·2°
∴ difference in time = 6·2 × 4 min = 24·8 min ≃ 25 min

∴ sunset at Fishguard is at 21.13 hrs.

The nautical mile

One **nautical mile** is defined as the length of an arc on a great circle which subtends an angle of 1′ at the earth's centre.

Hence 360 × 60 n miles = 4 × 10⁴ km
∴ 1 n mile = 1·852 km

A speed of one nautical mile per hour is called one **knot**: this unit of speed is almost universally used by seamen and by airmen.

N.B. The shortest distance between any two points on the surface of the earth is along the great circle which passes through these points.

Example 4 P *and* Q *are two points on the earth's surface in latitude* 56° N: *their longitudes are* 25° E *and* 95° E *respectively. Find the distance* PQ (i) *in km along the parallel of latitude* (ii) *in km along a great circle* (iii) *in nautical miles along a great circle.*

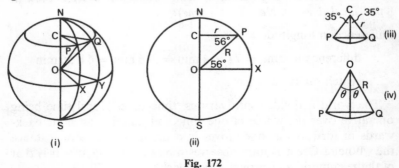

Fig. 172

Small circles and great circles. Latitude and longitude

(i) In Fig. 172 (iii) arc PQ $= \dfrac{70}{360}$ of $2\pi r$

$$= \dfrac{7}{36} \times 2\pi R \cos 56°$$

$$= \dfrac{7}{36} \times 4 \times 10^4 \cos 56° \text{ km}$$

No.	Log.
28×10^4	5·447 2
$\cos 56°$	$\bar{1}$·747 6
36	5·194 8
	1·556 3
4 350	3·638 5

$\simeq 4\,350$ km

(ii) From Fig. 172 (iii) PQ $= 2r \sin 35° = 2R \cos 56° \sin 35°$
from Fig. 172 (iv) PQ $= 2R \sin \theta$

$\therefore \sin \theta = \cos 56° \sin 35°$

$\therefore \ \theta = 18° \, 42'$
$\therefore \ \hat{POQ} = 2\theta = 37° \, 24' = 37·4°$

No.	Log.
$\cos 56°$	$\bar{1}$·747 6
$\sin 35°$	$\bar{1}$·758 6
$\sin 18° \, 42'$	$\bar{1}$·506 2

$\therefore$ arc PQ in Fig. 172 (iv) $= \dfrac{37·4}{360}$ of $2\pi R$

$$= \dfrac{37·4}{360} \times 4 \times 10^4 \text{ km}$$

$\simeq 4\,160$ km

(iii) $\hat{POQ} = 37° \, 24' = 2\,244'$
$\therefore$ arc PQ $\simeq 2\,240$ n miles

Check. 2 244 n miles $= 2\,244 \times 1·852$ km $\simeq 4\,160$ km

Ans. (i) 4 350 km (ii) 4 160 km (iii) 2 240 n miles.

Exercise 47b

1. What is the difference in latitude of two places 125 nautical miles apart and on the same meridian?

2. What is the distance in nautical miles between two places on the equator which have longitudes of 28° W and 14° E?

301

3. Two places on the equator are 780 nautical miles apart. What is the difference in their longitudes?

4. P and Q are two places 2 700 nautical miles apart, P being due south of Q. If Q is in latitude 36° 14′ N, what is P's latitude?

5. Find the differences in local time between places whose longitudes are

   (i) 34° 17′ W and 128° 53′ W (nearest minute)
   (ii) 16° 29′ W „ 48° 38′ E („ „)
   (iii) 13° 18′ E „ 14° 56′ E („ second)
   (iv) 74° 35′ E „ 159° 16′ W („ minute)

6. For the following places find (a) the time by the sun at the second when it is noon at the first, (b) their distance apart in km (3 sig. fig.) measured along the relevant parallel of latitude.

   (i) Dundalk 54° N, 6° 25′ W; Harrogate 54° N, 1° 33′ W
   (ii) Ipswich 52° 4′ N, 1° 10′ E; Killarney 52° 4′ N, 9° 29′ W
   (iii) New York 40° 24′ N, 73° 58′ W; Madrid 40° 24′ N, 3° 42′ W
   (iv) Windhoek 22° 56′ S, 17° 4′ E; Rio de Janeiro 22° 56′ S, 43° 14′ W.

7. A ship sails at a steady ten knots from Easter Island (27° S, 109° 30′ W) towards the Tubuai Islands (27° S, 144° W). How much longer does the route between the groups of islands take via the parallel of latitude than by the great circle route?

8. The difference in longitude of two places on the equator is 59° 14′. Find

   (i) the difference in local time between the places
   (ii) the distance between them in nautical miles
   (iii) the distance between them in km.

9. The latitudes of two places on the same meridian differ by 35° 27′. What is their distance apart, measured along the meridian, (i) in nautical miles? (ii) in km?

10. A and B are places in latitude 58° 24′ N, their longitudes being 148° W and 156° E respectively. What is the distance AB

(i) measured along the parallel of latitude? (ii) along a great circle? Answer in km.

11. Tokyo and Tehran are both in latitude 35° 41′ N and their respective longitudes are 139° 45′ E and 51° 28′ E. How far apart are they (i) by parallel of latitude? (ii) by great circle? Answer in km.

12. Lagos is 6° 31′N, 3° 26′ E; Georgetown is 6° 31′ N, 58° 12′ W. (i) I want to telephone someone in Lagos so as to catch him at 09.00 hours local time: at what time must I make the call in Georgetown?

How far apart are the two places
  (ii) by great circle (nautical miles)?
 (iii) by great circle (km)?
 (iv) by parallel of latitude (km)?

Chapter 48

Trigonometrical problems

Example 1   *A pyramid with a vertex O and edges $\overline{OA}$, $\overline{OB}$, $\overline{OC}$, $\overline{OD}$ each 10 cm long stands on a square base ABCD of side 8 cm. Find (i) the height OP of the pyramid (ii) the angle between the base and an edge (iii) the angle between the base and a sloping face.*

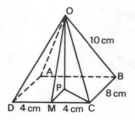

Fig. 173

Fig. 174

(i) $PC^2 = 4^2 + 4^2 = 16 + 16 = 32$ *Pythagoras*
   $OP^2 = OC^2 - PC^2$ *Pythagoras*
     $= 100 - 32$
     $= 68$
$\therefore$ $OP = 8{\cdot}246 \text{ cm} \simeq 8{\cdot}25 \text{ cm}$

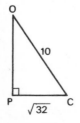

Fig. 175

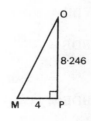

Fig. 176

304

(ii) Since $\overline{OP}$ is $\perp$ to the base the $\angle$ between $\overline{OC}$ and the base is $O\widehat{C}P$.

$$\cos O\widehat{C}P = \frac{\sqrt{32}}{10} = 0.565\ 7$$

$\therefore\ O\widehat{C}P = 55°\ 33'$

(iii) The $\angle$ between $\triangle OCD$ and the base is $O\widehat{M}P$ since $\overline{OM}$ and $\overline{MP}$ are both $\perp \overline{DC}$ of which M is the mid-point.

$$\tan O\widehat{M}P = \frac{8.246}{4} = 2.061\ 5$$

$\therefore\ O\widehat{M}P = 64°\ 7'$

Example 2 *A ramp is 16 m wide, 12 m long and slopes at 25° to the horizontal. Find the slope of the diagonal* $\overline{BD}$.

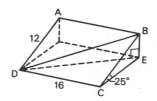

Fig. 177

$$BE = 12 \sin 25°$$

$$BD^2 = 12^2 + 16^2 = 400$$

$$\therefore\ BD = 20\ cm$$

$$\sin B\widehat{D}E = \frac{12 \sin 25°}{20}$$

$$= 0.6 \sin 25°$$

$$\therefore\ B\widehat{D}E = 14°\ 41'$$

No.	Log.
0·6	$\bar{1}$·778 2
sin 25°	1·625 9
sin 14° 41′	$\bar{1}$·404 1

Exercise 48a

1. A set square whose hypotenuse is 15 cm and shortest side is 7·5 cm is held with the hypotenuse horizontal and the right angle 5 cm above the level of the hypotenuse. Find the angles of slope of the two shorter sides. (Fig. 178)

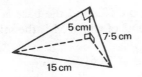

Fig. 178

2. The vertex of a pyramid on a square base of side 12 cm is 7 cm above the base. Calculate (i) the length of each sloping edge (ii) the angle between each sloping edge and the base (iii) the angle between each sloping face and the base.

3. A pyramid OABCD stands on a square base ABCD and OA = OB = OC = OD = 16 cm. BÔD is a right angle. Calculate the angle between each sloping face and the base.

4. ABCD is the sloping face of a wedge. $\overline{AB}$ and $\overline{DC}$ are horizontal with $\overline{AB}$ 4 cm higher than $\overline{DC}$, AB = 20 cm, AD = 16 cm. Calculate the slope of the plane and the slope of $\overline{BD}$. (Fig. 179)

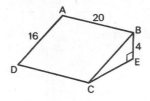

Fig. 179

5. ABCD is a tetrahedron (4-faced pyramid) with AB = AC = BC = 12 cm. AD̂B = AD̂C = BD̂C = 90°. BDC is horizontal and AD = 6 cm. Calculate the slope of $\overline{AC}$ and of △ABC.

6. A pyramid OABCDEF has a base ABCDEF which is a regular hexagon of side 4 cm. O is 8 cm vertically above the centre of the hexagon. Calculate the angle between each sloping edge and the base, and the angle between each sloping face and the base.

7. A wedge like the one in Fig. 179 has AB = 24 cm, AD = 7 cm and BE = 3 cm. X is a point in $\overline{AB}$ such that $A\hat{D}X = 45°$. Calculate the slope of $\overline{BD}$ and of $\overline{DX}$.

8. A pole is resting in a corner of a room. The top of the pole is 3·5 m above the floor and the bottom is 2 m from each wall. Find the length of the pole and the angle it makes with the ground.

9. A mast 45 m high is supported by 4 equal wires attached to the top of the mast and the corners of a square of side 60 m on the level ground. Calculate the inclination of each wire to the horizontal.

10. The base of a pyramid OABCD is a rectangle ABCD with AB = 4 m and BC = 6 m. O is 6 m vertically above the intersection of the diagonals of the rectangle. Calculate the length of each sloping edge and the angle it makes with the base. Calculate also the angle between △OBC and the base.

11. A screen consists of two rectangles each 2 m high and 1·5 m wide hinged along one side as in Fig. 180. If $D\hat{A}F = 60°$ calculate the slopes of (i) $\overline{DE}$ (ii) △ACE.

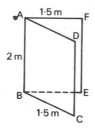

Fig. 180

12. ABCDSPQR is a rectangular cuboid with ABCD//PQRS. AB = 12 cm, AP = 8 cm, AD = 9 cm. Calculate the angles (i) between $\overline{BS}$ and PQRS (ii) between $\overline{BS}$ and BCRQ (iii) between $\overline{BS}$ and DCRS.

13. A triangular prism is 16 cm long, and the cross-section is an isosceles triangle whose equal sides are 12 cm long and third side is 8 cm. It is lying on one of the equal rectangular faces. Calculate the angle between the diagonal of the other equal face and the horizontal.

14. An open rectangular box has a base 7 cm long and 6 cm wide and its height is 6 cm. A rod 12 cm long rests with its lower end in one bottom corner and is supported by the opposite corner. Find the inclination of the rod to the horizontal and the height of its top end above the level of the base of the box.

15. A cylindrical cheese has a quadrant cut out of it and is resting on a horizontal table. The height of the cheese is 16 cm and its radius is 8 cm. Calculate the slope of $\overline{BC}$ and of $\triangle OCD$.

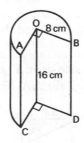

Fig. 181

Example 3   *From a point A the elevation of the top of a hill is 26° 12′, and from a point B, 1 000 m nearer the hill in a straight horizontal line from A, the elevation is 46° 4′. Find the height of the hill to 3 sig. fig.*

From Fig. 182 $1\,000 + x = h \cot 26° 12' = 2\cdot032\,3\,h$

$$x = h \cot 46° 4' = 0\cdot963\,5\,h$$

$$\overline{1\,000 \qquad\qquad\qquad = 1\cdot068\,8\,h}$$

$$\therefore \; h = \frac{1\,000}{1\cdot068\,8}$$

$$\therefore \; \text{height} \fallingdotseq 935 \text{ m.}$$

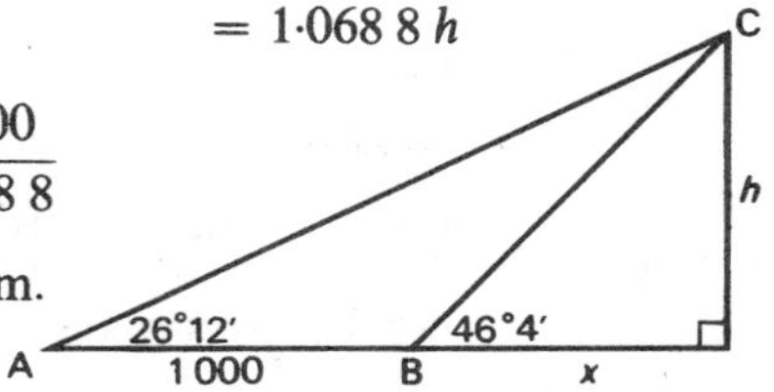

Fig. 182

Alternative method

In $\triangle ABC$, $A\hat{C}B = 46° 4' - 26° 12' = 19° 52'$

$$BC = h \operatorname{cosec} 46° 4'$$

$\therefore$ by sine formula

$$\frac{h \operatorname{cosec} 46° 4'}{\sin 26° 12'} = \frac{1\,000}{\sin 19° 52'}$$

$\therefore \; h = 1\,000 \operatorname{cosec} 19° 52' \sin 26° 12' \sin 46° 4'$

$\therefore \; h = 935$ m.

No.	Log.
$1\,000$	$3\cdot000\,0$
$\sin 26° 12'$	$\bar{1}\cdot644\,9$
$\sin 46° 4'$	$\bar{1}\cdot857\,4$
$\operatorname{cosec} 19° 52'$	$0\cdot468\,7$
$935\cdot4$	$2\cdot971\,0$

Example 4 *From a point A due east of a lighthouse the elevation of the top of the lighthouse is 7° 18', and from a point B due north of the lighthouse the elevation is 6° 12'. If AB is 1 200 m and $\overline{AB}$ is at sea level find the height of the top of the lighthouse above sea level.*

Let the height be h m

Then $AD = h \cot 7° 18'$

$\qquad BD = h \cot 6° 12'$

$\qquad AB = 1\,200$ m and $ADB = 90°$

$\therefore \; 1\,200^2 = (h \cot 7° 18')^2 + (h \cot 6° 12')^2$

$\qquad\quad = h^2(7\cdot806^2 + 9\cdot205^2)$

$\qquad\quad = h^2(60\cdot93 + 84\cdot73)$

$\therefore \; h^2 = \dfrac{1\,200^2}{145\cdot66}$

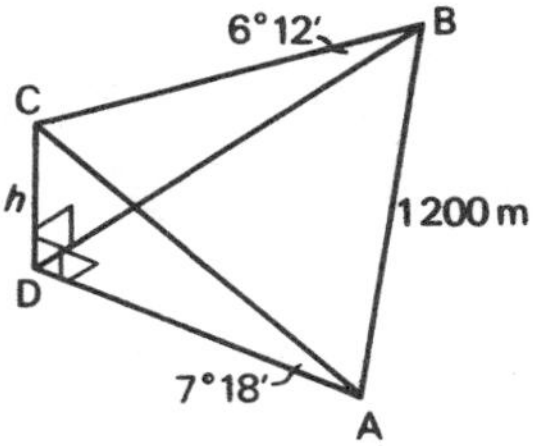

Fig. 183

$$\therefore \quad h = \frac{1\,200}{\sqrt{145\cdot7}}$$

$$= \frac{1\,200}{12\cdot07}$$

$$= 1\,200 \times 0\cdot082\,88 \text{ (using reciprocal tables)}$$

$$= 99\cdot456$$

$$\therefore \quad \text{height} \simeq 99\cdot5\,\text{m}$$

Exercise 48b

In Fig. 184 find to 3 sig. fig. the lengths marked x, all dimensions being in metres.

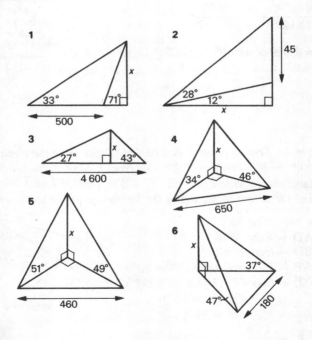

Fig. 184

7. Find the angles of triangles having sides (i) $\sqrt{3}$, $\sqrt{4}$, $\sqrt{5}$ cm (ii) $\sqrt{10}$, $\sqrt{6}$, $\sqrt{15}$ m (iii) $\sqrt{12}$, $\sqrt{35}$, $\sqrt{21}$ mm.

8. Fig. 185 represents the corner of a room in which OP = 2 m, OQ = 3 m, OR = 4 m. Find the angles of △PQR.

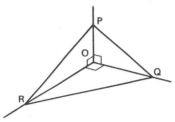

Fig. 185

9. An aircraft is observed from two points A and B which are 5 km apart, the elevation of the aircraft from these points being 26° 15′ and 32° 11′. If the aircraft is vertically over the line $\overline{AB}$ and is between A and B what is its height in metres?

10. A yacht sailing due south at 12 km h^{-1} is observed by a man in the clubhouse to be on a bearing 072°. Ten minutes later her bearing is 102°. What is the shortest distance between the yacht and the clubhouse?

11. From a coastguard lookout, two ships 1·2 km apart are visible, one on a bearing 061° and the other on a bearing 151°. If the angles of depression of the ships are respectively 6° 18′ and 5° 6′ find the height of the lookout above sea level in metres.

12. From the top of a lighthouse standing on a cliff the angle of depression of a boat out at sea is 10° 37′, and from the bottom of the lighthouse which is 30 m high the angle of depression is 10° 1′. Find how far away the boat is horizontally.

13. An aircraft in level flight at 1 200 km h^{-1} is observed at an elevation of 34° 5′. Two minutes later its elevation is 24° 9′, the aircraft having passed directly over the observer during this time. At what height is the aircraft flying?

14. From a point due south of a tower 120 m in height the top of the tower is at an angle of elevation of 26° 52′. What will be the angle of elevation when the observer has moved 400 m due west from his present position?

15. From the top of a mountain 1 020 m high the angles of depression of two points at sea level are both 11° 30′. If the bearing of one is 126° and the other 194°, how far apart are they?

Chapter 49

Gradients

Example 1 *Find the gradient of the line joining the points*
(i) $(-3, -1)$ and $(4, 2)$ (ii) $(-2, 4)$ and $(3, -4)$.

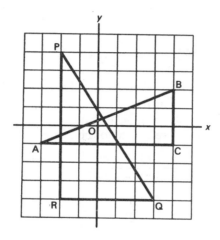

Fig. 186

(i) A and B are the points $(-3, -1)$ and $(4, 2)$ respectively.

From the figure,

the gradient of $\overline{AB} = \dfrac{CB}{AC} = \dfrac{3}{7}$.

The gradient of $\overline{AB}$ is said to be positive because, in going from A to B, y increases as x increases,
i.e. x of B > x of A and y of B > y of A.

313

Alternatively, without reference to the figure,

$$\text{the gradient of } \overline{AB} = \frac{y \text{ of B} - y \text{ of A}}{x \text{ of B} - x \text{ of A}}$$

$$= \frac{2 - (-1)}{4 - (-3)}$$

$$= \frac{3}{7}$$

(ii) P and Q are the points $(-2, 4)$ and $(3, -4)$ respectively.
From the figure,

$$\text{the gradient of } \overline{PQ} = \frac{RP}{QR} = \frac{8}{-5} = -\frac{8}{5}.$$

The gradient of $\overline{PQ}$ is said to be negative because, in going from P to Q, y decreases as x increases,
i.e. x of Q $> x$ of P but y of Q $< y$ of P.
Alternatively, without reference to the figure,

$$\text{the gradient of } \overline{PQ} = \frac{y \text{ of Q} - y \text{ of P}}{x \text{ of Q} - x \text{ of P}}$$

$$= \frac{-4 - 4}{3 - (-2)}$$

$$= -\frac{8}{5}$$

Example 2   *Find the gradient of the line whose equation is*
(i) $y = 3x - 2$ (ii) $5x + 2y - 4 = 0$.

(i) If the equation of a line is written in the form $y = mx + c$, then the gradient is **m**.
Hence the gradient of the line $y = 3x - 2$ is 3.

(ii) The equation $5x + 2y - 4 = 0$ may be written as

$$2y = -5x + 4$$

i.e. $y = -\frac{5}{2}x + 2$

This is of the form $y = mx + c$.
Hence the gradient is $-\frac{5}{2}$.

Exercise 49a
Find the gradients of the lines joining the following pairs of points.

1. $(9, 5), (1, 3)$ **2.** $(2, 7), (5, 1)$
3. $(6, 6), (-3, 1)$ **4.** $(3, -1), (-5, -3)$
5. $(-4, 5), (6, -3)$ **6.** $(4, 3), (-2, -7)$
7. $(-5, 2), (-2, -5)$ **8.** $(-7, -1), (-1, -3)$

Draw the graphs of the lines represented by the following equations, and in each case find the gradient by taking measurements.

9. $y = 2x + 1$ **10.** $y = 2x - 3$
11. $y = -3x + 1$ **12.** $y = -3x - 2$
13. $4x - 2y = 0$ **14.** $3x - 2y + 1 = 0$
15. $4x + 3y = 2$ **16.** $2x + 5y + 3 = 0$

In each of the following *write down* the gradient of the line represented by the given equation.

17. $y = 3x + 2$ **18.** $y = 3x - 2$
19. $y = \frac{1}{2}x$ **20.** $y = 1 - 2x$
21. $y = -\frac{2}{3}x + 4$ **22.** $3x - 4y = 5$
23. $2x + 3y = 1$ **24.** $3x + 5y + 2 = 0$
25. $7x - 2y + 4 = 0$

Example 3 *Draw the graph of* $y = x^2 + 2x - 3$ *for values of* x *from* -5 *to* 3 *and find the gradients at the points where* x *is* 2 *and* -3.
The table of values is constructed and the curve drawn.

x	-5	-4	-3	-2	-1	0	1	2	3
y	12	5	0	-3	-4	-3	0	5	12

P is the point on the curve at which $x = 2$.
A ruler is placed carefully against the curve at P and the tangent is drawn.

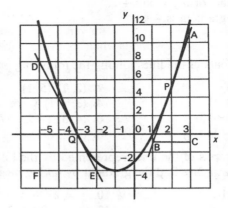

Fig. 187

On the tangent *any* two points A and B may be taken, but it is convenient to choose A to be the point at which $x = 3$, and B the point where $x = 1$.

Then BC = 2.

By measurement CA = 12.

$\therefore$ gradient of $\overline{AB} = \frac{12}{2} = 6$.

Q is the point on the curve at which $x = -3$.

The tangent at Q is drawn and on it two points D and E are chosen at which $x = -5$ and -2 respectively.

Then FE = 3.

By measurement FD = 12.

The gradient is clearly negative.

$\therefore$ gradient of $\overline{DE} = -\frac{12}{3} = -4$.

N.B. The method of drawing a tangent by placing a ruler against the curve can lead to considerable inaccuracy. The results should therefore be taken to be only approximate.

Exercise 49b

1. Draw the graph of $y = x^2 - 5x$ for values of x from -1 to 6, and find the gradients at the points where x has the values $-\frac{1}{2}$, 1 and 5.

In nos. 2–8 follow the instructions given for no. 1.

2.	$y = \frac{1}{3}x^2$	-4 to 4	3, 1, -2
3.	$y = 2x^2 - 3x$	-2 to 3	$2\frac{1}{2}$, 1, $-1\frac{1}{2}$
4.	$y = 3x - x^2$	-2 to 5	-1, 1, 3
5.	$y = x^2 - x - 5$	-3 to 4	$2\frac{1}{2}$, 2, -2
6.	$y = 5 - \frac{1}{2}x^2$	-4 to 4	2, -1, -3
7.	$y = x^2 + 2x - 5$	-5 to 3	-4, -2, 1
8.	$y = \cos x$	$0°$ to $180°$	$0°$, $30°$, $90°$, $120°$

Chapter 50

Area under a curve

Example 1 *Estimate the area enclosed between the curve $y = 18 + 3x - x^2$ and the axes (for positive values only of x and y) by (i) counting squares (ii) using the mid-ordinate rule.*

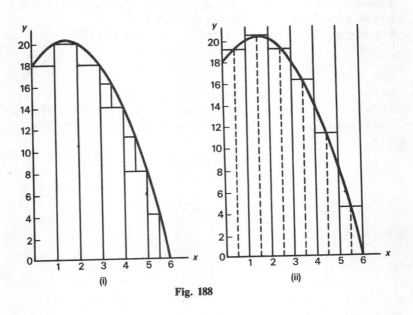

Fig. 188

In Fig. 188 the graphs have been drawn on paper ruled in 20-mm squares, each subdivided into 100 2-mm squares.

In (i) the total number of 2-mm squares is counted as 4 498
      100 of these squares form an area $1 \times 2 = 2$ units
    ∴ total area $= 4\,498 \div 50$ units $= 89{\cdot}96$ units $\simeq 90{\cdot}0$ units

318

In (ii) the successive mid-ordinates are $19\frac{1}{4}$, $20\frac{1}{4}$, $19\frac{1}{4}$, $16\frac{1}{4}$, $11\frac{1}{4}$, $4\frac{1}{4}$

Successive rectangles are $19\frac{1}{4} \times 1$, $20\frac{1}{4} \times 1$, ... units

$\therefore$ total area $= 19\frac{1}{4} + 20\frac{1}{4} + \dots$ units

$\quad\quad\quad\quad\quad = 90\frac{1}{2}$ units

N.B.   In a velocity-time graph the area under the curve gives the distance, since distance = velocity × time. Since the gradient of the curve measures the rate of change of velocity with time, the curve can also be used to find the acceleration at any given time, as in the following example.

Example 2   *The speed of a car entering a built-up area is recorded at half-minute intervals in the following table*:

Time (min)	0	$\frac{1}{2}$	1	$1\frac{1}{2}$	2	$2\frac{1}{2}$	3
Speed (km h^{-1})	50	30	25	$28\frac{1}{2}$	40	46	42

Estimate the distance travelled in metres during these three minutes and also the acceleration in m s^{-2} at times 2 min, $\frac{1}{2}$ min from the start.

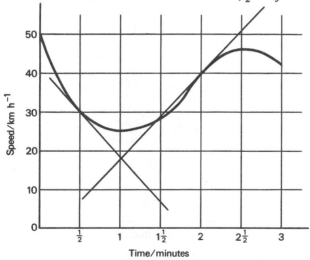

Fig. 189

The velocity–time curve is drawn on 20-mm squared paper.
Under the curve there are 2 126 2-mm squares.
One 2-mm square represents $1 \text{ km h}^{-1} \times \frac{1}{20}$ minutes,

$$= \frac{1\,000}{3\,600} \text{ m s}^{-1} \times 3 \text{ s}$$

$$= \frac{5}{6} \text{ m}$$

$\therefore$ distance travelled $= 2\,126 \times \frac{5}{6} \text{ m}$
$$\simeq 1\,770 \text{ m}$$

At time 2 minutes, acceleration $= \dfrac{\text{increase of speed}}{\text{time}}$

$$= \frac{22 \text{ km h}^{-1}}{1 \text{ min}}$$

$$= \frac{22\,000}{3\,600} \text{ m s}^{-1} \div 60 \text{ s}$$

$$= \frac{22\,000}{216\,000} \text{ m s}^{-2}$$

$$\simeq 0 \cdot 102 \text{ m s}^{-2}$$

At time $\frac{1}{2}$ min, acceleration $= \dfrac{-23 \text{ km h}^{-1}}{1 \text{ min}}$

i.e. deceleration $= \dfrac{23\,000}{216\,000} \text{ m s}^{-2}$

$$\simeq 0 \cdot 107 \text{ m s}^{-2}$$

Exercise 50

1. Use the mid-ordinate rule to find the distance travelled by the
   car in worked Example 2, drawing the graph and taking six
   ordinates. Find also the initial deceleration in m s^{-2}.

2. Draw on squared paper a quadrant of a circle of radius 10 cm,
   centred at the origin. Estimate the area of the quadrant by

counting squares, and also by the mid-ordinate rule, taking five ordinates.

3. Draw the curve $y = 5x - x^2$ for values of x from 0 to 5, taking 20-mm as the unit for both x and y.

   Find (i) the gradient when $x = 1$, $x = 2$, $x = 4$.

   (ii) the area enclosed by the curve, the x-axis and the ordinates $x = 0$, $x = 5$; use both methods.

4. An object is constrained to move in such a way that its velocity (v cm s^{-1}) at various times (t s) is given by the equation $v = 20t - 3t^2$.

   Plot v against t for values of t from 0 to 6.

   Estimate (i) the distance covered in the 6 seconds,

   (ii) the maximum velocity attained,

   (iii) the acceleration in cm s^{-2} when $t = 2$.

5. The shape of a river-bed 60 m wide is found by taking soundings at 5-m intervals from the bank in a line straight across the river: successive soundings are (in metres) 0, 5, 15, 22, 25, 26, 25, 23, 21, 20, 17, 11, 0.

   Draw an accurate cross-section of the river and estimate its area in square metres. Deduce the flow in litres per second if the river is flowing at 5 km h^{-1}, giving the answer in standard form.

6. The speed of a car accelerating from rest is shown in the table:

Time from start (s)	0	10	20	30	40	50	60
Speed (km h^{-1})	0	10	30	50	64·5	70·5	75

   Estimate the distance covered (in metres) during the 60 seconds and also the maximum acceleration in m s^{-2}.

7. Draw the graph of $y = \dfrac{6}{x}$ from $x = 1$ to $x = 6$. Estimate the area between the curve and the axis of x between these limits. Find also the gradient when $x = 3$.

8. A particle moves along a straight line in such a way that its velocity (v cm s^{-1}) after t seconds from the start of its observed motion is given by the equation $v = \frac{1}{20}t^3$. Plot v against t for values of t from 0 to 5. Estimate the distance covered in the 5 seconds, and also the acceleration when $t = 3$.

9. A locomotive's speed is automatically recorded at 5-second intervals, and successive speeds are found to be (in m s^{-1}) 20, 22·3, 24·2, 25·8, 27, 27·8, 28·3, 28·3, 28, 27·3, 26·2, 25·6, 25·3.

Plot v against t and estimate the distance covered during the time involved, and find also the accelerations after 20 seconds and after 45 seconds from the start.

10. Draw the graphs of $y = \sqrt{3x}$ from $x = 0$ to $x = 5$ and of $y = \dfrac{9}{x}$ from $x = 2$ to $x = 5$, taking positive values only of y.

Estimate the area enclosed between both curves, the x-axis and the ordinate $x = 5$. Find also the gradients of both curves at their intersection.

Chapter 51

Differentiation

If $y = x^n$, then $\dfrac{dy}{dx} = nx^{n-1}$.

If $y = Ax^n$, then $\dfrac{dy}{dx} = Anx^{n-1}$.

For example,

if $y = x^5$,

then $\dfrac{dy}{dx} = 5x^{5-1} = 5x^4$

if $y = 3x^7$

then $\dfrac{dy}{dx} = 3 \times 7x^{7-1} = 21x^6$

if $y = 5x = 5x^1$

then $\dfrac{dy}{dx} = 5 \times 1x^{1-1} = 5 \times x^0 = 5 \times 1 = 5$

if $y = 7 = 7x^0$

then $\dfrac{dy}{dx} = 7 \times 0x^{0-1} = 7 \times 0 = 0$

if $y = 4x^2 + 5x - 7$

then $\dfrac{dy}{dx} = 4 \times 2x + 5 \times 1 = 8x + 5$

if $y = \dfrac{1}{x^3} = x^{-3}$

then $\dfrac{dy}{dx} = -3x^{-3-1} = -3x^{-4} = -\dfrac{3}{x^4}$

if $y = \dfrac{7}{x^2} = 7x^{-2}$

then $\dfrac{dy}{dx} = 7 \times -2x^{-2-1} = -14x^{-3} = -\dfrac{14}{x^3}$

if $y = \dfrac{5}{x^3} - \dfrac{6}{x^2} + \dfrac{3}{x} + 2 = 5x^{-3} - 6x^{-2} + 3x^{-1} + 2$

then $\dfrac{dy}{dx} = -15x^{-4} + 12x^{-3} - 3x^{-2} + 0$

$\qquad = -\dfrac{15}{x^4} + \dfrac{12}{x^3} - \dfrac{3}{x^2}$

Exercise 51a

Write down the differential coefficients with respect to x of the following functions.

1. x^4 **2.** x^7 **3.** $5x^3$ **4.** $3x^6$

5. $\dfrac{1}{x^4}$ **6.** $\dfrac{4}{x^2}$ **7.** $\dfrac{6}{x}$ **8.** $-\dfrac{2}{x^3}$

9. $\dfrac{1}{5x^2}$ **10.** $-\dfrac{1}{3x^3}$ **11.** $3x - 2$ **12.** $2x^3 + 6$

13. $x^4 + 5x^2$ **14.** $x^2 - \dfrac{1}{x}$ **15.** $2x + \dfrac{1}{x^2}$ **16.** $x^5 - 5x^4$

17. $3x^2 - 4x + 2$ **18.** $x^2 - 2 - \dfrac{1}{x^2}$ **19.** $x^3 + x^2 + x + 1$

20. $3x^3 + 2x^2 + x$ **21.** $2x^4 - 5x^2 + 3$ **22.** $\dfrac{1}{x^3} + \dfrac{2}{x^2} - \dfrac{3}{x}$

23. $\dfrac{2}{x^6} - \dfrac{5}{x^4} - \dfrac{3}{x^2}$ **24.** $5x^7 + 3x^5 - 2x^3 - 4x$

25. $\dfrac{2}{3x^3} + \dfrac{3}{2x^2} + \dfrac{5}{4x}$

Gradients

Example 1 *Find the gradient of the curve* $y = 3x^2 - 5x + 4$ *at the point on it where* (*i*) $x = 3$ (*ii*) $x = 1$ (*iii*) $x = -2$.

The gradient is measured by the rate of change of y compared with x, i.e. by $\dfrac{dy}{dx}$.

$$y = 3x^2 - 5x + 4$$
$$\therefore \frac{dy}{dx} = 6x - 5$$

  (i) If $x = 3$, gradient $= 6 \times 3 - 5 = 13$
 (ii) If $x = 1$,   ,, $= 6 \times 1 - 5 = 1$
(iii) If $x = -2$, ,, $= 6 \times (-2) - 5 = -17$

Example 2 *Find the points on the curve* $y = 2x^3 - 3x^2 - 12x + 4$ *at which the gradient is* (*i*) 0 (*ii*) 24.

$$y = 2x^3 - 3x^2 - 12x + 4$$
$$\therefore \frac{dy}{dx} = 6x^2 - 6x - 12$$

(i) If the gradient is 0,

    then $6x^2 - 6x - 12 = 0$
        $\therefore \ x^2 - x - 2 = 0$
     $\therefore \ (x - 2)(x + 1) = 0$
              $\therefore \ x = 2 \text{ or } -1$

$\therefore$ the gradient is 0 at the points on the curve at which $x = 2$ or -1.

If $x = 2$, then
    $y = 2 \times 2^3 - 3 \times 2^2 - 12 \times 2 + 4 = 16 - 12 - 24 + 4$
      $= -16$
If $x = -1$, then
    $y = 2 \times (-1)^3 - 3 \times (-1)^2 - 12 \times (-1) + 4$
      $= -2 - 3 + 12 + 4 = 11$

$\therefore$ the gradient is 0 at the points $(2, -16)$ and $(-1, 11)$.

325

(ii) If the gradient is 24,
    then $6x^2 - 6x - 12 = 24$
    $\therefore\ 6x^2 - 6x - 36 = 0$
    $\therefore\ x^2 - x - 6 = 0$
    $\therefore\ (x - 3)(x + 2) = 0$
        $\therefore\ x = 3 \text{ or } -2$

$\therefore$ the gradient is 24 at the points on the curve at which $x = 3$ or -2.

If $x = 3$, then
    $y = 2 \times 3^3 - 3 \times 3^2 - 12 \times 3 + 4$
        $= 54 - 27 - 36 + 4$
        $= -5$

If $x = -2$, then
    $y = 2 \times (-2)^3 - 3 \times (-2)^2 - 12 \times (-2) + 4$
        $= -16 - 12 + 24 + 4$
        $= 0$

$\therefore$ the gradient is 24 at the points $(3, -5)$ and $(-2, 0)$.

Exercise 51b

1. By substitution verify that the points $(5, 11)$, $(3, -1)$, $(1, -5)$, $(0, -4)$, $(-2, 4)$ lie on the curve $y = x^2 - 2x - 4$. Calculate the gradient at each of these points and sketch the graph.

2. Verify that the curve $y = x^3 - 4x + 3$ passes through the points $(3, 18)$, $(2, 3)$, $(1, 0)$, $(0, 3)$, $(-1, 6)$, $(-2, 3)$, $(-3, -12)$. Calculate the gradient at each of these points and sketch the graph.

3. Calculate the gradient of the curve $y = 2x^2 - 2x - 5$ at the points where $x = 4, 2, 0, -2, -4$. Sketch the graph.

4. Find the co-ordinates of the point on the graph of $y = x^2 - 2x + 5$ at which the gradient is equal to 2.

5. Find the co-ordinates of the point on the graph of $y = x^2 - 3x + 1$ at which the gradient is zero.

6. Calculate the gradient of the curve $y = \dfrac{6}{x}$ at the points where $x = 6, 4, 2, -1, -3$. Sketch the graph.

7. Find the co-ordinates of the point on the graph of $y = 3 - 2x - x^2$ at which the tangent is parallel to the x-axis.

8. If $y = 3x^2 - 4x + 1$, find the co-ordinates of the point on the graph at which the gradient is equal to 8.

9. Find the co-ordinates of the point on the graph of $y = 2x^2 + x - 3$ at which the tangent makes an angle of 45° with the positive direction of the x-axis.

10. Calculate the gradient of the curve $y = 3 - 4x - x^2$ at the points where $x = 1, 0, -2, -3, -5$. Sketch the graph.

11. Find the co-ordinates of the points on the graph of $y = x^3 - 3x^2 - 9x + 3$ at which the gradient is zero.

12. Find the co-ordinates of the points on the graph of $y = 2x^3 - 9x^2 + 3x + 8$ at which the gradient is equal to -9.

13. Calculate the gradient of the curve $y = \dfrac{2}{x}$ at the points where $x = 4, 2, \frac{1}{2}, -\frac{1}{2}, -1, -3$. Sketch the graph.

14. Find the co-ordinates of the points on the graph of $y = 3x^3 + 6x^2 - x - 2$ at which the gradient is equal to -4.

15. Find the co-ordinates of the points at which the graph of $y = (x^2 - 9)(x + 2)$ cuts the x-axis. Find the gradient at each of these points and hence sketch the graph.

Velocity and acceleration

If a particle is moving along a straight line, and after t seconds its distance from a fixed point in the line is x metres,
then the **velocity** of the particle is measured by the rate of change of x compared with t,

i.e. velocity $= \dfrac{dx}{dt}$.

Similarly the **acceleration** is measured by the rate of change of velocity compared with time.

Hence if the velocity is v m s^{-1} after t seconds,

then acceleration $= \dfrac{dv}{dt}$.

If a graph is drawn, plotting distance against time, then the gradient at any point gives the velocity, since it measures the rate of change of distance compared with time.

Similarly on a graph connecting velocity and time, the gradient at any point gives the acceleration.

Example 3 *After t seconds a particle has travelled a distance x cm, where $x = 2t^3 - 21t^2 + 60t$. How far has it gone after 4 seconds? When is the velocity zero? When is the acceleration zero? Find the velocity and the acceleration after (i) 4 seconds (ii) 6 seconds.*

$x = 2t^3 - 21t^2 + 60t$

$\therefore$ after 4 seconds, distance gone $= (2 \times 64 - 21 \times 16 + 60 \times 4)$
$$\text{cm}$$

$$= (128 - 336 + 240)\,\text{cm}$$

$$= (368 - 336)\,\text{cm}$$

$$= 32\,\text{cm}$$

$x = 2t^3 - 21t^2 + 60t$

$\therefore \ v = \dfrac{dx}{dt} = 6t^2 - 42t + 60$

and acceleration $= \dfrac{dv}{dt} = 12t - 42$

If the velocity is zero,

then $6t^2 - 42t + 60 = 0$
$\qquad \therefore \ t^2 - 7t + 10 = 0$
$\qquad \therefore \ (t - 2)(t - 5) = 0$
$\qquad\qquad\qquad \therefore \ t = 2 \text{ or } 5$

$\therefore$ the velocity is zero after 2 seconds and after 5 seconds.

If the acceleration is zero,
then $12t - 42 = 0$
$\qquad\quad \therefore \ 2t = 7$
$\qquad\quad \therefore \ t = 3\frac{1}{2}$

$\therefore$ the acceleration is zero after $3\frac{1}{2}$ seconds.

(i) When $t = 4$,

velocity in cm s^{-1} $= 6 \times 4^2 - 42 \times 4 + 60$
$\qquad\qquad\qquad\quad = 96 - 168 + 60$
$\qquad\qquad\qquad\quad = -12$

and acceleration in cm s^{-2} $= 12 \times 4 - 42$
$\qquad\qquad\qquad\qquad\qquad = 48 - 42$
$\qquad\qquad\qquad\qquad\qquad = 6$

(ii) When $t = 6$,
velocity in cm s^{-1} $= 6 \times 6^2 - 42 \times 6 + 60$
$\qquad\qquad\qquad\quad = 216 - 252 + 60$
$\qquad\qquad\qquad\quad = 24$

and acceleration in cm s^{-2} $= 12 \times 6 - 42$
$\qquad\qquad\qquad\qquad\qquad = 72 - 42$
$\qquad\qquad\qquad\qquad\qquad = 30$

$\therefore$ after 4s, vel. is -12 cm s^{-1} and accel. is 6 cm s^{-2}
$\qquad$ after 6s, vel. is $\quad$ 24 cm s^{-1} and accel. is 30 cm s^{-2}.

Exercise 51c

1. A particle moves along a straight line, and after t seconds the distance gone is x metres, where $x = t^2 + 3t$. Draw the distance-time graph for values of t from 0 to 5, and by measuring the gradient find the velocity of the particle after 2 seconds and after 4 seconds. Check the results by differentiation.

2. A particle moves along a straight line, and after t seconds its velocity is v m s^{-1}, where $v = \frac{1}{2}t^2 + t$. Draw the velocity-time graph for values of t from 0 to 5, and by measuring the gradient find the acceleration after 2 seconds and after 4 seconds. Check the results by differentiation.

3. The distance moved by a body in t seconds is x cm, where $x = 3t^2 - 2t + 4$. Calculate the velocity after 4 seconds. Prove that the acceleration is constant, and find its value.

4. After t seconds the velocity of a body is v cm s^{-1}, where $v = 3t + 2$. By drawing the velocity-time graph, show that the acceleration is constant, and find its value. Check by differentiation.

5. After t seconds the distance which a particle has moved is x metres, where $x = 2t - 3$. By drawing the distance-time graph, show that the velocity is constant, and find its value. Check by differentiation.

6. The distance moved by a particle in t seconds is x cm, where $x = 3 + 7t - t^2$. By differentiation, calculate the velocity after 2 seconds and after 5 seconds. Prove that the acceleration is constant, and find its value. When is the particle momentarily at rest?

7. After t seconds the velocity of a moving body is v m s^{-1}, where $v = 5 + 8t - t^2$. Calculate the acceleration after 1 second and after 3 seconds.

8. After t seconds a moving body has gone x cm, where $x = 3 - 7t + 12t^2 - 2t^3$.
   (i) How far has it gone after 2 seconds?
   (ii) After how many seconds is the acceleration zero?
   (iii) Find the velocity and acceleration after 3 seconds.

9. A moving body has gone x cm after t seconds, where $x = t^3 - 9t^2 + 24t + 5$.

  (i) After how many seconds is the velocity zero?

 (ii) After how many seconds is the acceleration zero?

(iii) Find the velocity and acceleration after 5 seconds.

10. A marble is projected up a sloping groove, and after t seconds its distance from the starting point is x cm, where $x = 20t - 4t^2$.

   (i) Find its initial velocity.

  (ii) Find its acceleration.

 (iii) After how many seconds does it reach its furthest point?

 (iv) Find its velocity after 2 seconds.

  (v) Find the distance gone after 4 seconds.

 (vi) Find its greatest distance from the starting point.

(vii) Find the total time taken to return to the starting point.

Chapter 52

Maxima and minima

Example 1 *Find the maximum and minimum values of the function* $x^3 + 3x^2 - 9x - 8$. *Hence sketch the curve whose equation ·is* $y = x^3 + 3x^2 - 9x - 8$.

If $y = x^3 + 3x^2 - 9x - 8$ then $\dfrac{dy}{dx} = 3x^2 + 6x - 9$.

At a maximum or minimum point the tangent to the curve is parallel to the x-axis,

i.e. $\dfrac{dy}{dx} = 0$ $\therefore\ 3x^2 + 6x - 9 = 0$

$\therefore\ 3(x^2 + 2x - 3) = 0$

$\therefore\ 3(x - 1)(x + 3) = 0$

$\therefore\ x = 1$ or -3.

Hence the **turning points** occur where $x = 1$ or -3, and it remains to distinguish between them.

(i) If x is a little less than 1

$x - 1$ is negative and $x + 3$ is positive

$\therefore\ 3(x - 1)(x + 3)$ is negative.

If x is a little greater than 1

$x - 1$ is positive and $x + 3$ is positive

$\therefore\ 3(x - 1)(x + 3)$ is positive.

$\therefore$ as x passes through the value 1, $\dfrac{dy}{dx}$ passes from negative to positive.

$\therefore$ a minimum occurs when $x = 1$ (see Fig. 190), and this minimum value of $x^3 + 3x^2 - 9x - 8$

is $1^3 + 3 \times 1^2 - 9 \times 1 - 8 = 1 + 3 - 9 - 8 = -13$.

(ii) If x is a little less than -3 (e.g. -3.1)

$x - 1$ is negative and $x + 3$ is negative

$\therefore\ 3(x - 1)(x + 3)$ is positive.

Fig. 190

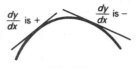

Fig. 191

If x is a little greater than -3 (e.g. -2.9)

$x - 1$ is negative and $x + 3$ is positive

$\therefore$ $3(x - 1)(x + 3)$ is negative.

$\therefore$ as x passes through the value -3, $\dfrac{dy}{dx}$ passes from positive to negative.

$\therefore$ a maximum occurs when $x = -3$ (see Fig. 191), and this maximum value of $x^3 + 3x^2 - 9x - 8$

is $(-3)^3 + 3 \times (-3)^2 - 9 \times (-3) - 8$

$= -27 + 27 + 27 - 8$

$= 19.$

The curve cuts the y-axis where $x = 0$,

i.e. where $y = 0^3 + 3 \times 0^2 - 9 \times 0 - 8$

$\qquad = -8.$

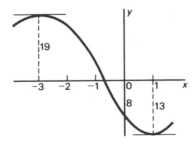

Fig. 192

The characteristic features of the curve are now known, and it may be sketched as in Fig. 192.

Notice that this a *rough* sketch, and that graph paper is not needed.

333

Example 2 *Investigate the turning points, if any, of* $x^3 - 6x^2 + 12x - 4$ *and sketch the graph of the function.*

Let $y = x^3 - 6x^2 + 12x - 4$

then $\dfrac{dy}{dx} = 3x^2 - 12x + 12$

At a turning point $\dfrac{dy}{dx} = 0$

$\therefore\ 3(x^2 - 4x + 4) = 0$
$\therefore\ 3(x - 2)^2 = 0$
$\therefore\ x = 2$ twice

$\therefore$ the gradient is zero only at the point where $x = 2$.

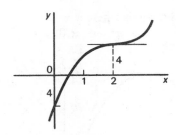

Fig. 193

If x is a little less than 2, $3(x - 2)^2$ is positive.
If x is a little greater than 2, $3(x - 2)^2$ is positive.
$\therefore$ the gradient is *positive* on *both* sides of the point at which it is zero.

Hence there is a **point of inflexion** where $x = 2$, and there is no maximum or minimum.

If $x = 2$, $y = 2^3 - 6 \times 2^2 + 12 \times 2 - 4$
$$= 8 - 24 + 24 - 4$$
$$= 4$$

∴ the point of inflexion is at $(2, 4)$.

If $x = 0$, $y = 0^3 - 6 \times 0^2 + 12 \times 0 - 4$
$$= -4$$

∴ the curve cuts the y-axis at $(0, -4)$.

The curve may now be sketched and is as in Fig. 193.

Exercise 52a

For the following functions find the values of x at which turning points occur, and distinguish between them. Find the value of the function at each turning point, and sketch the graph.

1. $x^2 - 4x + 5$	**2.** $5 - 6x - x^2$	**3.** $4x - x^2$
4. $x^2 + 5x$	**5.** $3x^2 - 2x^3$	**6.** $x^3 - 12x + 1$
7. $4x^2 - 2x + 3$	**8.** $1 - 9x - 3x^2$	
9. $2x^3 + 3x^2 - 12x - 5$	**10.** $x^3 + 6x^2 + 12x + 5$	
11. $2 - x^3$	**12.** $1 + 12x + 3x^2 - 2x^3$	
13. $2 - 3x + 3x^2 - x^3$	**14.** $4 + 36x - 3x^2 - 2x^3$	
15. $x^3 + 5x^2 + 7x + 3$		

Problems

The examples which have just been done involved finding the turning points of a function which was given. In each of the problems which follow, a variable is chosen and the function of this variable has to be constructed.

Notice that the constructed function must be in terms of *only one* variable, so that if two letters are originally used, one must be expressed in terms of the other by means of a geometrical connection.

Example 3 *Find the maximum area of a rectangle whose perimeter is 36 cm.*

Let the rectangle measure x cm by y cm.
Then since the perimeter is 36 cm,
$2x + 2y = 36$
$\quad \therefore \; y = 18 - x$

If the area is A cm^2,
then $A = xy$
$\qquad = x(18 - x)$　　**(N.B.** *a single variable x)*
$\qquad = 18x - x^2$
$\therefore \; \dfrac{dA}{dx} = 18 - 2x$

For a maximum or minimum $\dfrac{dA}{dx} = 0$

$\therefore \; 18 - 2x = 0$
$\qquad \therefore \; x = 9$
If x is slightly < 9, $18 - 2x$ is positive
If x is slightly > 9, $18 - 2x$ is negative
$\therefore \; x = 9$ gives a maximum.
　Also $y = 18 - 9 = 9$
$\therefore$ the rectangle of maximum area is a square of side 9 cm.
i.e. its area is 81 cm^2.

Example 4 *Find the volume of the largest circular cone that can be cut from a solid sphere of radius a cm.*

Let the altitude of the cone be x cm and the radius of base r cm.

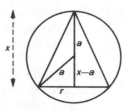

Fig. 195

Then, in Fig. 195, $r^2 = a^2 - (x - a)^2$

$$= a^2 - x^2 + 2ax - a^2$$

$$= 2ax - x^2$$

Let volume of cone be V cm^3.

Then $V = \frac{1}{3}\pi r^2 x$

$$= \frac{1}{3}\pi(2ax - x^2)x$$

$$= \frac{\pi}{3}(2ax^2 - x^3)$$

$$\therefore \frac{dV}{dx} = \frac{\pi}{3}(4ax - 3x^2)$$

$$= \frac{\pi}{3}x(4a - 3x)$$

$\therefore$ for a maximum or minimum,

$$\frac{\pi}{3}x(4a - 3x) = 0$$

$\therefore$ $x = 0$ or $\frac{4}{3}a$

From the figure, $x = 0$ clearly gives a minimum

and $x = \frac{4}{3}a$ gives a maximum.

$\therefore$ $V = \frac{2}{3}\pi ax^2 - \frac{1}{3}\pi x^3$ where $x = \frac{4}{3}a$

$$= \frac{2}{3}\pi a\frac{16}{9}a^2 - \frac{1}{3}\pi\frac{64}{27}a^3$$

$$= \pi a^3(\frac{32}{27} - \frac{64}{81})$$

$$= \pi a^3 \frac{96 - 64}{81}$$

$$= \frac{32}{81}\pi a^3$$

$\therefore$ the volume of the largest cone is $\frac{32}{81}\pi a^3$ cm^3.

Exercise 52b

1. If $A = xy$ where $4x + y = 20$, find the maximum value of A.

2. If $P = 2x + 5y$ where $xy = 40$, find the minimum value of P, taking x and y to be both positive.

3. A farmer has 80 metres of fencing with which to enclose a rectangular sheep-pen, using a wall for one side. Find the maximum area that he can enclose.

4. A farmer has some 2-metre hurdles with which to enclose a rectangular pen of area $512 \, \mathrm{m}^2$. If one side of the pen is a river bank and needs no fencing, find the minimum number of hurdles needed.

5. A rectangular sheet of metal measures 16 cm by 10 cm. From each corner a square of side x cm is removed, and the flaps so formed are bent up to make an open box. Show that the volume of the box is $(4x^3 - 52x^2 + 160x) \, \mathrm{cm}^3$, and find its maximum value.

6. Sheet metal is used for making an oil-tank, open at the top, on a square base. If the volume of the tank is to be $4 \, \mathrm{m}^3$, find the least area of sheet metal required.

7. Sheet metal of total area $294 \, \mathrm{cm}^2$ is to be used for making a closed rectangular box with square ends. Find the greatest possible volume of the box.

8. An object is projected into the air and its height, h metres, after t seconds is given by the formula $h = 196t - 4 \cdot 9t^2$. Find the greatest height to which it rises.

9. A cylindrical can is open at the top and stands on a circular base. If the can has a volume of $64\pi \, \mathrm{cm}^3$, find the least area of sheet metal needed to make the can. (Leave π in the answer.)

10. A rectangular box with square ends is to be made, such that the sum of the length of the box and the perimeter of an end is 4 m. Find the greatest possible volume of the box.

11. A cylindrical container with circular ends is to be made, such that the sum of the length of the cylinder and the circumference of an end is 4 m. Find the greatest possible volume of the cylinder. (Leave π in the answer.)

12. The ends of an open trough are right-angled isosceles triangles, and are perpendicular to the sides. If the trough is made of sheet metal of total area 2 028 cm^2, find the maximum volume possible.

13. If the trough in no. 12 is to have a volume of 2 916 cm^3, find the least area of sheet metal needed.

14. A lawn is in the shape of a rectangle with a semicircle at one end, the diameter of the semicircle being equal to the width of the rectangle. Find the radius of the semicircle if the area of the lawn is a maximum, the perimeter being 60 metres. (Leave π in the answer.)

15. Find the volume of the largest circular cylinder that can be cut from a solid sphere of radius a cm. (Leave π in the answer.)

Chapter 53

Integration

If $\dfrac{dy}{dx} = x^n$, then $y = \dfrac{x^{n+1}}{n+1} + c$

where c is an arbitrary constant.

Alternatively, using the symbol for integration,

$$\int x^n \, dx = \frac{x^{n+1}}{n+1} + c$$

Notice also that $\displaystyle\int ax^n \, dx = \dfrac{ax^{n+1}}{n+1} + c.$

For example

$$\int x^5 \, dx = \frac{x^6}{6} + c$$

$$\int x \, dx = \int x^1 \, dx = \frac{x^2}{2} + c$$

$$\int 3 \, dx = \int 3x^0 \, dx = \frac{3x^1}{1} + c = 3x + c$$

$$\int 6x^2 \, dx = 6 \times \frac{x^3}{3} + c = 2x^3 + c$$

$$\int \frac{1}{x^4} \, dx = \int x^{-4} \, dx = \frac{x^{-3}}{-3} + c = -\frac{1}{3x^3} + c$$

$$\int \frac{8}{x^3} \, dx = \int 8x^{-3} \, dx = 8 \times \frac{x^{-2}}{-2} + c = -\frac{4}{x^2} + c$$

Example 1 *If* $\dfrac{dy}{dx} = x^3 - 5x^2$, *find* y.

$$\dfrac{dy}{dx} = x^3 - 5x^2$$

$$\therefore \; y = \dfrac{x^4}{4} - 5 \times \dfrac{x^3}{3} + c$$

$$= \dfrac{x^4}{4} - \dfrac{5x^3}{3} + c$$

Example 2 *Integrate the expression* $x^4 - 3x^2 + 5 - \dfrac{2}{x^2}$.

$$\int \left(x^4 - 3x^2 + 5 - \dfrac{2}{x^2} \right) dx = \int (x^4 - 3x^2 + 5x^0 - 2x^{-2}) \, dx$$

$$= \dfrac{x^5}{5} - \dfrac{3x^3}{3} + 5x - \dfrac{2x^{-1}}{-1} + c$$

$$= \dfrac{x^5}{5} - x^3 + 5x + \dfrac{2}{x} + c$$

Exercise 53a

Integrate the following expressions.

1. $4x^3$

2. $\dfrac{x^2}{3}$

3. $\dfrac{1}{x^2}$

4. $-\dfrac{1}{2x^5}$

5. 8

6. $4x - 5$

7. $2x + 1$

8. $6x^2 + x - 2$

9. $2x^3 - 3x^2 - 3x + 2$

10. $3x^4 + 2x^2 - 5$

11. $x + \dfrac{2}{x^2}$

12. $3x^3 - \dfrac{1}{3x^3}$

13. $x^7 - 2x^5 + 5x^3$ **14.** $\dfrac{1}{x^2} - \dfrac{2}{x^3} + \dfrac{3}{x^4}$

15. $\dfrac{2}{x^4} + \dfrac{3}{x^3} - \dfrac{4}{x^2}$

In particular cases the value of the arbitrary constant can be calculated from the information given in the question, as in Examples 3, 4, 5, 6 which follow.

Example 3 *A curve passes through the point* $(2, -5)$, *and its gradient at any point is given by* $3x^2 - 8x + 5$. *Find the equation of the curve.*

The gradient is given by $\dfrac{dy}{dx}$.

$\therefore \dfrac{dy}{dx} = 3x^2 - 8x + 5$

$\therefore y = x^3 - 4x^2 + 5x + c$

But this equation is satisfied by the co-ordinates of the point $(2, -5)$.

$\therefore -5 = 2^3 - 4 \times 2^2 + 5 \times 2 + c$

$\qquad = 8 - 16 + 10 + c$

$\qquad = 2 + c$

$\therefore c = -7$

$\therefore$ the equation of the curve is $y = x^3 - 4x^2 + 5x - 7$.

Example 4 *A particle moves in a straight line, and its velocity after* t *seconds is* $(3t^2 - 5t - 4)\,\text{m s}^{-1}$. *The distance of the particle from a fixed point on the line after* t *seconds is* $x\,\text{m}$, *and* $x = 11$ *when* $t = 4$. *Find the formula for* x *in terms of* t.

The velocity is given by $\dfrac{dx}{dt}$.

$\therefore \dfrac{dx}{dt} = 3t^2 - 5t - 4$

$\therefore x = t^3 - \dfrac{5t^2}{2} - 4t + c$

But $x = 11$ when $t = 4$,

$\therefore \ 11 = 4^3 - \dfrac{5 \times 4^2}{2} - 4 \times 4 + c$

$\qquad = 64 - 40 - 16 + c$

$\qquad = 8 + c$

$\therefore \ c = 3$

$\therefore \ x = t^3 - \dfrac{5t^2}{2} - 4t + 3$

Example 5 *A particle moves in a straight line with a constant acceleration of $4\,cm\,s^{-2}$. If its velocity after t seconds is $v\,cm\,s^{-1}$, find v in terms of t, given that the velocity after 3 seconds is $15\,cm\,s^{-1}$. Hence find the initial velocity and the velocity after 5 seconds.*

The acceleration is given by $\dfrac{dv}{dt}$.

$\therefore \ \dfrac{dv}{dt} = 4$

$\therefore \ v = 4t + c.$

But $v = 15$ when $t = 3$,

$\therefore \ 15 = 4 \times 3 + c$

$\qquad = 12 + c$

$\therefore \ c = 3$

$\therefore \ v = 4t + 3.$

If $t = 0$, $v = 4 \times 0 + 3 = 3$

$\therefore$ initial velocity $= 3\,cm\,s^{-1}$.

If $t = 5$, $v = 4 \times 5 + 3 = 23$

$\therefore$ velocity after 5 seconds $= 23\,cm\,s^{-1}$.

Example 6 *A particle moves in a straight line in such a way that its velocity after t seconds is $(3t + 2)\,m\,s^{-1}$. Find the total distance travelled in the 2nd, 3rd and 4th seconds.*

Let the distance after t seconds be x metres.

Then velocity $= \dfrac{dx}{dt}$.

$\therefore \dfrac{dx}{dt} = 3t + 2$

$\therefore x = \dfrac{3t^2}{2} + 2t + c$

When $t = 1$, $x = \frac{3}{2} + 2 + c = 3\frac{1}{2} + c$.
When $t = 4$, $x = 24 + 8 + c = 32 + c$.
$\therefore$ the total distance gone in the 2nd, 3rd and 4th seconds
$\qquad = [(32 + c) - (3\frac{1}{2} + c)]$ metres
$\qquad = 28\frac{1}{2}$ metres.

Exercise 53b

1. Two variables x and y are such that $\dfrac{dy}{dx} = 2x - 1$, and $y = 8$ when $x = 3$. Find y in terms of x.

2. If u and v are two variables such that $\dfrac{dv}{du} = 6u^2 - 4u - 3$, and $v = -3$ when $u = 2$, find v in terms of u.

3. Find the equation of the curve whose gradient is given by $4x - 5$, and which passes through the point $(3, 7)$.

4. Find the equation of the straight line with gradient 4 which passes through the point $(-2, -5)$.

5. A particle is projected along a straight line from a point A in the line, and its velocity after t seconds is $(28 - 4t)\,\text{cm s}^{-1}$. If its distance from A after t seconds is x cm, find x in terms of t. Hence find the time that elapses before the particle is back again at A. (Initially $x = 0$ and $t = 0$.)

6. A particle moves along a straight line in such a way that its acceleration after t seconds is $(t + 2)\,\text{cm s}^{-2}$. If its velocity after t seconds is $v\,\text{cm s}^{-1}$, find v in terms of t, given that $v = 19$ when $t = 4$. Hence find its velocity after 2 seconds.

7. Find the equation of the curve which passes through the point $(-2, -4)$, and whose gradient at any point is given by $3x^2 - 4x - 5$.

8. A particle is moving in a straight line in such a way that its velocity after t seconds is $(3t^2 - 2t)\,\mathrm{m\,s^{-1}}$. Find the distance gone in the first 4 seconds.

9. A curve passes through the point $(-2, -3)$, and its gradient is given by $7 - 4x - 6x^2$. Find the equation of the curve.

10. A curve passes through the point $(3, -5)$, and its gradient at any point is $2x - 2$. Find the points where the curve crosses the axis of x.

11. A body is projected vertically into the air, and its upward velocity after t seconds is $(78\cdot4 - 9\cdot8t)\,\mathrm{m\,s^{-1}}$. If its height after t seconds is h metres, find the formula giving h in terms of t. Find also the greatest height reached.

12. A body is moving along a straight line, and its acceleration after t seconds is $(8 - 3t)\,\mathrm{cm\,s^{-2}}$. Its velocity after t seconds is $v\,\mathrm{cm\,s^{-1}}$, and its initial velocity is $4\,\mathrm{cm\,s^{-1}}$. Find v in terms of t.

13. The gradient of a curve is given by $x^2 - 2x + \dfrac{3}{x^2}$. Find the equation of the curve if the point $(3, -4)$ lies on it.

14. A particle moves along a straight line in such a way that its velocity after t seconds is $(2t^2 - 6t + 3)\,\mathrm{m\,s^{-1}}$. The distance of the particle from a fixed point A in the line is x metres after t seconds, and $x = 4$ when $t = 3$. Find the distance of the particle from A (i) initially (ii) after 2 seconds (iii) after 4 seconds.

15. A body is projected vertically into the air with an initial velocity of $117\cdot6\,\mathrm{m\,s^{-1}}$, and the constant deceleration due to gravity is $9\cdot8\,\mathrm{m\,s^{-2}}$. If the velocity after t seconds is $v\,\mathrm{m\,s^{-1}}$, find v in terms of t. Find also h in terms of t, where h metres is the height after t seconds. Hence find the height after (i) 10 seconds (ii) 14 seconds. What do these last two results imply?

Definite integral

The expression is first integrated. Then the upper and lower limits are substituted in turn for the variable, and the second result subtracted from the first. Notice that the arbitrary constant disappears, and may therefore be omitted when calculating a definite integral.

This process is known as **integrating between limits**.

For example,

$$\int 6x^2 \, dx = 2x^3 + c$$

and $\int_4^5 6x^2 \, dx = [2x^3 + c]_4^5$

$$= [2 \times 5^3 + c] - [2 \times 4^3 + c]$$

$$= 250 + c - 128 - c$$

$$= 122.$$

Example 7   *Evaluate* $\int_3^5 (3x^2 - 4x + 1) \, dx$.

$\int_3^5 (3x^2 - 4x + 1) \, dx = [x^3 - 2x^2 + x]_3^5$

$$= [5^3 - 2 \times 5^2 + 5] - [3^3 - 2 \times 3^2 + 3]$$

$$= [125 - 50 + 5] - [27 - 18 + 3]$$

$$= 80 - 12$$

$$= 68.$$

Exercise 53c

Evaluate the following definite integrals.

1. $\int_2^4 3x \, dx$ 2. $\int_1^4 x^2 \, dx$ 3. $\int_0^2 2x^3 \, dx$

4. $\int_1^6 \dfrac{3}{x^2} \, dx$ 5. $\int_{-3}^4 3x^2 \, dx$ 6. $\int_{-2}^{-1} \dfrac{1}{x^4} \, dx$

7. $\displaystyle\int_{3}^{5} (x - 5)\,dx$

8. $\displaystyle\int_{-1}^{1} (x^2 + x)\,dx$

9. $\displaystyle\int_{2}^{3} \left(x^2 - 2 - \frac{1}{x^2}\right) dx$

10. $\displaystyle\int_{-2}^{2} (6x^2 + 8x - 3)\,dx$

11. $\displaystyle\int_{2}^{5} (3x^2 - 5x + 2)\,dx$

12. $\displaystyle\int_{-1}^{5} (4x^2 - 3x - 1)\,dx$

Areas

Suppose that in Fig. 196 it is required to calculate the area lying between the curve and the x-axis.

Divide the area into a very large number of very narrow strips parallel to the y-axis.

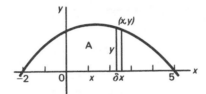

Fig. 196

If the area as far as (x, y) is A, then for a small increase δx in x, the corresponding increase in A is δA.

$\therefore \quad \delta A \simeq y\,\delta x$

i.e. $\dfrac{\delta A}{\delta x} \simeq y.$

The required area is the sum of all such strips between the limits -2 and 5, since the curve cuts the x-axis where $x = -2$ and $x = 5$.

$\therefore \quad A = \displaystyle\int_{-2}^{5} y\,dx.$

Example 8 *Find the area lying between the x-axis and the curve*
$y = 4 + 3x - x^2$.

The curve cuts the y-axis where $x = 0$,
      i.e. where $y = 4$.
There is a maximum of $6\frac{1}{4}$ where $x = 1\frac{1}{2}$.
The curve cuts the x-axis where $y = 0$,
      i.e. where $4 + 3x - x^2 = 0$
      i.e. where $(4 - x)(1 + x) = 0$
      i.e. where $x = 4$ or -1.

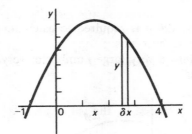

Fig. 197

These values are therefore the limits of integration.

$$\therefore \ A = \int_{-1}^{4} y \, dx$$

$$= \int_{-1}^{4} (4 + 3x - x^2) \, dx$$

$$= \left[4x + \frac{3x^2}{2} - \frac{x^3}{3} \right]_{-1}^{4}$$

$$= [16 + 24 - 21\tfrac{1}{3}] - [-4 + 1\tfrac{1}{2} + \tfrac{1}{3}]$$

$$= 18\tfrac{2}{3} - [-2\tfrac{1}{6}]$$

$$= 20\tfrac{5}{6}.$$

$\therefore$ the required result is $20\frac{5}{6}$ units of area.

Exercise 53d

1. Find the area enclosed between the curve $y = x^2$, the x-axis, and the lines $x = 2$ and $x = 5$.

2. Find *by integration* the area bounded by the straight line $y = \frac{1}{2}x + 2$, the x-axis, and the ordinates $x = 1$ and $x = 3$.

3. Find the area lying between the curve $y = 2x^2 - 1$ and the x-axis, for values of x from 3 to 6.

4. Find the area lying between the curve $y = x^2 + 2x - 3$, the x-axis, and the lines $x = 2$ and $x = 4$.

5. Find the area lying between the curve $y = x^2 + 2x + 1$, the x-axis, and the line $x = 1$.

6. Find the area bounded by the curve $y = 6 + x - x^2$ and the x-axis.

7. Find the area lying between the curve $y = 2x^2 - 4x + 5$, the x-axis, the y-axis, and the ordinate $x = 3$.

8. Find the area enclosed by the two axes, the line $x = 2$, and the curve $y = x^2 + 3x + 2$.

9. Find the area lying between the x-axis and the curve $y = 15 + 2x - x^2$.

10. Find the area bounded by the curve $y = 3x - \dfrac{1}{x^2}$, the x-axis, and the ordinates $x = 1$ and $x = 4$.

11. Find the area lying between the curve $y = \frac{1}{3}x^2$ and the straight line $y = 3x$. (*Difference of two areas.*)

12. Find the area lying between the curves $y = 4x^2$ and $y = x^3$.

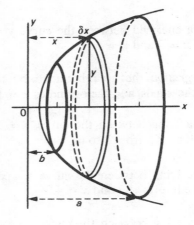

Fig. 198

Volumes of revolution

Suppose that in Fig. 198 it is required to calculate the volume obtained by revolving about the x-axis that part of the curve which lies between the limits $x = a$ and $x = b$.

Divide the volume into a very large number of very thin circular slices to each of which the x-axis is perpendicular.

If the required volume is V, then the volume of a typical elementary circular slice is δV.

$$\therefore \quad \delta V \simeq \pi y^2 \, \delta x$$

i.e. $\dfrac{\delta V}{\delta x} \simeq \pi y^2.$

The required volume is the sum of all such slices between the limits a and b for x.

$$\therefore \quad V = \int_b^a \pi y^2 \, dx.$$

Example 9 *The curve xy = 4 is revolved about the x-axis. Find the volume generated by that part of the curve which lies between x = 2 and x = 5.*

Divide the volume into elementary circular slices each perpendicular to the x-axis.

Volume of an elementary slice = $\pi y^2 \, \delta x$.

$$\therefore \ V = \int_2^5 \pi y^2 \, dx$$

$$= \int_2^5 \pi \frac{16}{x^2} \, dx \quad \text{since } y = \frac{4}{x}$$

$$= 16\pi \int_2^5 \frac{1}{x^2} \, dx$$

$$= 16\pi \left[-\frac{1}{x} \right]_2^5$$

$$= 16\pi[-\tfrac{1}{5} - (-\tfrac{1}{2})]$$

$$= 16\pi \times \tfrac{3}{10}$$

$$= \frac{24\pi}{5}$$

$\therefore$ the required result is

$\dfrac{24\pi}{5}$ units of volume.

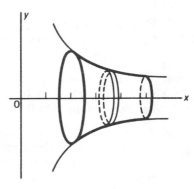

Fig. 199

351

Exercise 53e

In calculating these answers, do not substitute for π.

1. Find the volume obtained by rotating about the x-axis that part of the curve $y^2 = 4x$ which lies between the limits $x = 1$ and $x = 4$.

2. Find the volume generated by rotating about the x-axis that part of the curve $y^2 = 2x - 1$ which lies between $x = 2$ and $x = 5$.

3. The curve $y = \frac{1}{2}x^2$ is revolved about the x-axis. Find the volume generated by that part of the curve which lies between the origin and $x = 2$.

4. Find, *by integration*, the volume of the cone formed by rotating about the x-axis the line $y = 3x$ for values of x from 0 to 2.

5. Find the volume generated by rotating about the x-axis that part of the curve $y = \dfrac{3}{x}$ which lies between $x = 1$ and $x = 7$.

6. The equation $x^2 + y^2 = 4$ represents a circle of radius 2 units, with its centre at the origin. By integrating between the limits -2 and $+2$, find the volume of a sphere of radius 2 units.

7. Find, by integration, the volume of the frustum of a cone formed by rotating about the x-axis the line $y = \frac{1}{2}x$ for values of x from 2 to 6.

8. The curve $y = x^2 + 2x$ is rotated about the x-axis. Find the volume generated by the part of the curve which lies between its intersections with the x-axis.

9. The equation $x^2 + y^2 = 25$ represents a circle of radius 5 units, with its centre at the origin. Find the volume of the slice of a sphere of radius 5 units, cut off by parallel planes on the same side of the centre and at distances of 2 units and 4 units from it.

10. Find the volume obtained by rotating about the x-axis that part of the curve $y = x^2 + 1$ which lies between the limits $x = 2$ and $x = 3$.

Revision examples

I

1. Three landmarks A, B and C on a coastline are such that B is 5 km due south of A and C is 5 km due south of B. The captain of a ship X observes that A is on a bearing of 031° and C is on a bearing of 169°.

    Calculate (a) the distance of the ship X from A,
    (b) the distance of the ship X from B.   *(L)*

2. (i) Use tables to calculate, correct to 3 significant figures, the value of

    $$3.754 \times \sqrt{\frac{28.73}{125.3}}.$$

    (ii) A bucket is raised from a well by means of a rope which is wound round a wheel of diameter 75 cm. Given that the bucket ascends in 1 minute 12 seconds with a uniform speed of 1.3 metres per second, calculate the number of complete revolutions the wheel makes in raising the bucket. (Take π to be 3.142.) *(C)*

3. A cylindrical cauldron of radius 60 cm contains 7 equal cylindrical drums full of tar whose horizontal bases just fit that of the cauldron, with one drum in the middle and the centres of the others as vertices of a regular hexagon. What is the radius of the drum?

    The height of the cauldron is 126 cm and of each drum 108 cm. The drums are removed and the tar poured into the cauldron. Find

    (i) the fraction of the capacity of the cauldron occupied by tar,

    (ii) the depth of the surface of the tar below the rim of the cauldron.   *(S)*

4. A sector of a circle contains an angle of 216° at the centre O. The radius of the circle is r cm. The sector is cut from thin card and folded to form the curved surface of a cone, vertex O. Show that the radius of the circle of card needed to form the base of the cone is 0·6r and find, in terms of r, the height of the cone. If S cm^2 is the total area of cardboard used to form the cone and V cm^3 is the volume of the cone, prove that $10V = Sr$.

(O)

5. (a) In Fig. 200 DEFG is a rectangle and A, B are fixed points. Copy the figure and, by using two reflections, find the shortest route from A to B which passes through a point on DE and a point on EF.

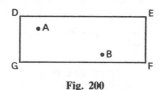

Fig. 200

(b) If $y = \dfrac{a}{3x^2 + b}$, express x in terms of y, a and b.

(c) Use the Remainder Theorem to find one factor of $6x^3 - 19x^2 + 11x + 6$ and hence find the other factors. *(W)*

6. A body moves in a straight line OA, and at time t seconds after it leaves O its displacement from O is x m and its velocity is v m s^{-1}, where $\dfrac{dv}{dt} = 4 - 2t$. Initially the body leaves O with a velocity of 5 m s^{-1}.

(i) Find formulae for v and x in terms of t, and hence prove that the distance moved by the body in reaching its maximum velocity is $15\frac{1}{3}$ m.

(ii) Find the time at which the body is momentarily at rest, and its displacement from O at that time.

(iii) Find the velocity and acceleration of the body when $t = 6$. State the direction of motion of the body at that time, and also

355

state whether its velocity is increasing or decreasing, giving
your reasons clearly. (*MME*)

7. On the staff of a college 48 men have a licence to drive a car,
a motor cycle or a public-service vehicle. Of these, 35 can drive
a car, 8 can drive a public-service vehicle and 5 can drive both
a car and a motor cycle. All those who can drive a public-service
vehicle can also drive a car. The number who can drive a car
only is twice the number who can drive a motor cycle only.

   (i) Denoting by x the number of men who can drive all three
types of vehicle, draw a Venn diagram to show the above facts.
Write down an equation in x and hence find the value of x.

   (ii) If one of the men is chosen at random, what is the
probability that he can drive a motor cycle?

   (iii) If one of the men who can drive a motor cycle is chosen
at random, what is the probability that he can also drive a
public-service vehicle? (*N*)

8. The following table gives the result of an examination in a
cumulative-frequency form. Against the given score is shown
the number of pupils with a score less than or equal to the
given score.

Score ⩽	Number of pupils
0	0
10	10
20	34
30	80
40	138
50	214
60	282
70	344
80	392
90	414
100	420

Draw a cumulative-frequency curve for this distribution and determine the median and semi-interquartile range for the distribution. How many pupils achieved a mark greater than 75?   (*S*)

9. Taking 2 cm as the unit for both x and y, draw the graph of $y = (x - 1)(5 - x)$ for values of x from 1 to 5. Using the same axes and scales draw the graph of $y = \dfrac{4}{x}$ for values of x from 1 to 5. Explain clearly how your graphs may be used to find approximate values of roots of each of the equations

   (i) $(x - 1)(5 - x) = 2$,
   (ii) $x^3 - 6x^2 + 5x + 4 = 0$,

   and hence find approximately two roots of each equation.
   (*MME*)

10. A toy consists of a circular track with two additional tracks which are perpendicular diameters of the circle. A, B, C, D, X are junctions, and a mechanical car can travel at uniform speed along the track.

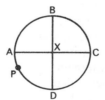

Fig. 201

   If one of the junctions A, B, C, D is approached along the circumference of the circle, then the probability that the car will continue along the circumference when it reaches the junction is $\frac{4}{5}$. If however one of these junctions is approached from X, then it is equally likely that the car will turn left or right on reaching the junction. If the junction X is approached, then the probability that the car will continue straight across the junction is $\frac{1}{2}$, while that of turning left or right is $\frac{1}{4}$ each.

A car is set in motion at P moving towards A. What is the probability that the car will return to P

(a) having travelled only round the circumference?

(b) in the shortest possible time?

(c) having passed through each junction once and once only?

(*MEI*)

II

1. (i) A rectangular block of metal measuring 20 cm by 4 cm by 3 cm is melted down and made into 8 000 identical spherical ball-bearings. Calculate the volume of one ball-bearing, giving your answer in cubic millimetres.

   It is decided to manufacture a larger size of ball-bearing with diameter twice as big as before. Find how many of these larger ball-bearings could be made from an identical block of metal.

   (ii) Calculate the amount of money obtained if £1 500 is invested for 12 years, compound interest at $6\frac{1}{2}\%$ being added annually. (*MEI*)

2. The flow diagram describes a computer programme to read four numbers A, B, C and X, and to print the result of an arithmetical calculation with them.

   (i) Find the number which will be printed when A = 3, B = -4, C = -1 and X = 2.

   (ii) Find the general formula which the programme is designed to evaluate for any values of A, B, C and X.

   (iii) Modify the programme so that the computer will print out a series of results for X = 1, 2, 3, 4, ..., 10 (A, B and C remaining constant).

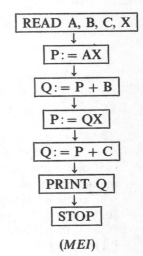

READ A, B, C, X

↓

P: = AX

↓

Q: = P + B

↓

P: = QX

↓

Q: = P + C

↓

PRINT Q

↓

STOP

(*MEI*)

3. (a) Solve the equation $2x^2 - 5x - 2 = 0$, giving the answers correct to two decimal places.

(b) Calculate the maximum and minimum points on the curve $y = x^3 - 3x^2 + 1$, carefully distinguishing between them.

(c) Calculate the area A, which is shown shaded in Fig. 202, bounded by the curve $y = 6x^2 + 5$, the x-axis and the lines $x = 1$ and $x = 2$.

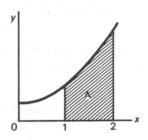

Fig. 202

4. (i) Two points A and B in the same latitude are in longitudes 30° E and 24° W respectively, and the distance AB, measured along the parallel of latitude, is 2 400 km. Taking the earth to be a sphere of radius 6 370 km, calculate the latitude of A and B.

(ii) A ship travels due south from a point P (12° 10′ N, 60° 20′ E) to a point Q at an average speed of 22 knots for 95 hours. Calculate the latitude and longitude of Q.   *(L)*

5. The distance in which a car can be stopped from different speeds when the road surface is dry is given in the following table.

Speed in km h^{-1}	0	20	40	60	80	100	120
Stopping distance in m	0	8	20	36	58	86	119

Taking scales of 2 cm to represent 20 m on one axis and 2 cm to represent 20 km h^{-1} on the other, draw a graph to represent this data, joining the points by a smooth curve. Use your graph to estimate

    (i) the stopping distance from a speed of 50 km h^{-1},

    (ii) the speed of the car if it is stopped in 70 m.

If the road surface is wet the stopping distance for any speed is doubled. Use your graph to estimate the speed on a wet day which has the same stopping distance as a speed of 100 km h^{-1} on a dry day.   (C)

6. The curve whose equation is $y = 2x^2 + bx + c$ passes through the points P, Q, R whose co-ordinates are (0, 5), (1, 4), (2, 7) respectively.

    (i) Find the values of b and c.

    (ii) Find the area of the region enclosed by the arc PR of the curve, the x-axis from $x = 0$ to $x = 2$, and the ordinates $x = 0$ and $x = 2$.

    (iii) Find the area of the region enclosed by the line segments PQ and QR, the x-axis from $x = 0$ to $x = 2$, and the ordinates $x = 0$ and $x = 2$.   (N)

7. Each of a party of climbers is to carry emergency rations. These are obtainable in units of two types A and B. The contents and cost of each type are shown in the following table, along with a man's daily requirements of each constituent.

	Proteins	Minerals	Vitamins	Cost
Unit A	5 g	200 mg	2 mg	6p
Unit B	7·5 g	50 mg	1·5 mg	4p
Daily requirement	75 g	1 g	15 mg	

A pack is to be made up, suitable for one man for one day. If it contains x units of type A and y of type B, state the inequalities (other than $x \geqslant 0$, $y \geqslant 0$) to be satisfied by x and y. Indicate by the use of shading a graphical region in which possible solutions (x, y) must be, and find the cheapest solution and its cost.　　　　　　　　　　　　　　　　　　　　(*O*)

8. The three components of the vector (x, y, z) represent displacements in easterly, northerly and vertically upward directions, all measured in metres, so that $(10, 0, 0)$ represents a displacement of 10 m to the east.

Vectors *a*, *b*, *c*, *d*, *e* are defined as follows:

$$a = (2, 4, 2),\ b = (1, 2, 0),\ c = (1, 2, 2),\ d = (1, 3, 2),\ e = (3, 6, 1).$$

Write in this form the vectors $a + b$, $a - b$, $3a$.
Show that $a + 4b = 2e$, and that $a - d$ is a horizontal displacement.
Calculate the length of the vector *c*.

Find an integer n which will ensure that $a + nb$ is a displacement which is vertical.　　　　　　　　　　　　　　　　　(*S*)

9. The square OABC has vertices O $(0, 0)$, A $(1, 0)$, B $(1, 1)$, C $(0, 1)$.

The transformation T_1 with matrix $P = \begin{pmatrix} 1 & -1 \\ 1 & 1 \end{pmatrix}$ maps the

square OABC on to $OA_1B_1C_1$. Find the co-ordinates of A_1, B_1 and C_1, and show the square OABC and its image in a diagram. State the lengths of OA_1 and OC_1, and the sizes of the angles AOA_1 and A_1OC_1, and hence describe the transformation T_1 in geometrical terms.

A second transformation T_2 is a reflection in the line $y = x$. Write down the matrix Q of this transformation.

A third transformation T_3, with matrix R, is obtained by applying first T_1, then T_2. Find the matrix R. Show in a clearly lettered diagram the square OABC and its image $OA_3B_3C_3$ under the transformation T_3, stating the co-ordinates of A_3, B_3, C_3.

Write down the inverse of the matrix R. Find the image of the point B_3 under the inverse of the transformation T_3.　(*MME*)

10. An empty storage tank is filled with water so that t hours later it contains V gallons where

$$V = 1\,080t - 10t^3.$$

The tank is completely full when $t = 6$. What is its capacity?

   Plot a graph of V against t for values of t from 0 to 6. As scales use 2 cm to represent one hour on the t-axis and 500 gallons on the V-axis. From your graph determine the value of t at which the tank is half full.

   An attendant who knows the capacity of the tank assumes that it fills at a steady rate, m gallons per hour. What value does he give m?

   Superimpose on your graph the straight lines representing

$$V = mt \quad \text{and} \quad V = mt + 500$$

using the value you have obtained for m. Hence find between what values of t the attendant makes an error of more than 500 gallons in estimating the volume of the water. $\qquad (O)$

III

1. (a) Use the Remainder Theorem to find one factor of $2x^3 - 7x^2 + 9x - 6$ and hence find the other factor.

   (b) O is the origin and A, B and C have co-ordinates $(-3, 1)$, $(1, -2)$ and $(2, 1)$ respectively. Calculate

   (i) the vector $\boldsymbol{BC}$ in the form $\begin{pmatrix} x \\ y \end{pmatrix}$ where x, y are numbers,

   (ii) the co-ordinates of D if ABCD is a parallelogram,

   (iii) the co-ordinates of E if $\boldsymbol{BC} = \boldsymbol{CE}$,

   (iv) the size of angle BAC,

   (v) the co-ordinates of F if $\boldsymbol{OF} = 3\boldsymbol{AC}$. $\qquad (W)$

2. VABCD is a right pyramid with a square base ABCD of side 5 cm. Each of the four triangular faces is inclined at 75° to the base. Calculate

   (a) the perpendicular height of the pyramid,

(b) the length of the slant edge VA,

(c) the angle between the edge VA and the base plane ABCD,

(d) the area of the face VAB.

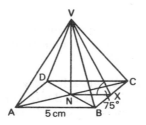

Fig. 203

3. A model of a car is made to a scale of $1:10$.

(i) If the length of the car is 4.5 m, find the length of the model in cm.

(ii) If the area of the windows in the car is 5 m^2, find the area of the windows in the model in cm^2.

(iii) If the car's fuel tank holds 80 litres, how much could the model's tank hold? Express your answer as a decimal of a litre.

(*N*)

4. P is the point where $x = 2$ on the curve $y = x^3 - 3x + 1$. Calculate the y-co-ordinate at P and the gradient of the tangent at P, and hence find the equation of the tangent at P.

If Q is the point $(-1, -1)$ calculate the distance PQ.

On the curve $y = x^3 - 3x + 1$ calculate the maximum and minimum points, carefully distinguishing between them.

Find where the curve cuts the y-axis, and sketch the curve.

(*W*)

5. A satellite is describing a circular orbit of radius r km about the earth as centre. The speed of the satellite is v km s^{-1}. If it takes T seconds to complete one circuit of the earth, write down a formula for T in terms of r, v and π.

It is known that v and r are connected by the approximate formula

$$v = \frac{630}{\sqrt{r}};$$

deduce that $T = \frac{1}{100}\sqrt{r^3}$ approximately, and use this formula to calculate the radius of a circular orbit which a satellite will complete in 24 hours. (*MEI*)

6. In the diagram A represents a house which lies due west of a church C. Roads run from A to B and from B to C, and a path leads from B to the point D on AC. Given that AB = 60 m, BD = 70 m, AD = 100 m and that $\hat{BCA} = 25°$, calculate
   (i) the bearing of B from A,
   (ii) the distance DC,
   (iii) the distance that B lies to the west of C. (*C*)

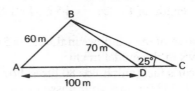

Fig. 204

7. The owner of a small business employs a craftsman who works for not more than 42 hours a week. The owner himself can spend not more than 34 hours a week in the workshop. Two types of article, an ordinary and a superior model, are manufactured; the ordinary model requires one hour's work by the craftsman and two by the owner, whereas the superior model requires three hours' work by the craftsman and one by the owner. At least six ordinary and at least six superior models must be made each week.

   If in a week x ordinary and y superior models are made, express the above information in the form of inequalities in terms of x and y.

If the profit on an ordinary model is £3 and on a superior model £5, find how many of each model should be made each week in order to obtain the greatest profit, and find the profit in this case. (*MME*)

8. In a recent disaster it was necessary to fly 160 tons of food and 160 personnel to the disaster area. There were only two types of aircraft, X and Y, available. Each aircraft X could carry 8 tons of food and 12 personnel; each aircraft Y could carry 12 tons of food and 10 personnel. Given that there were only 12 aircraft of each type available, find by a graphical method, or otherwise, the least number of aircraft necessary to transport the food and personnel to the disaster area. (*N*)

9. Matrices P, Q, R and S are defined by

$$P = \begin{pmatrix} 4 & 5 \\ 3 & 4 \end{pmatrix}, Q = \begin{pmatrix} 2 & 0 \\ -1 & 1 \end{pmatrix}, R = PQ, S = QP.$$

Evaluate R and S. Write down the inverses (P^{-1} and Q^{-1}) of P and Q, and determine which of the statements

$$P^{-1}Q^{-1} = R^{-1} \quad \text{and} \quad P^{-1}Q^{-1} = S^{-1}$$

is correct.
Solve $P\begin{pmatrix} x \\ y \end{pmatrix} = \begin{pmatrix} -1 \\ 1 \end{pmatrix}.$

Show that any point on the line $y = -x$ is transformed by the matrix operator P into a point on the line $y = x$. (*O*)

10. The velocity v in m s^{-1} of a particle during the first four seconds of its motion is given by the equation $v = \sqrt{(16 - t^2)}$, where t is the time in seconds.

Using a graphical method with the time divided into four equal intervals, or any other method, estimate the distance travelled by the particle, and deduce its average velocity during these four seconds. (Give your answers to two significant figures.) (*MEI*)

IV

1. Solve the simultaneous equations $x^2 + xy + y^2 = 7$
$$x + 2y = 1. \qquad (L)$$

2. The depth of the water in a rectangular swimming bath increases uniformly from 1 metre at the shallow end to 3·5 metres at the deep end. The bath is 25 metres long and 12 metres wide. Calculate the volume of the water in the bath, giving your answer in cubic metres.

    The bath is emptied by means of a cylindrical pipe of internal radius 9 cm. The water flows down the pipe at a speed of 3 metres per second. Calculate the number of litres emptied from the bath in 1 minute, giving your answer to the nearest 10 litres. (Take π to be 3·142.) $\qquad (C)$

3. (i) The curve whose equation is $y = ax^3 - bx$, where a and b are numerical constants, passes through the point $(1, 2)$ and its gradient at that point is 8. Find the values of a and b.

    (ii) Show that a line whose equation is $y = x + 2$ meets the curve $y = 4 - x^2$ at the points whose co-ordinates are $(-2, 0)$ and $(1, 3)$. Find by integration the finite area between the line and the arc of the curve intercepted by the line. $\qquad (O)$

4. Three students A, B and C at a certain examination obtained the following marks in the subjects stated:

	A	B	C
English	62	64	52
French	70	60	60
Mathematics	28	43	60
Science	30	37	48
Geography	66	38	52

    Calculate the mean mark for each student and place them in order.

    An employer with particular interest in the scientific capabilities of the students asks that the marks be combined with weights English 1, French 1, Mathematics 3, Science 3,

Geography 2. Calculate the weighted mean in this case, and place the students in order. (*S*)

5. Prove that in a right-angled triangle the square described on the hypotenuse is equal to the sum of the squares on the other two sides.

   PQR is a triangle right-angled at P. X is the mid-point of RP and Y is the mid-point of QP.

   Prove that $4(QX^2 + RY^2) = 5QR^2$. (*W*)

6. A sundial consists of a triangular style-plate PQR, with the angle PQR = 90° and angle PRQ = 53°. This is mounted on a horizontal dial in such a way that PQ is vertical and QR is horizontal. QR measures 20 cm and lies in a North-South direction with Q north of R. The sun shines from the South-East and its altitude is 30°. Calculate the lengths of the sides of the triangular shadow cast at this time. (*S*)

7. Given that x belongs to the set of real numbers, state which of the following statements are true and which are false. In each of the cases in which the statement is false illustrate this fact by using a numerical value of x.

   (i) $(x - 4)(x + 1) > 0 \Rightarrow x > 4$.
   (ii) $x > 4 \Rightarrow (x - 4)(x + 1) > 0$.
   (iii) $x^2 > x \Rightarrow x > 0$.
   (iv) $x^2 - 2x + 1 \leqslant 0$.
   (v) $x^2 + 2x + 1 \geqslant 0$.
   (vi) $0 \leqslant \cos x^c \leqslant 1$.
   (vii) $x > 4 \Rightarrow \dfrac{1}{x} < \dfrac{1}{4}$. (*N*)

8. An amateur dramatic society is putting on a small entertainment. The audience can be seated partly in easy chairs and partly in upright chairs for which tickets will be cheaper. The number of easy chairs is x and the number of upright chairs is y, and previous experience allows us to assume that $y \leqslant 2x$.

   The hall has a floor area of 90 m²; easy chairs require 1 m² and upright chairs 0·6 m² of space. The organisers must allow for an audience of at least 100, but there are only 50 easy chairs available. Write down these relations in the form of inequalities involving x and y.

Illustrate all four relations on a graph. Assuming that easy chairs must be put in rows of ten and upright chairs in rows of twelve, mark clearly on your diagram the points which represent possible numbers of each chair which will satisfy all the conditions.

If tickets for an easy chair cost 40p and those for upright chairs cost 35p, which layout will be most profitable to the society, assuming that all seats are sold? (*MEI*)

9. A pack of 20 playing cards consist of the 2, 3, 4, 5 and 6 of each of the four suits. A card is drawn at random from the pack. This card is then replaced, and for a second time a card is drawn at random from the pack.

Find the probability of each of the following events:

(i) The first card is a heart.

(ii) The first card is a 2.

(iii) The first card is a 2 or a heart or both.

(iv) The first card is a heart and the second is even-numbered.

(v) Either the first card is a heart or the second is even-numbered, but not both.

(vi) The sum of the numbers on the first card and the second card is a multiple of 3. (*MME*)

10. The function f is defined by

$f(x) \equiv 2x^3 - 3x^2 - 12x + 1$.

(i) By evaluating $f(x)$ for $x = -3, -2, -1, \ldots, 3, 4$, show that the equation $f(x) = 0$ has one solution between 3 and 4.

Give the locations of the other solutions to the same degree of accuracy.

(ii) Draw a *sketch* of the curve.

(iii) Assuming that the curve may be approximately represented by a straight line between $x = 3$ and $x = 4$, calculate to two significant figures the value of the solution between $x = 3$ and $x = 4$. From your answer to (ii) state whether you expect this answer to be too big or too small. (*MEI*)

V

1. A cylindrical measuring jar containing water has an internal radius of 3 cm. When a metal sphere is placed in the water it is completely submerged, but only just, and the level of the water rises 0·5 cm. Calculate the radius of the sphere and the volume of water. *(S)*

2. In the diagram a circular metal plate, centre N, is supported horizontally by three equal chains OA, OB, OC. The angles BOC, COA, AOB are each equal to 90°. The points A, B, C on the circumference of the circle are such that $\widehat{ANB} = 120°$ and the chords AB, BC and CA are each 25 cm long. Calculate
   - (i) the radius of the circle,
   - (ii) OA,
   - (iii) the inclination of OA to the horizontal. *(C)*

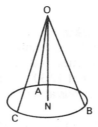

Fig. 205

3. The notation $a * b$ will be used to mean the average of two numbers a and b, that is

$$a * b = \frac{a + b}{2}.$$

   - (i) Solve the following equations:
     - (a) $x * 5 = 7$
     - (b) $(2 * y) * 7 = 5$
     - (c) $z * (3 * 8) = -2$

(ii) Is it possible to find an identity element for this operation? If so, state its value, or if not, explain why an identity does not exist.

(iii) If $(a * b) * c = a * (b * c)$, what can you deduce about a, b and c? (*MEI*)

4. In the triangle OAB, L is the mid-point of OA, and M is a point on OB such that $\dfrac{OM}{MB} = 2$. P is the mid-point of LM, and the line AP is produced to meet OB at Q.

Given that $\overrightarrow{OA} = \mathbf{a}$ and $\overrightarrow{OB} = \mathbf{b}$, find in terms of $\mathbf{a}$ and $\mathbf{b}$, (i) $\overrightarrow{OP}$, (ii) $\overrightarrow{AP}$. If $\overrightarrow{AQ} = h\overrightarrow{AP}$ and $\overrightarrow{OQ} = k\overrightarrow{OB}$, find h, k, $\dfrac{AP}{PQ}$ and $\dfrac{OQ}{QB}$. (*MME*)

5. A and B are towns 200 km apart. A car leaves A at noon at 50 km h^{-1} and travels for one hour at this speed; then stops for one hour; then continues to B at 60 km h^{-1}.

A second car leaves B at 12.30 p.m. and travels for one hour at 40 km h^{-1}. It then travels at a constant speed and arrives at A at 4.30 p.m.

Using scales of 2 cm to 20 km and 4 cm to 1 hour draw travel graphs to illustrate the two journeys. Use them to estimate

(i) the distance from A and the time at which the cars pass each other,

(ii) the time of arrival of the first car at B.

Estimate also the speed to which the second car should change at 1.30 p.m. in order that the cars should pass each other at 2.35 p.m., the speed of the first car being unchanged. (*W*)

6. The table shows the frequency distribution of the life times, in hours to the nearest hour, of 500 electric light bulbs.

Life time (hours)	Frequency
200–	16
400–	48
600–	70
800–	105
1 000–	92
1 200–	76
1 400–	57
1 600–	24
1 800–2 000	12
Total	500

Draw a graph of the cumulative frequency distribution. From your graph estimate
(i) the median life time,
(ii) the semi-interquartile range of this distribution,
(iii) the percentage of bulbs with life times between 750 and 1 250 hours. (*N*)

7. The container of a petrol tanker is a cylinder with its axis horizontal. Its internal length is 7 m and its internal diameter is 3 m.

The diagram shows the vertical section of the cylinder at a time when the maximum depth of petrol it contains is 0·75 m, AB indicating the level of the petrol. Calculate

(a) the angle AOB, where O is the centre of the circular section,

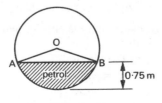

Fig. 206

    (b) the area of the sector AOB,

    (c) the area shown shaded in the diagram,

    (d) the weight of the petrol in the tanker at this time, given that one cubic metre of petrol weighs 700 kg.   *(L)*

8. Draw on graph paper the parallelogram OPQR where O, P, Q and R are respectively the points $(0, 0)$, $(2, 0)$, $(3, 1)$ and $(1, 1)$. Find and draw the image of OPQR under the transformation whose matrix is M, where

$$M = \begin{pmatrix} 0{\cdot}8 & -0{\cdot}6 \\ 0{\cdot}6 & 0{\cdot}8 \end{pmatrix},$$

and state what transformation this is.

    Form the product MN, where

$$N = \begin{pmatrix} 0{\cdot}6 & -0{\cdot}8 \\ 0{\cdot}8 & 0{\cdot}6 \end{pmatrix},$$

and state what transformation corresponds to MN.

    Hence, or otherwise, find what transformation corresponds to N.   *(L)*

9. In an audience research survey 720 people, all of whom had seen television on the previous day, were asked which of the three channels ITV, BBC 1 and BBC 2 they had watched. ITV alone had been watched by 190 people, BBC 1 alone by 220 and BBC 2 alone by 150. Eighty viewers had watched both BBC channels and of this number 20 had also watched ITV. Equal numbers had watched the two combinations ITV with BBC 1 and ITV with BBC 2. Represent this information in a Venn diagram and calculate

    (a) how many people in all had watched BBC 2,

    (b) how many people had not watched ITV.   *(S)*

10. The following transformations are defined:

M_x is a reflection in the x-axis,

M_y is a reflection in the y-axis,

M_1 is a reflection in $y = x$,

M_2 is a reflection in $y = -x$,

R is an anticlockwise quarter turn about the origin.

By considering the effects on the rectangle formed by $(0, 0)$, $(2, 0)$, $(2, -1)$ and $(0, -1)$ show that

$$M_1 M_x = M_y M_1 = R.$$

(Show each of these three transformations in separate diagrams.)

If S is an anticlockwise quarter turn about $(2, 0)$ show, by using the same rectangle, that SR is equivalent to a single rotation and state the centre and amount of turn. *(O)*

VI

1. (a) Solve the simultaneous equations $\quad\quad 3x - y = 7$
$$2x^2 - 2xy + y^2 - 13 = 0.$$

(b) Use the Remainder Theorem to find one factor of $2x^3 - 7x^2 + 3x + 6$, and hence find the other factor.

(c) Use the Remainder Theorem to find the value of k if the expression $6x^3 - 19x^2 + kx + 6$ leaves a remainder of 4 when divided by $x - 1$. *(W)*

2. (a) Numbers p, x and y are related by the formula $p^3 = \dfrac{x + y}{x - y}$.

    (i) Use tables to evaluate p, correct to three significant figures, when $x = 13\cdot73$ and $y = 6\cdot47$.

    (ii) Calculate, giving your answer to the nearest whole number, the value of $\dfrac{x}{y}$ when $p = 1\cdot1$.

    (iii) Express y in terms of x and p.

(b) Find the remainders when $x^3 - x^2 - 14x + 24$ is divided by $x - 1$, or by $x - 2$, or by $x - 3$, or by $x + 1$.

Hence write down the three factors of $x^3 - x^2 - 14x + 24$. *(O)*

3. $\overline{AB}$ and $\overline{CD}$ are two chords of a circle intersecting internally at X. AX = 21 cm, XB = 9 cm. The distance of the chord $\overline{AB}$ from the centre O is 8 cm; angle OXD = 30°. (D is on the same side of $\overline{AB}$ as O.) Calculate the length of (i) OX (ii) the radius of the circle (iii) the chord CD. *(S)*

4. Use a slide-rule to solve the following simultaneous equations, giving your answers correct to 2 significant figures.

$3.5x + 4.1y + 5.2z = 5.3$
$2.7x + 0.7y - 2.3z = -2.1$
$1.4x - 2.4y + 0.8z = 8.3.$ (*MME*)

5. Without using set-square or protractor construct in the same diagram

   (i) the triangle XYZ in which XY = 7·5 cm, XZ = 6 cm and $Z\hat{X}Y = 60°$,

   (ii) the point P which is on the opposite side of YZ to X such that $Y\hat{P}Z = 90°$ and ZP = 5·5 cm,

   (iii) the point W on XY produced such that the area of the triangle XWZ is equal to the area of the quadrilateral XYPZ. Measure the length of XW.   (*C*)

6. (a) Calculate the gradient of the tangent at P $(2, -4)$ on the curve $y = 3x^2 - 8x$, and hence find the equation of the tangent at P.

   (b) On the curve $y = x^3 - 6x^2 + 13$ calculate the maximum and minimum points, carefully distinguishing between them.

   (c) If $7x - 3y = 2x + y$ find the ratio of x to y.   (*W*)

7. The diagram represents a heavy girder which is to be moved lengthwise across horizontal ground on three cylindrical rollers, each of radius 20 cm. The point O is the centre of a circular cross-section of one of the rollers, and U is its initial point of contact with the girder. V is the point *of the girder* initially in contact with the point U.

The rollers now carry the girder forward without slipping in the direction indicated until the point U is on the ground.

   (a) Through what angle have the rollers rotated?

   (b) Calculate the distance through which the point O has moved.

   (c) Through what total distance has the point V moved?

   (d) If the centre of each roller is moving steadily at a speed of 0·4 m s^{-1}, at what speed is the girder moving?   (*MEI*)

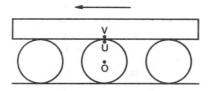

· **Fig. 207**

8. P and Q are points on the surface of the earth situated on the same parallel of latitude 50° N. The longitudes of P and Q are 15° W and 20° E respectively. X and Y are the two points on the equator such that X is due south of P and Y is due south of Q. Two alternative routes from X to Q are
   (i) from X due north to P, and then due east to Q,
   (ii) from X due east to Y, and then due north to Q.
Calculate which of these two routes is the shorter and by how many nautical miles.

If two travellers set out at the same time from X and travel by routes (i) and (ii) respectively, at the same speed, calculate the latitude and longitude of the point reached by the traveller taking the longer route at the instant when the other traveller reaches Q.

(Candidates who wish to do so may take the earth to be a sphere of radius 3 438 nautical miles.)   (*L*)

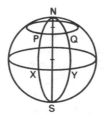

Fig. 208

9. (i) Evaluate the matrix product $\begin{pmatrix} 3 & 2 \\ 6 & 4 \end{pmatrix}\begin{pmatrix} -2 & -4 \\ 3 & 6 \end{pmatrix}$.

(ii) Evaluate $\begin{pmatrix} k & 0 \\ 0 & k \end{pmatrix}\begin{pmatrix} x \\ y \end{pmatrix}$.

S is the set of points (x, y) in the region defined by the three inequalities $0 \leqslant x$, $0 \leqslant y$, $x + y \leqslant 1$.

The matrix $\begin{pmatrix} k & 0 \\ 0 & k \end{pmatrix}$, where $k > 0$, maps S on to T which is the set of points in a region R.

Write down sufficient inequalities to define R.   (C)

10. In an experiment on a certain type of plant the lengths of 150 leaves were recorded to the nearest mm, the results being as follows:

Length (mm)	20–24	25–29	30–34	35–39	40–44	45–49
Frequency	10	18	40	52	24	6

Rewrite this information as a cumulative frequency table.
Draw a cumulative frequency diagram to represent information, and use the diagram to estimate
   (i) the median length,
   (ii) the semi-interquartile range of the lengths,
   (iii) the percentage of leaves whose lengths were over 40 mm.
                                                         (N)

VII

1. The ends of the roof of a barn are segments of circles of radius 5 m. In Fig. 209, O is the centre of one of these circles and $A\hat{O}B = 90°$; the shaded portion represents one end of the roof. The length of the roof is 12 m.
   Find
   (i) the area of one end of the roof of the barn,
   (ii) the area of the curved surface of the roof,
   (iii) the total cost, to the nearest £, of covering the two ends and the curved surface with corrugated iron costing £1·90 per square metre. (Take π to be 3·142.)   (C)

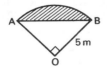

Fig. 209

2. (*Give answers in standard form.*)

(a) The universe has $1{\cdot}5 \times 10^{10}$ galaxies, each with 10^{11} suns. What is the number of suns in the universe?

(b) Find to 2 significant figures the number of seconds in a year.

(c) The speed of light is $3{\cdot}00 \times 10^7 \text{ km s}^{-1}$. Find to one significant figure how many years it takes to travel from the furthest point of the known universe $9{\cdot}3 \times 10^{21}$ km away. (*S*)

3. In the figure ST is the common tangent at P to the two circles. PVW and PQR are straight lines. QS bisects $P\hat{S}R$ and PV = PS.
   Prove that
   (i) QV and RW are parallel,
   (ii) SR = VW. (*C*)

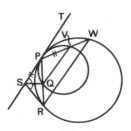

Fig. 210

4. A coal merchant has two depots P and Q, at which his stocks are respectively 50 tonnes and 30 tonnes. Customer A orders 40 tonnes and customer B orders 25 tonnes. The merchant sends x tonnes to A and y tonnes to B from depot P, and completes the order from depot Q.

Obtain inequalities which restrict the possible values of x and y. Draw a Cartesian graph of these inequalities and indicate clearly the region which represents the set of possible ordered pairs (x, y).

If the distances in km from each depot to each customer are shown in the table, prove that the number of tonne-km required is $3x + 2y + 235$, and use your graph to find the values of x and y for which this number is least.

	A	B
P	7	5
Q	4	3

(*MME*)

5. A box in the shape of a cuboid has a square base of side l cm and a height of h cm. Its volume is V cm^3. Complete the following table for a box for which $h + l = 9$.

l	0	1	2	3	4	5	6	7	8	9
h	9	8	7			4			1	
V		8	28			100			64	

Draw a graph to show how V varies as h varies from 0 to 9, taking 2 cm as one unit for h and 2 cm as ten units for V. Use your graph to estimate

(i) the possible heights of a box whose volume is 90 cm^3,

(ii) the volume of a box whose height is 6·4 cm,

(iii) the height of the box of greatest volume. (*W*)

6. A particle starts from rest at a point A and moves along a straight line, coming to rest again at another point B. During the motion its velocity, v metres per second, after time t seconds, is given by $v = 9t^2 - 2t^3$. Calculate

   (i) the time taken for the particle to reach B,

   (ii) the distance travelled during the first two seconds.

   (iii) the time taken for the particle to attain its maximum velocity,

   (iv) the maximum velocity attained,

   (v) the maximum acceleration during the motion.   *(L)*

7. A solid cylinder of metal 2 cm in radius and 2 cm long, turning about its own axis which is along the x-axis of co-ordinates, is shaped by a lathe to conform to the outline $y = 2x(2 - x)$ where units are centimetres. Calculate the volume of metal remaining when the job has been done, in cm^3 as a multiple of π.

   Calculate also the percentage of metal wasted.   *(MEI)*

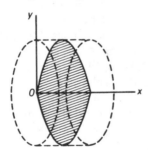

Fig. 211

8. In a breeding experiment there are 120 rabbits each of which belongs to at least one of the sets lop-eared (L), giant (G) and blue (B). There are 50 lop-eared, 69 giant and 71 blue. Of those which are lop-eared 19 are also giant and 31 are also blue. Of those which are blue 35 are giant.

   Draw a Venn diagram and, taking x as the number of rabbits which belong to all three sets, insert the appropriate numbers involving x in each of the other six compartments. Hence determine x.

Shade in a *second* Venn diagram the region $(L \cup G) \cap B$ and determine the number of rabbits in this set. *(O)*

9. The speed of an electric train is noted at 2-s intervals:

t (s)	0	2	4	6	8	10	12
$V(\text{m s}^{-1})$	0	4·6	8·4	11·4	13·6	15	15·6

Plot the speed-time graph. From the graph find (i) the acceleration when $t = 4$ and (ii) the distance travelled in 10 s. *(S)*

10. In a simplified form of Bingo used at a children's party there are thirty similar balls numbered 1 to 30 in a box. These are drawn out at random one by one and are not replaced. Each child has a card with five numbers between 1 and 30 on it, and whenever a ball with one of those numbers on it is drawn out the child crosses out that number. The first child to cross out all five numbers on his card wins. On this occasion there are only two children playing, A and B; A's card has 1, 8, 18, 19, 27 on it and B's has 1, 8, 10, 13, 29.

(i) Write down the probabilities that on the first draw
  (a) A will cross off a number,
  (b) neither A nor B will cross off a number.

(ii) Find the probability that A will cross off a number on both the first and second draws.

(iii) Find the probability that on the first draw A will cross off a number but B won't. Show also that the probability that this happens and that then, on the second draw, B will cross off a number but A won't is $\frac{3}{290}$. *(MEI)*

VIII

1. A closed cylindrical container has base radius r cm, height h cm, and total surface area (including the two ends) A cm^2.

Write down a formula for A in terms of π, r and h. If the volume of the cylinder is 16π cm^2, use this fact to express h in terms of r only, and hence prove that $A = 2\pi r^2 + \dfrac{32\pi}{rh}$.

If the volume of the cylinder remains constant, prove that as r varies the surface area has a minimum value, and find this value, leaving your answer in cm^2 as a multiple of π. (*MME*)

2. (a) If $(x + 2)$ is a factor of $8x^3 + 6x + a$, calculate the value of a.

(b) On graph paper draw a semi-circle of radius 10 cm. Use the mid-ordinate rule with 10 strips and the diameter as base to estimate the area of the semi-circle. From this area, find an approximate value of π, giving your answer correct to 2 decimal places. (*W*)

3. The diagonals PR, QS of a cyclic quadrilateral PQRS intersect at X. Given that PS = SR prove that
   (i) $P\hat{X}Q = S\hat{R}Q$,
   (ii) the triangles SXR and SRQ are similar,
   (iii) $SR^2 = SQ \times SX$. (*C*)

4. A gardener has room for 80 rows of vegetables and wishes to plant some beans and some carrots, both of which grow well on his land. The cost of seeds for one row is 12p for beans and 8p for carrots. He does not wish his outlay to be more than £8·40. If he decides to plant x rows of beans and y rows of carrots, write down two linear constraints on x and y from this information and show these on a linear programming diagram. If the profit from the sale of produce is £1·50 from a row of beans and 75p from a row of carrots, calculate the maximum profit which he can obtain with the best use of his available land. (*S*)

5. Two bags contain coloured marbles. The first bag contains 5 white and 3 red marbles; the second 3 white and 2 red marbles. A marble is taken at random out of the first bag and placed in the second; then a marble is taken at random out of the second

bag and placed in the first. Find the probability that both these marbles are (i) white, (ii) red. Hence find the probability that the first bag now contains 5 white and 3 red marbles.

(*N*)

6. In 1971 rates were paid to the Council by the householders of a certain district at 55p on each £1 of rateable value of their property. Out of each 55p it received the Council spent 20p on education.

Calculate the amount paid in rates by a man whose house had a rateable value of £134.

If the Council's expenditure on education amounted to £750 000, calculate

(a) the total rateable value of the district in 1971,

(b) the total sum raised by the rates in 1971.

For the year 1972 it was estimated that the cost of education would rise by $7\frac{1}{2}\%$, other costs remaining the same, and that the rateable value of the district would rise by £250 000.

Calculate to the nearest penny the new rate in the £ that had to be levied.

(*L*)

7. $A = \begin{pmatrix} 2 & 0 \\ 0 & 2 \end{pmatrix}, B = \begin{pmatrix} 3 \\ 0 \end{pmatrix}, C = \begin{pmatrix} 1 & 0 \\ 0 & -1 \end{pmatrix}, D = \begin{pmatrix} -3 \\ 0 \end{pmatrix}$ and the transformations which map (x, y) into (x', y') and (x', y') into (x'', y'') are defined by $\begin{pmatrix} x' \\ y' \end{pmatrix} = A \begin{pmatrix} x \\ y \end{pmatrix} + B, \begin{pmatrix} x'' \\ y'' \end{pmatrix} = C \begin{pmatrix} x' \\ y' \end{pmatrix} + D$. Explain what happens geometrically to the unit square with vertices P $(0, 0)$, Q $(0, 1)$, R $(1, 1)$, S $(1, 0)$, when the two transformations are carried out one after the other. By substituting from the first equation above into the second, derive a matrix expression for a single transformation equivalent to the double transformation. Simplify the expression and check that the point $(3, 1)$ is mapped correctly by the new single transformation.

(*S*)

8. The duration to the nearest second of each of 200 trunk calls was noted at a telephone exchange and the results were tabulated as follows:

Duration in seconds	0–19	20–39	40–59	60–79	80–99
No. of calls	2	3	19	36	42

Duration in seconds	100–119	120–139	140–159	160–179
No. of calls	48	27	16	7

Prepare a cumulative frequency table and draw the cumulative frequency graph. From your graph estimate (i) the median, (ii) the upper and lower quartiles, (iii) what percentage of the calls lasted more than 130 seconds. (*O*)

9. A triangle has vertices A, B and C. D is a point on BC such that $BD = \frac{1}{2}DC$. Vectors p and q are defined by $p = \overrightarrow{AB}$, $q = \overrightarrow{AC}$. Find a vector expression for the displacement $\overrightarrow{AD}$.

Both X and Y are defined by $\overrightarrow{DX} = \frac{1}{2}\overrightarrow{AD}$ and $\overrightarrow{XY} = \overrightarrow{AX}$. Find vector expressions for $\overrightarrow{BX}$ and $\overrightarrow{CY}$. Show that BX is parallel to AC, and find the ratio of the lengths CY : AB. (*S*)

10. It is expected that the values of s and t resulting from an experiment will approximately satisfy the formula $s = at^2 + b$, where a and b are constants.

What are the most appropriate quantities to plot to obtain a straight-line graph to confirm this formula? Describe how you would then determine a and b from the graph.

Use this method and the following data to obtain values for a and b, and so estimate a value of s for $t = 20$.

s	2·5	3	4·5	5
t	10	11	13	14

(*MEI*)

New General Mathematics Revision

IX

1. U is the 'universal set' $\{1, 2, 3, 4, 5, 6, 7, 8, 9, 10\}$. $A = \{1, 3, 5, 7, 9\}$, $B = \{1, 2, 3, 4, 5\}$, $C = \{3, 4, 5, 6, 7\}$. List the sets C', $A \cap B$, $B \cap C'$, $(A \cap B) \cup (B \cap C')$. *(MME)*

2. On the sides AB and AC of a triangle ABC equilateral triangles ABF and ACE are described outside the triangle. The circumcircles of the equilateral triangles intersect again at H.

   Prove that B, H and E are collinear and that C, H and F are collinear.

   Prove also that, if AH is produced to meet the circumcircle of triangle BHC at D, then BCD is an equilateral triangle. *(O)*

3. (*Tables must **not** be used in this question.*)
   (i) Simplify $32^{\frac{2}{5}}$ and $(27 x^6)^{-\frac{1}{3}}$.

   (ii) Find the value of $\dfrac{2\sqrt{a}}{b}$ when $a = 1.21 \times 10^{-4}$ and $b = 4.4 \times 10^{-6}$, giving your answer in the form $A \times 10^n$, where n is a whole number and A is a number between 1 and 10.

   (iii) Solve the equation $2^{x+1} = 32$.
   (iv) Solve the equation $\log(3y + 4) = \log(y - 2) + 3\log 2$. *(C)*

4. If $P = \begin{pmatrix} 0 & 1 \\ 1 & 0 \end{pmatrix}$, $Q = \begin{pmatrix} 0 & -1 \\ -1 & 0 \end{pmatrix}$, $PQ = R$ and $R^2 = S$ express R and S as square matrices.

   Identify P, Q, R and S as simple geometrical transformations.

   A fifth matrix is defined by $T = \begin{pmatrix} 0 & -1 \\ 1 & 0 \end{pmatrix}$.

   Express PT and TP as square matrices and identify T, PT and TP as simple geometrical transformations. *(O)*

5. (a) If $\dfrac{1}{v} + \dfrac{1}{u} = \dfrac{1}{f}$, calculate the negative value of v when $u = v + 4$ and $f = 3\frac{3}{4}$.

   (b) The plan of a pyramid on a rectangular horizontal base is a rectangle PQRS with the diagonals meeting at M. If

384

PQ = 12 cm, QR = 16 cm and the vertex V is 8 cm above M, calculate

   (i) the angle between PV and the plane PQRS,

   (ii) the angle between the planes PVS and QVR.   (*W*)

6. At a garden fête side-show a rectangular board measuring 2·4 m by 1·6 m has 192 cards pinned to it. Each card is rectangular measuring 8 cm by 5 cm, and the cards do not overlap. A lady throws darts at random towards the board, and any that miss the board are returned to her to be thrown again. Assuming that in a valid throw all points of the board are equally likely to be hit, show that the probability that a card will be hit is $\frac{1}{5}$.

   Calculate the probability that in two valid throws

   (i) a card will be hit on both occasions,

   (ii) the same card will be hit on both occasions.

What is the probability that in three valid throws at least one card will be hit?   (*N*)

7. (a) X is a point on the side PQ of a triangle PQR, and XY is drawn parallel to QR to meet PR in Y. Given that the area of triangle PQR is 48 cm^2 and that PX:PQ = 3:4, calculate the areas of the triangles PXY and RXY.

   (b) As illustrated in Fig. 212, the angle of elevation of the top B of a flagpole AB from a point D on the ground is 30°, and the angle of elevation of B from a point C 2 m vertically above D is 25°.

   Calculate the angle CBD, the length of CB, and the height of the flagpole.   (*W*)

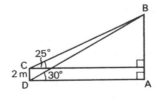

Fig. 212

8. Philadelphia and Reno are two cities on the same circle of latitude north of the equator. The longitude of Philadelphia is 75° W and of Reno 120° W. Given that the distance between the cities is 3 830 km, measured along the circle of latitude, find this latitude. (Take the earth to be a sphere and the length of the equator to be 4×10^4 km.)

Clearwater Lake is 1 900 km due north of Philadelphia and Dawson Creek is 1 900 km due north of Reno. Find the distance between Clearwater Lake and Dawson Creek measured along their common circle of latitude. (*C*)

9. 200 eggs were weighed and the table shows the frequency distribution obtained.

Plot the cumulative frequency curve, and from it determine the median of the distribution. What is the interquartile range?

If the heaviest 10% of the eggs are to be classified as 'large' what is the minimum mass of a 'large' egg? (Give your answers to the nearest gram.)

Mass (in grams)	Under 55	55–	60–	65–	70–
Frequency	7	17	16	25	46

Mass (in grams)	75–	80–	85–	90 and over
Frequency	41	34	10	4

(*MEI*)

10. Copy and complete the table of values of the function $y = x^2(x + 1) - 5$.

x	0	0·5	1	1·5	2
y		−4·625		0·625	

By drawing the graph of $y = x^2(x + 1) - 5$, obtain an approximate value of the root of the equation $x^2 = \dfrac{5}{x + 1}$.

Use a suitable method of numerical approximation to obtain the root correct to 3 significant figures. (*MME*)

X

1. (a) Three men, Jones, Morgan and Williams, agreed to form a business partnership. Jones invested £4 000 for 2 years; Morgan £2 500 for 3 years, and Williams invested his money for 4 years. They agreed that the profits should be shared in proportion to the amount invested and the time for which it was invested. How much did Williams invest if Jones' share of the profit of £6 450 was £2 400?

(b) A man agrees to buy a car for £2 000, paying £800 down and the remainder in instalments of £400, paid at the end of each of the first three quarters, together with a final payment at the end of the fourth quarter to clear the debt. Interest at 3% *per quarter* reckoned on the amount owing at the beginning of each quarter, is added at the end of each quarter. Working to the nearest penny, calculate the amount of his final payment to clear the debt. (*W*)

2. (i) A wire of length 24 cm is cut into two pieces, each of which is bent into the form of a square. If the length of the side of one square is x cm, find an expression for the length of the side of the other square.

Given that the total area of the two squares is $18\frac{1}{2}$ cm², find the lengths of the two pieces of wire.

(ii) The force acting on a body moving with speed v in a circle of radius r is proportional to the square of the speed and inversely proportional to the radius.

    (a) If the speed is doubled and the radius halved, by what factor is the force altered?

    (b) If the force is unaltered and the speed is trebled, by what factor is the radius changed?   (*C*)

3. O is the origin and points A, B have position vectors $\overline{OA} = a$, $\overline{OB} = b$. L is the midpoint of OB, M is the midpoint of AB and N the midpoint of AM. The lines ON and LM produced meet at P. Find the position vectors of L, M, N and prove that $\overline{OP} = \frac{3}{2}a + \frac{1}{2}b$. Hence or otherwise, show that BP is parallel to LN and twice its length.   (*O*)

4. A car starting from rest accelerates with constant acceleration $3 \, \text{m s}^{-2}$ for 4 seconds, then constant acceleration $2 \, \text{m s}^{-2}$ for 6 seconds. It travels with constant speed for a further 12 seconds, and then comes to rest with constant retardation in 8 seconds. Draw the speed-time graph, taking 1 cm (or $\frac{1}{2}$ inch) to $2 \, \text{m s}^{-1}$ vertically and 1 cm (or $\frac{1}{2}$ inch) to 2 seconds horizontally.

    By finding the area under the graph, or otherwise, find the total distance travelled. Calculate the average speed for the journey.   (*S*)

5. Sketch the curve $y = \frac{1}{4}x^2$ for $-4 \leqslant x \leqslant +4$. (There is no need to use squared paper.)

    Find the equation of the tangent at P, a point on this curve where $x = 4a$ and $y = 4a^2$. Write down the co-ordinates of the point R where this tangent meets the x-axis and of the point S where it meets the y-axis. Find also the equation of the line perpendicular to this tangent through the point R. (Answers so far include a.)

    Find the co-ordinates of the point Q where this line meets the y-axis and show all these points and lines in your diagram.

    Hence show that, wherever P may be on the curve as a alters in value, (i) Q is always the same point, (ii) PR = RS, (iii) PQ = QS.   (*MEI*)

6. A communications satellite moves in a circular path so that it is at all times directly above the equator and at a fixed distance from the earth's surface. An observer in latitude 11° 30′ N

finds that when the satellite crosses his meridian its elevation from his horizontal direction is 8°.

Show by calculation that the height of the satellite above the equator is about 320 km (taking the earth's circumference at the equator to be 4×10^4 km). Calculate also, to the nearest degree, the most northerly latitude from which the satellite can be seen (i.e. the latitude of an observer for whom the satellite is on his horizon as it crosses his meridian). *(O)*

7. An examination paper contains three sections I, II, III. The number of questions answered from section I must be
    (a) at least half the number answered from section II,
    (b) not less than the number answered from section III.
A candidate has to answer 12 questions altogether, and answers x questions from section I and y questions from section II.
    (i) Write down, in terms of x and y, the number of section III questions answered.
    (ii) Explain why $x + y \leqslant 12, y \geqslant 0, y \leqslant 2x$ and $2x + y \geqslant 12$.
    (iii) Show on graph paper the region containing the points whose co-ordinates (x, y) satisfy all the inequations in part (ii). (Use a scale of 1 cm to 1 unit on both axes.)

If questions in I, II, III are each worth 1, 3, 4 marks respectively, show that the highest mark the candidate can obtain is $48 - 3x - y$. Find the values of x and y which make this as great as possible. *(N)*

8. In the diagram the triangle OAB is right-angled at A. The triangle OPQ is an enlargement of the triangle OAB with centre O and scale factor k. The line OCR is the image of OBQ under reflection in the line OP. The line CQ crosses OP at X. (Fig. 213)

Show that triangle XPQ is an enlargement of triangle XAC and state the scale factor in terms of k. Hence show that $CX:XQ = OC:OQ$.

If triangle OAB is taken to have unit area, calculate, in terms of k, the areas of the triangles OPQ, OQR and OCQ. *(L)*

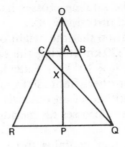

Fig. 213

9. The co-ordinates of the vertices of $\triangle ABC$ are $(0,0)$, $(2,0)$ and $(1,2)$, and $\triangle A_1B_1C_1$ is the image of $\triangle ABC$ under the transformation T_1 whose matrix is $\begin{pmatrix} 1 & 1 \\ 0 & 1 \end{pmatrix}$. Find the co-ordinates of A_1, B_1, and C_1. $\triangle A_2B_2C_2$ is the image of $\triangle A_1B_1C_1$ under the transformation T_2 whose matrix is $\begin{pmatrix} 3 & 0 \\ 0 & 3 \end{pmatrix}$. Find the co-ordinates of A_2, B_2 and C_2. Describe the transformations T_1 and T_2.

   Find the matrix of the single transformation under which $\triangle A_2B_2C_2$ is the image of $\triangle ABC$. (*C*)

10.

Value of x	1	2	3	4
Frequency	2	4	8	12

Value of x	5	6	7	8
Frequency	11	9	3	1

For the frequency distribution shown in the table,
   (i) state the median value of x,

(ii) calculate the mean value of x,

(iii) calculate the probability that a randomly selected x deviates from the mean of the distribution by more than 2.

(MME)

Answers

Exercise 1a (p. 2)

1. 15	**2.** 40	**3.** 165
4. 1 573	**5.** 3 517	**6.** 8
7. 23	**8.** 68	**9.** 238
10. 334	**11.** 1 022	**12.** 65
13. 17 406	**14.** 35	**15.** 2 253
16. 344	**17.** 22 544	**18.** 45
19. 20 535	**20.** 255 203	

Exercise 1b (p. 3)

1. 110	**2.** 1 011	**3.** 10 101
4. 100 101	**5.** 110 001	**6.** 111 101
7. 1 010 111	**8.** 1 100 111	**9.** 11 001 001
10. 100 001 110	**11.** 3	**12.** 5
13. 9	**14.** 10	**15.** 25
16. 27	**17.** 12	**18.** 23
19. 8	**20.** 127	

Exercise 1c (p. 4)

1. 1 000	**2.** 10 100	**3.** 10 001
4. 11 000	**5.** 100 101	**6.** 1 000 001
7. 1 100 111	**8.** 10 000 100	**9.** 10
10. 110	**11.** 11	**12.** 1 010
13. 1 000	**14.** 10 110	**15.** 11 000
16. 100 001		

Exercise 1d (p. 5)

1. 11 010	**2.** 100 001	**3.** 1 000 110
4. 10 100 010	**5.** 11 011 100	**6.** 101 000 100

7. 111 100 110   **8.** 11 111 100   **9.** 1 001
10. 1 010   **11.** 1 011   **12.** 110
13. 101   **14.** 101   **15.** 11
16. 111

Exercise 2a (p. 8)

1. Oak is inflammable.
2. All kings are heads of state.
3. All rhombuses are quadrilaterals.
4. All men in the armed forces are allowed to vote in elections.
5. No.
6. A satchel contains a ruler and a rubber.
7. {2, 4, 5, 6, 7, 8, 10, 12}, {1, 4, 5, 6, 7, 8, 11, 12}, {4, 5, 6, 7, 8, 12}, {4, 5, 6, 7, 8, 12}, {1, 2, 4, 5, 6, 7, 8, 10, 11, 12}, {1, 2, 4, 5, 6, 7, 8, 10, 11, 12}.
8. All who study metalwork also study mathematics.
9. All judges are lawyers.
10. Nothing.
11. Tables are dangerous.
12. Slide rules can be called computers and desk calculators can be called computers.

Exercise 2b (p. 11)

1. 25   **2.** 200   **3.** 23%   **4.** 18
5. 7   **6.** 2   **7.** 29   **8.** 18, 25, 6

Exercise 3 (p. 15)

1. £26·55   **2.** $3\frac{1}{2}$ yr   **3.** 8 yr   **4.** $2\frac{1}{2}$%
5. £320·50   **6.** £3·64   **7.** £124·20   **8.** £102·17
9. 5%   **10.** £541·67   **11.** 1 yr 9 mth   **12.** $4\frac{1}{2}$%
13. £59·94   **14.** £159·78   **15.** 5·56%

Exercise 4 (p. 17)

1. (2, 1), (5, 5), (3, 7)   **2.** (1, 6), (4, 10), (2, 12)
3. (5, 7), (7, 7), (7, 9), (5, 9)   **4.** (7, 5), (9, 5), (9, 7), (7, 7)

5. (6, 4), (2, 7), (8, 15), (12, 12)   **6.** (1, 2), (−3, 5), (3, 13), (7, 10)
7. (2, 0), (1, −4), (5, −1), (6, 3)   **8.** (−4, 3)
9. (0, 0), (1, −2), (−3, −3), (−4, 3)
10. (3, −1), (4, −3), (0, −4), (−1, 2)
11. (0, −2), (1, 0), (0, 2), (−1, 0)
12. (0, 1), (1, 3), (0, 5), (−1, 3)

Exercise 5 (p. 22)

1. 4·6, 4, 4
2. 6·5, 7, 7
3. $6\frac{1}{3}$, 6, 6
4. 117·1, 113 or 118, 117·5
5. $13\frac{1}{2}$, 10–18, 11–15, $14\frac{1}{6}$
6. $34\frac{1}{2}$, 26–41, 31–40, 33
7. 29, 24–35, 27–33, 29
8. 3·3, 2, 3
9. 34, 20–29, 29, $22\frac{1}{2}$–52
10. 50, 50·5, 39–60·5, 41·5
11. $59\frac{1}{4}$, 56–61, 59·2
12. 49·6, 50, 46–52

Exercise 6a (p. 29)

1. 1 800
2. 2 300
3. 2 430
4. 28 000
5. 940
6. 3 050
7. $9a^2 + 6a + 1$
8. $b^2 - 8b + 16$
9. $4c^2 - 20cd + 25d^2$
10. $16m^2 + 24mn + 9n^2$
11. $(3c - d)(3m - 4n)$
12. $(a + b)(c + 2d)$
13. $(x + 4a)(x - 4a)$
14. $(2c + 5d)(2c - 5d)$
15. $(a + 2)(a - 5)$
16. $(a + 2b)(a - 5b)$
17. $(ab + 2)(ab - 5)$
18. $5(m - 3n)(m + 3n)$
19. $(h - 2k)(m - 2n)$
20. $(2a + b)(a + 4b)$
21. $(3m - 1)(m - 3)$
22. $(cd - 9)(cd + 9)$
23. $(4x + 3am)(4x - 3am)$
24. $(2n + 3)(3n + 2)$
25. $(2a + 5)^2$
26. $9(h - 2k)(h + 2k)$
27. $(a - 2b)(a - 4b)$
28. $(5abc + 3d)(5abc - 3d)$
29. $\left(\dfrac{m}{3} - \dfrac{n}{2}\right)\left(\dfrac{m}{3} + \dfrac{n}{2}\right)$
30. $(3s + t)(u - 2v)$
31. $(3x - 2y)^2$
32. $(4d - 1)(3d + 2)$
33. $(x^2 + y)(x^2 - y)$
34. $(2mn - 3)(5mn + 4)$
35. $(4 + n^2)(2 + n)(2 - n)$
36. $(a + b + c)(a + b - c)$
37. $(x + m - n)(x - m + n)$
38. $2(m + 2n)(a + b)$
39. $(2 + 5h)(1 - 3h)$
40. $(2a - b)(m - 3n)$

41. $(a - 6b)(a - 9b)$ **42.** $(m - 18n)(m + 3n)$
43. $(c - 2d - 3e)(c - 2d + 3e)$ **44.** $(3x + 2y)(4x + 9y)$
45. $(h - k)(3h - 4k)$ **46.** $2a(3x + 2y)(c - 2d)$
47. $(2a - 9x)(3a + 4x)$
48. $(5a + 2m + 4n)(5a - 2m - 4n)$
49. $(7a - 4b)(3a + 4b)$ **50.** $4b(3a - b)$

Exercise 6b (p. 31)

1. $(a + 2)(a^2 - 2a + 4)$ **2.** $(2 - m)(4 + 2m + m^2)$
3. $(1 - 2u)(1 + 2u + 4u^2)$ **4.** $(3x + 2y)(9x^2 - 6xy + 4y^2)$
5. $(2 - 5x)(4 + 10x + 25x^2)$ **6.** $8(2m + 1)(4m^2 - 2m + 1)$
7. $2(a^2 + 2)(a^4 - 2a^2 + 4)$ **8.** $(m^2 - n)(m^4 + m^2n + n^2)$
9. $(2a^3 + 3b^3)(4a^6 - 6a^3b^3 + 9b^6)$
10. $(2abc + x)(4a^2b^2c^2 - 2abcx + x^2)$
11. $\left(\dfrac{a}{m} - 1\right)\left(\dfrac{a^2}{m^2} + \dfrac{a}{m} + 1\right)$ **12.** $\left(2 + \dfrac{m}{x}\right)\left(4 - \dfrac{2m}{x} + \dfrac{m^2}{x^2}\right)$
13. $2(x - 3ab)(x^2 + 3abx + 9a^2b^2)$
14. $(1 + m)(1 - m)(1 - m + m^2)(1 + m + m^2)$
15. $(x - y)(x^2 - 8xy + 19y^2)$ **16.** $(m - n)(m^2 + 7mn + 19n^2)$
17. $(x + 3)(19x^2 - 21x + 9)$ **18.** $5a(13a^2 + 9ab + 3b^2)$
19. $(2a - 3)(13a^2 + 3a + 3)$ **20.** $7(5x - a)(x^2 - ax + a^2)$

Exercise 7 (p. 33)

1. 950 kg   **2.** 650   **3.** £1·05
4. £1 050   **5.** $5\frac{1}{2}\%$ decrease   **6.** $22\frac{1}{2}\%$
7. 432 kg   **8.** 102 litres   **9.** $6·51\%$
10. $9·6\%$ **11.** $10\frac{1}{4}\%$ **12.** £806
13. £12   **14.** £16   **15.** $27\frac{1}{2}\%$
16. £35·20   **17.** $24·5\%$ **18.** $5·03\%$
19. $2\frac{1}{4}\%$ less   **20.** £12 784   **21.** £413·77
22. £656

Exercise 8a (p. 36)

1. $10a^3$ **2.** $20a^3$ **3.** $250a^5$
4. $\dfrac{10}{a}$ **5.** $\dfrac{5}{4a}$ **6.** $250a$

7. $\frac{1}{16}$ **8.** 4   **9.** $\pm\frac{1}{8}$

10. $\pm 1\frac{1}{4}$ **11.** ± 3 **12.** 4

13. ± 0.3 **14.** 1   **15.** ± 2

16. $\pm\frac{64}{27}$ **17.** $\frac{25}{9}$ **18.** $\frac{2}{a^2}$

19. $\frac{1}{x^3}$ **20.** $\frac{x}{y}$ **21.** $\frac{1}{xy}$

22. $\frac{b^3}{a^2}$ **23.** $\frac{a^2}{b^6}$ **24.** $\frac{3}{x^{\frac{1}{2}}}$

25. 9   **26.** 8   **27.** $\pm\frac{1}{4}$

28. 2   **29.** $\pm\frac{1}{27}$ **30.** ± 8

Exercise 8b (p. 39)

1. 1 909   **2.** 51·45   **3.** 62·98

4. 4·038   **5.** 1·963   **6.** 7·819

7. 58·02   **8.** 2·759   **9.** 1·914

10. 243·6   **11.** 4·852   **12.** 257·9

13. 48·43   **14.** 1·854   **15.** 22·43

16. 30·35   **17.** 1·644   **18.** 1·950

19. 1·677   **20.** 2·834   **21.** 4·687

22. 10·02

Exercise 8c (p. 41)

1. 0·769 5   **2.** 0·024 06   **3.** 0·293 1

4. 0·055 4   **5.** 0·246   **6.** 8·559

7. 0·246 8   **8.** 0·436 6   **9.** 3·058

10. 1·182

Exercise 8d (p. 43)

1. 0·267 1   **2.** 0·060 57   **3.** 0·609 2

4. 0·497 8   **5.** 0·314 9   **6.** 0·369 8

7. 0·855 1   **8.** 0·746 6   **9.** 0·060 42

10. 0·430 9   **11.** 0·311 7   **12.** 0·008 872

13. 1·940   **14.** 0·225 7   **15.** 1.95×10^{13}

16. 2.429×10^{-1} **17.** 1.37×10^{-9} **18.** 5.38×10^{11}

19. 3.05×10^{-2} **20.** 0·589 1

Exercise 9a (p. 45)

1. 3
2. 9
3. 7
4. 9
5. 14
6. 44
7. 37 m
8. 8 m
9. 7 cm, 84 cm^2
10. 20 cm
12. 5·39
13. 3·74
14. 6·48
15. 7·28
16. 7·55
17. 9·54
18. 29·3 m
19. 2·74 cm, 11·8 cm^2
20. 6·26 m^2
21. 4·36 m
22. 1·68 cm
23. 10·6 cm
24. 32·0 cm, 896 cm^2
25. 5·6 cm, 6·5 cm
26. 240 km, 318°
27. 9·85 cm, 7·31 cm
28. 7 cm

Exercise 10a (p. 51)

1. 3, 7
2. $-1, -2$
3. 2, -3
4. 5, -2
5. 1, -2
6. 0, -3
7. 2, $1\frac{1}{2}$
8. $-2, -\frac{3}{4}$
9. 2, -2
10. 0, 4
11. $-1, -2\frac{1}{2}$
12. 4, $-\frac{2}{3}$
13. $1\frac{1}{2}, \frac{3}{4}$
14. $2\frac{1}{4}, -\frac{2}{3}$
15. $1\frac{1}{2}, -1\frac{3}{4}$
16. $x^2 - 7x + 10 = 0$
17. $x^2 - x - 12 = 0$
18. $x^2 - 5x = 0$
19. $4x^2 - 16x + 15 = 0$
20. $12x^2 + 7x - 49 = 0$

Exercise 10b (p. 53)

1. 6, -2
2. 5, -1
3. $-2 \pm \sqrt{10}$
4. $2 \pm \sqrt{2}$
5. -3 twice
6. $4 \pm \sqrt{7}$
7. $-5 \pm \sqrt{26}$
8. 1, -11
9. $\dfrac{-3 \pm \sqrt{5}}{2}$
10. $\dfrac{5 \pm \sqrt{37}}{2}$
11. 2, -1
12. $\dfrac{1 \pm \sqrt{13}}{2}$
13. $-4 \pm \sqrt{3}$
14. $\dfrac{-7 \pm \sqrt{5}}{2}$
15. $\dfrac{9 \pm \sqrt{89}}{2}$

Exercise 10c (p. 55)

1. 3·41, 0·59
2. 5, −1
3. imag.
4. 0·74, −6·74
5. −1, −5
6. 0·56, −3·56
7. 1·62, −0·62
8. 3·62, 1·38
9. 1, $2\frac{1}{2}$
10. 5·08, −1·08
11. imag.
12. 5·62, −0·62
13. 5, $-\frac{1}{2}$
14. 2·53, −0·53
15. 0·71, −4·21
16. −2, $-1\frac{1}{2}$
17. 2·76, 0·24
18. 7·34, −0·34
19. 0·39, −1·72
20. 1·54, −0·87

Exercise 10d (p. 56)

1. 3
2. 9, 11 or −9, −11
3. 7, 8, 9 or −7, −8, −9
4. 39, 13
5. 9
6. 3 m
7. 4 m
8. 14·8 cm
9. 22 p
10. 2 s or 5 s
11. 10·57 cm
12. 30 cm square
13. 3 m
14. $1\frac{1}{2}$ m
15. 8 m
16. 2·41 cm

Exercise 10e (p. 59)

1. 1, 3
2. 1, −3
3. 1·5, −4
4. imag.
5. 1, −1·5
6. −0·44, −4·56
7. 3·30, −0·30
8. 1·43, 0·23
9. 0·87, −1·54
10. −0·42, −3·58
11. 3·77, −0·27
12. 1·37, −1·70
13. 1·29, 0·31
14. 2·18, 0·57
15. 0·24, −1·64
16. 3·41, −1·08

Exercise 11 (p. 61)

1. 625 cm²
2. 6·4 litres
3. 750 g
4. 9 cm
5. 1·2 kg
6. 1·2 cm
7. 24 cm
8. 7·9 cm
9. 4 times; $\frac{1}{4}$
10. 800 kg
11. 440 litres
12. 1·2 m, 9 000 cm²

Exercise 13a (p. 67)

1. 7·13
2. 6·02
3. 15·27
4. 46·7
5. 34·3
6. 315

7. 24 200	**8.** 100 600	**9.** 529
10. 121·8	**11.** 1·783	**12.** 13 140 000
13. 64·5	**14.** 0·000 606	**15.** 125·8
16. 60·4	**17.** 847	**18.** 12·04
19. 20 800	**20.** 2 010	**21.** 5 470
22. 692	**23.** 482	**24.** 20 300
25. 63 600	**26.** 3 850	**27.** 0·499
28. 0·000 389	**29.** 0·046 4	**30.** 0·008 55

Exercise 13b (p. 67)

1. 1·5	**2.** 0·444	**3.** 0·846
4. 1·235	**5.** 2·29	**6.** 0·507
7. 1·374	**8.** 0·883	**9.** 1·462
10. 10·65	**11.** 0·985	**12.** 1·406
13. 0·023 5	**14.** 0·784	**15.** 0·065 3
16. 0·094 3	**17.** 13·24	**18.** 32·6
19. 0·018 99	**20.** 0·4	**21.** 1·636
22. 0·758	**23.** 0·150 5	**24.** 5·19
25. 0·000 093 5	**26.** 0·011 34	**27.** 0·000 328
28. 6·09	**29.** 268 000	**30.** 0·152 6

Exercise 13c (p. 69)

1. 10·3	**2.** 73·3	**3.** 630
4. 5 230	**5.** 0·173	**6.** 0·677
7. 177 000	**8.** 0·002 14	**9.** 0·000 282
10. 3 690 000	**11.** 61 300 000	**12.** 0·000 000 482

Exercise 13d (p. 70)

1. 1·414	**2.** 5·48	**3.** 2·51
4. 7·82	**5.** 12·33	**6.** 42·3
7. 241	**8.** 793	**9.** 0·621
10. 0·182 2	**11.** 0·073 2	**12.** 0·001 463
13. 4·24	**14.** 1·08	**15.** 55
16. 46·3	**17.** 1·06	**18.** 1·743
19. 10·19	**20.** 3·27	

Exercise 14 (p. 73)

1. 181 m   2. 6° 23′   3. 147 m
4. 16·2 m   5. 48° 11′   6. 59°
7. 030° 35′, 12·8 km   8. 2 030 m
9. 70° 32′   10. 276 m   11. 3·35 m
12. 085° 12′, 7·81 m   13. 45·9 m
14. 66° 25′   15. 6·73 m   16. 31° 20′
17. 304 m   18. 3 835 m   19. 2° 58′
20. 55° 47′

Exercise 15a (p. 76)

1. (a) £34·75   (b) £80·62
2. (a) £72·81   (b) £3·28   (c) £12·77   (d) £11·91
3. 48·8%   4. £178
5. (a) £14·10   (b) £25·12   (c) 85p
6. £568 232   7. $54\frac{1}{2}$p in the £   8. 3p

Exercise 15b (p. 79)

1. £15·20   2. £6·38   3. £4·34
4. £19·39   5. £7·60   6. £9·44
7. £16·69   8. £8·43

Exercise 15c (p. 82)

1. £618·75   2. £14 856·25   3. £341·55
4. £36·30   5. £1 509·70   6. £448·80
7. £735·90   8. £1 292·94   9. £7 031·74
10. £30 927·22 ; 63·6%

Exercise 16 (p. 84)

1. $2a^3 - 7a^2 + 8a - 3$ 2. $10d^3 + 31d^2 - 9$
3. $6m^3 - 13m^2 + 4m + 3$ 4. $u^3 + uv^2 - 2v^3$
5. $6x^3 - x^2y - 9xy^2 + 4y^3$ 6. $m^2 - n^2 - 2n - 1$
7. $6a^2 - 7ab + 2b^2 + 17a - 10b + 12$
8. $2c^4 - c^3 - 15c^2 + 2c + 5$

9. $2d^5 + 4d^4 - 3d^3 + 4d^2 - 13d + 6$

10. $m^4 - m^3 - 4m^2 + 19m - 15$

11. $x^2 + 3x - 4$　　**12.** $m^2 - 4m + 6$, rem. -2

13. $2a^2 + 3a - 4$　　**14.** $2d^2 + 5d + 2$, rem. 6

15. $2a^2 - 4ab - b^2$, rem. b^3

16. $3m^2 + 4mn + 6n^2$, rem. $-4n^3$

17. $5x - 3$　　**18.** $5c + 2d$, rem. $-2d^3$

19. $x^3 - 2x^2 - 5x + 4$, rem. 5　　**20.** $4m^2 + 6m - 3$

21. $a^2 + 8a - 13$　　**22.** m

23. $5x^2 - 5y^2 - 10x + 10y$　　**24.** $2c^3$　　**25.** $5a$

Exercise 17a (p. 87)

1. $\dfrac{b+c}{b-c}$　　**2.** $\dfrac{a}{b}$　　**3.** N.S.F.

4. $-\dfrac{a+b}{a}$　　**5.** $\dfrac{x-2y}{x}$　　**6.** $\dfrac{m-n}{m+n}$

7. $\dfrac{q}{p-q}$　　**8.** N.S.F.　　**9.** $\dfrac{a^2+ab+b^2}{a+b}$

10. $-\dfrac{x+3}{x+2}$　　**11.** $\dfrac{4y^2}{3x(3x-2y)}$　　**12.** $-\dfrac{b}{4a}$

13. $\dfrac{p}{2q}$　　**14.** $\dfrac{m+2n}{m}$　　**15.** $\dfrac{1}{3}$

16. $\dfrac{c+d}{b-d}$　　**17.** $-\dfrac{x^2}{y^2}$　　**18.** $\dfrac{p(p-q)}{q(p+q)}$

19. $\dfrac{1}{a-2}$　　**20.** $\dfrac{x-3y}{3x+y}$

Exercise 17b (p. 89)

1. $\dfrac{8z-9x}{12xyz}$　　**2.** $\dfrac{4q-p}{q}$　　**3.** $\dfrac{a}{b(a-b)}$

4. $\dfrac{1}{3(a-2b)}$　　**5.** $\dfrac{1}{x-2}$　　**6.** $-\dfrac{a+b}{ab}$

7. $\dfrac{1}{(x-1)(2x-3)}$　　**8.** $\dfrac{6}{(a-4)(a+2)}$

9. $\dfrac{5p}{(p - 2q)^2(p + 3q)}$

10. $\dfrac{1}{a(3a - b)}$

11. $\dfrac{2 - x}{1 + x}$

12. $\dfrac{y(2x + 3y)}{(x + y)(3x - y)(x + 2y)}$

13. $\dfrac{8b - 7}{1 - 4b}$

14. $\dfrac{3y + 1}{y - 3}, \dfrac{1 + y^2}{y - 3}$

15. $\dfrac{5y + 2}{3 - 2y}; 7, 1$

Exercise 17c (p. 91)

1. $-2, \frac{1}{2}$ **2.** $3, -1$ **3.** $3, -2$

4. $0, -4$ **5.** $4, -1$ **6.** $5, -1\frac{1}{4}$

7. $8, -4$ **8.** $8, -2$ **9.** $-3, \frac{7}{9}$

10. $6, 0$ **11.** 5 **12.** 7

13. 5 **14.** $3, \frac{2}{3}$ **15.** $4, 1\frac{1}{2}$

Exercise 17d (p. 94)

1. $200 \, \text{km h}^{-1}$ **2.** 9 **3.** £50

4. $20 \, \text{km h}^{-1}$ **5.** $75 \, \text{km h}^{-1}$ **6.** 20

7. $10p$

8. 16 and $18 \, \text{km h}^{-1}$ *or* 30 and $32 \, \text{km h}^{-1}$

9. $6 \, \text{km h}^{-1}$ **10.** $24 \, \text{cm}$

11. $75 \, \text{km h}^{-1}$ and $48 \, \text{km h}^{-1}$ **12.** $15 \, \text{km h}^{-1}$; No

Exercise 18a (p. 97)

1. $\dfrac{q}{1 - p}$ **2.** $\dfrac{m}{p - n}$ **3.** $\dfrac{abc}{b - a}$

4. $\dfrac{n(1 - m)}{m}$ **5.** $\dfrac{mn}{m - n}$ **6.** $\dfrac{bc}{a + 2b}$

7. $\dfrac{q(3p - 2)}{2p + 3}$ **8.** a^2 **9.** $\dfrac{b^2}{a^2}$

10. $\dfrac{4b^2}{a}$ **11.** $b^2 - a$ **12.** $(b - a)^2$

13. $\pm\sqrt{b^2 - a^2}$ **14.** $1 + \dfrac{q^2}{p^2}$ **15.** 0

16. $q - p$ **17.** $a^2 + ab + b^2$ **18.** $-\dfrac{p + q}{2}$

19. $2a - b$ **20.** $2p, -\dfrac{p}{2}$

Exercise 18b (p. 98)

1. $M = N - RD$ **2.** $N = \pm\sqrt{\dfrac{T - a}{b}}$

3. $Q = \dfrac{P(y + 3x)}{x - 3y}$

4. $s = \dfrac{u^2 - v^2}{2a}, u = \pm\sqrt{v^2 + 2as}$

5. $u = \pm\sqrt{v^2 - \dfrac{2Eg}{m}}$ **6.** $p = \dfrac{P(1 - eT)}{1 - et}$

7. $W = \dfrac{Tgx}{gx + v^2}$ **8.** $g = \dfrac{4\pi^2 l}{t^2}$ **9.** $h = \dfrac{V}{\pi r^2} - \dfrac{2}{3}r$

10. $h = \dfrac{v^2 - gd}{3g}, d = \dfrac{v^2 - 3gh}{g}$

11. $h = \pm\sqrt{\dfrac{A^2}{\pi^2 r^2} + r^2}$ **12.** $Q = \dfrac{P}{d^3} + P, P = \dfrac{d^3 Q}{1 + d^3}$

13. $k = \pm\sqrt{\dfrac{T^2 gh}{2\pi^2} - h^2}$ **14.** $t = \dfrac{k(1 + e^2)}{1 - e^2 k^2}$

15. $p = \pm m\sqrt{\dfrac{1 - 2n^2}{2 + n^2}}$ **16.** $V = \dfrac{C^2 h}{4\pi}$

17. (i) $A = \pi r(2C - r)$ (ii) $A = \pi(C^2 - h^2)$

18. $V = \dfrac{Sr}{2} - \dfrac{5}{6}\pi r^3$

Exercise 19a (p. 101)

1. 7 cm   **2.** 6 cm   **3.** 15 cm
4. 4 cm, 8 cm   **5.** 8·66 cm
12. $AB^2 - CD^2 = 4PQ(OP + OQ)$

Exercise 19b (p. 103)

1. 33°   **2.** 45°   **3.** 67°
4. 72°   **5.** 12°   **6.** 62°

Exercise 20 (p. 106)

1. $3\sqrt{2}$ **2.** $2\sqrt{7}$ **3.** $6\sqrt{3}$
4. $2\sqrt{11}$ **5.** $5\sqrt{7}$ **6.** $\sqrt{24}$
7. $\sqrt{63}$ **8.** $\sqrt{150}$ **9.** $\sqrt{288}$

10. $\sqrt{147}$ **11.** $\dfrac{2\sqrt{3}}{3}$ **12.** $4\sqrt{2}$

13. $3\sqrt{7}$ **14.** $\dfrac{5\sqrt{6}}{3}$ **15.** $\sqrt{2}$

16. $3\sqrt{5}$ **17.** $2\sqrt{3}$ **18.** $\dfrac{4\sqrt{5}}{3}$

19. $\dfrac{2\sqrt{6}}{5}$ **20.** $3\sqrt{7}$ **21.** 0

22. $4\sqrt{2}$ **23.** $\dfrac{2\sqrt{2}}{3}$ **24.** $\dfrac{2\sqrt{2}}{3}$

25. $\dfrac{\sqrt{6}}{3}$ **26.** $\sqrt{3}$ **27.** 9

28. 12   **29.** $9\sqrt{5}$ **30.** 60

31. $3\sqrt{3}$ **32.** 8   **33.** $54\sqrt{2}$

34. $10\sqrt{7}$ **35.** $3\sqrt{6}$ **36.** $\dfrac{\sqrt{3}}{3}$

37. $\frac{6}{7}$ **38.** $\sqrt{5}$ **39.** $\sqrt{5}$

40. $\dfrac{4\sqrt{15}}{5}$

Exercise 21 (p. 110)

1. 5 cm, $5\sqrt{2}$ cm   **2.** $2\sqrt{2}$ cm, $2\sqrt{2}$ cm

3. $\dfrac{7\sqrt{2}}{2}$ cm, $\dfrac{7\sqrt{2}}{2}$ cm   **4.** 6 cm, $3\sqrt{3}$ cm

5. $2\sqrt{3}$ cm, $4\sqrt{3}$ cm   **6.** $2\frac{1}{2}$ cm, $\dfrac{5\sqrt{3}}{2}$ cm

7. 10 cm, $5\sqrt{3}$ cm   **8.** 4 cm, $4\sqrt{3}$ cm
9. $3\sqrt{3}$ cm, $6\sqrt{3}$ cm   **10.** 12 cm
11. $6\sqrt{2}$ cm   **12.** $6\sqrt{3}$ cm   **13.** 8 cm
14. $2\sqrt{6}$ cm   **15.** $\sqrt{6}$ cm   **16.** $(3\sqrt{2} - \sqrt{6})$ cm
17. $4\sqrt{6}$ cm   **18.** 3 cm   **19.** $14\sqrt{3}$ m
20. $3\sqrt{3}$ cm, 3 cm   **21.** $180\sqrt{3}$ m
22. 800 m, $400\sqrt{3}$ m   **23.** 1·5 cm, 60°
24. $10\sqrt{3}$ m   **25.** $8(\sqrt{3} - 1)$ m   **26.** $10\sqrt{3}$ m
27. $3x$ cm   **28.** $4\sqrt{6}$ m, $6\sqrt{2}$ m

Exercise 22a (p. 113)

1. 2   **2.** 3   **3.** $\frac{1}{2}$ **4.** $1\frac{2}{3}$ **5.** $1\frac{1}{2}$
6. $-\frac{1}{2}$ **7.** $-\frac{2}{3}$ **8.** -2 **9.** -2 **10.** $-1\frac{1}{2}$

Exercise 22b (p. 114)

1. (i) 0·903 0   (ii) 1·908 4   (iii) 0·908 4   (iv) 1·602 0
     (v) 1·322 2   (vi) 0·889 1   (vii) 1·574 1   (viii) 1·088 2
2. (i) 2·59   (ii) 0·387   (iii) 1·87   (iv) $-0·060\,7$
3. (i) $\log 30$ (ii) $\log \frac{4}{3}$ (iii) $\log 216$ (iv) $\log 7$ (v) $\log \frac{1}{16}$
     (vi) $\log 50$ (vii) $\log 5$ (viii) $\log \frac{9}{2}$ (ix) $\log 4$ (x) $\log 8$
4. (i) 1 000   (ii) 3   (iii) 256
5. (i) 3   (ii) $1\frac{1}{2}$ (iii) $\frac{3}{4}$ (iv) -1 (v) 1   (vi) $\frac{2}{3}$
6. (i) $x = a^b$ (ii) $x = ay$ (iii) $ax = 1$ (iv) $x = a^3y^2$ (v) $x = yz^2$
7. (i) 0   (ii) 2   (iii) $\frac{1}{4}$ (iv) 0, 1   (v) 1   (vi) $-1,2$
8. $3, \frac{1}{3}$; $\pm 1·10$

Exercise 23a (p. 117)

1. 15·84 m   **2.** 150°   **3.** 50   **4.** 5·28 kg
5. $31\frac{1}{4}\%$ **6.** 20 m   **7.** 39·6 m   **8.** 113 m
9. 120°, $25\frac{1}{7}$ cm **10.** 88·5 cm²   **11.** 424 cm³   **12.** 27·5 m²

Exercise 23b (p. 120)

1. 18·48 l min⁻¹   **2.** 1·98 kg
3. 52 500 litres   **4.** 1·6 m
5. 1·188 kg   **6.** 1·12 m

7. 20 250 cm³, 16·2 kg   **8.** 0·79 litres
9. 13·7 cm   **10.** 20·4 kg
11. $6\frac{1}{4}$ **12.** 9 m
13. 7 min 12·s   **14.** $\frac{3}{4}$ cm
15. (i) $1\frac{1}{2}$ cm (ii) $1\frac{1}{3}$ cm

Exercise 23c (p. 124)

1. (i) 8 cm, 60°   (ii) 6 cm, 97° 11′   (iii) $6\frac{1}{4}$ cm, 49° 15′
2. 60π cm², 96π cm³   **3.** 216°   **4.** 195π cm², 700π cm³
5. $\dfrac{760\pi}{3}$ cm³, 125   **6.** 500π tonnes

Exercise 23d (p. 126)

1. 27 cm   **2.** 54   **3.** 1 728   **4.** $3\frac{3}{8}$ cm
5. (i) $\frac{2}{3}$ (ii) $\frac{1}{3}$. Equal   **6.** 37·0 cm   **7.** 186 g
8. 11 cm, 336 cm³   **9.** 20·2 kg   **10.** 1·26 kg
11. 38·1 m³   **12.** 1·51 kg   **13.** 172 cm³
14. 11·4 kg   **15.** 225 kg

Exercise 24a (p. 129)

1. 2·75, −5·25, −1·41 ; 4·7 or −1·7, −1 or 4, 3·3 or −0·3 ; 1·5, −6·25
2. 1·75, −2·25 ; 3·41 or 0·59, 4·65 or −0·65 ; 2, 4
3. 3·36, −4·56 ; 5·37 or −0·37, 3·52 or 1·48 ; −6·25, 2·5
4. 5·04, −1·61, 6·75 ; 3·54 or −2·54, 1·62 or −0·62, 2·56 or −1·56
5. −1·76, 4·64, 1·76 ; 0·41 or −2·41, 1·24 or −3·24, 1·83 or −3·83 ;
    −1, 5.

Exercise 24b (p. 132)

1. 3·56, −0·56 ; 2·62, 0·38 ; 3·30, −0·30 ; 0, 3 ; 3·79, −0·79 ; 4, −1
2. −0·27, −3·73 ; 0·24, −4·24 ; −0·59, −3·41 ; −2 twice ; imag. ;
    0·65, −4·65
3. 2·87, −0·87 ; 3·12, −1·12 ; 2·58, −0·58 ; imag. ; 1·71, 0·29 ; 3·55,
    −1·55

4. 0·33, −1; 0, −0·67; imag.; 1·23, −1·90; 0·72, −1·39; 1·69, −2·36
5. imag.; 0, 1·67; 1·85, −0·18; 2·26, −0·59; 2·57, −0·91; 2·92, −1·25

Exercise 24c (p. 134)

1. ±1·73, $x^2 − 3 = 0$ **2.** ±1·87, $2x^2 − 7 = 0$
3. 2·27, −1·77
4. −0·61, 3·28; $3x^2 − 8x − 6 = 0$
5. (2, 1), (−1·5, −1·33)   **6.** (1·92, 0·72)
7. (−0·83, 0·59), (4·83, 3·41)
8. −1, 1·38, 3·62; $x^3 − 4x^2 + 5 = 0$
9. −1 twice, 2; $x^3 − 3x − 2 = 0$ **10.** 2·11, −0·25, −1·86

Exercise 25a (p. 137)

1. 3 cm, 4 cm, 6 cm   **2.** 4 cm, 5 cm, 10 cm
3. 9·22 cm   **4.** 67°
5. 62°, 56°, 62°   **6.** 64°
7. 4 cm, 5 cm   **8.** 4 cm, 3 cm

Exercise 25b (p. 140)

1. (i) 56°, 68°, 56°   (ii) 76°, 70°, 34°   (iii) 38°   (iv) 25°   (v) 86°

Exercise 25c (p. 144)

1. 8·78 cm   **2.** 4·12 cm   **3.** 7·75 cm   **4.** 7·14 cm
5. 3·57 cm   **6.** 5·08 cm   **7.** 6·58 cm   **8.** 1·91 cm
9. 2·31 cm   **10.** 2·24 cm   **11.** 1·94 cm
12. 2·83 cm, 3·97 cm, 6·61 cm   **13.** 2 cm, 3 cm, 4 cm
14. 3 cm   **15.** 2 cm

Exercise 26a (p. 148)

1. 96 km h^{-1} **2.** 6 s
3. 25 s, 1·28 km   **4.** 13½ s
5. 50 s   **6.** (i) 11·4 s   (ii) 6·6 s

7. (i) 21 km h^{-1} (ii) $17\frac{1}{2} \text{ min}$ **8.** $1 \text{ h } 38\frac{1}{3} \text{ min}$
9. $1 \cdot 08 \times 10^5 \text{ km h}^{-1}$ **10.** $32 \cdot 4 \text{ s}$

Exercise 26b (p. 150)

1. $2:1$ **2.** $5:2$ **3.** $4:3$ **4.** 3   **5.** $7:4$
6. 5p less   **7.** $1:4:3$ **8.** 96p   **9.** 60% **10.** 7p

Exercise 26c (p. 151)

1. 3 min   **2.** 12 min   **3.** $4\frac{1}{2}$ min   **4.** 2 days
5. $2\frac{1}{2}$ days   **6.** 2 days   **7.** 3 days   **8.** 10 days
9. $7\frac{1}{2}$ days   **10.** Irene; just under 28 hours

Exercise 27a (p. 154)

1. $\begin{pmatrix} 7 & 1 \\ 2 & 2 \end{pmatrix}, \begin{pmatrix} -3 & 5 \\ 0 & -4 \end{pmatrix}, \begin{pmatrix} 13 & 5 \\ 4 & -5 \end{pmatrix}, \begin{pmatrix} 8 & 17 \\ 5 & 0 \end{pmatrix}$

2. $\begin{pmatrix} 2 & 1 & 4 \\ 6 & 11 & 8 \end{pmatrix}, \begin{pmatrix} 4 & 1 & -2 \\ -2 & -7 & -6 \end{pmatrix}$, Not possible, Not possible

3. Not possible, Not possible, $\begin{pmatrix} 273 & 152 \\ -57 & 31 \end{pmatrix}, \begin{pmatrix} -6 & -10 & -11 \\ 68 & 109 & 25 \\ 118 & 196 & 201 \end{pmatrix}$

4. Not possible, Not possible, $\begin{pmatrix} 31 & 39 & 24 \\ 7 & 0 & 29 \end{pmatrix}$, Not possible

5. $\begin{pmatrix} 8 & 0 \\ 0 & 8 \end{pmatrix}, \begin{pmatrix} 4 & 6 \\ -2 & -4 \end{pmatrix}, \begin{pmatrix} 15 & 0 \\ 0 & 15 \end{pmatrix}, \begin{pmatrix} 15 & 0 \\ 0 & 15 \end{pmatrix}$

6. $\begin{pmatrix} 2 & -1 & 9 \\ 3 & 1 & 7 \\ 14 & 10 & -1 \end{pmatrix}, \begin{pmatrix} 0 & 1 & -5 \\ 3 & -3 & 5 \\ -4 & -6 & -1 \end{pmatrix}, \begin{pmatrix} 19 & 15 & 7 \\ 57 & 43 & 20 \\ -4 & -9 & 37 \end{pmatrix}, \begin{pmatrix} 33 & 15 & -11 \\ 11 & 0 & 11 \\ 33 & -8 & 66 \end{pmatrix}$

7. $(5 \quad 3 \quad 0), (-1 \quad -1 \quad -2)$, Not possible, Not possible

8. Not possible, Not possible, (7), $\begin{pmatrix} 6 & 3 & -3 \\ 4 & 2 & -2 \\ 2 & 1 & -1 \end{pmatrix}$

9. Not possible, Not possible, $\begin{pmatrix} 34 & 30 \\ 45 & 15 \\ 30 & -37 \end{pmatrix}$, Not possible

10. $\begin{pmatrix} 2\cdot5 & -0\cdot5 \\ -1\cdot5 & 2\cdot5 \end{pmatrix}, \begin{pmatrix} -0\cdot5 & 1\cdot5 \\ 0\cdot5 & -0\cdot5 \end{pmatrix}, \begin{pmatrix} 1 & -0\cdot25 \\ -1\cdot75 & 2 \end{pmatrix}, \begin{pmatrix} 2 & -0\cdot25 \\ -1\cdot75 & 1 \end{pmatrix}$

11. $\begin{pmatrix} 10 & 5 & 2 \\ 12 & 3 & 3 \end{pmatrix} \begin{pmatrix} 4\frac{1}{2} & 3\frac{1}{2} \\ 6\frac{1}{2} & 5 \\ 10 & 7 \end{pmatrix} = \begin{pmatrix} 97\frac{1}{2} & 74 \\ 103\frac{1}{2} & 78 \end{pmatrix}$

12. $\begin{pmatrix} 6 & 5 & 4 & 3 \\ 10 & 4 & 3 & 2 \\ 8 & 3 & 6 & 0 \end{pmatrix} \begin{pmatrix} 2\frac{1}{2} & 3 \\ 3\frac{1}{2} & 4\frac{1}{2} \\ 3 & 4 \\ 4 & 5 \end{pmatrix} = \begin{pmatrix} 56\frac{1}{2} & 71\frac{1}{2} \\ 56 & 70 \\ 48\frac{1}{2} & 61\frac{1}{2} \end{pmatrix}$

Exercise 27b (p. 157)

1. $\begin{pmatrix} 1 \\ 2 \end{pmatrix}$ **2.** $\begin{pmatrix} 3 \\ -2 \end{pmatrix}$ **3.** $\begin{pmatrix} 5 \\ 4 \end{pmatrix}$

4. $\begin{pmatrix} -2 \\ 5 \end{pmatrix}$ **5.** $\begin{pmatrix} 2\frac{1}{2} \\ 3 \end{pmatrix}$ **6.** No solution

7. $\begin{pmatrix} 3 \\ 2 \end{pmatrix}$ **8.** $\begin{pmatrix} 2 \\ -1 \end{pmatrix}$ **9.** $\begin{pmatrix} 2\frac{1}{2} \\ 1\frac{1}{2} \end{pmatrix}$

10. $\begin{pmatrix} 1\frac{1}{3} \\ \frac{1}{2} \end{pmatrix}$ **11.** $\begin{pmatrix} 2 & -3 \\ -3 & 5 \end{pmatrix}, \begin{pmatrix} -3 & 11 \\ 7 & -16 \end{pmatrix}$

12. $\begin{pmatrix} 0 & -7 \\ 2 & 19 \end{pmatrix}$

Exercise 27c (p. 161)

1. $\begin{pmatrix} 1 \\ -1 \end{pmatrix}, \begin{pmatrix} 1 \\ -3 \end{pmatrix}, \begin{pmatrix} 2 \\ -3 \end{pmatrix}, \begin{pmatrix} 2 \\ -1 \end{pmatrix}$

2. $\begin{pmatrix} -1 \\ 1 \end{pmatrix}, \begin{pmatrix} -1 \\ 3 \end{pmatrix}, \begin{pmatrix} -2 \\ 3 \end{pmatrix}, \begin{pmatrix} -2 \\ 1 \end{pmatrix}$

3. $\begin{pmatrix} -1 \\ -1 \end{pmatrix}, \begin{pmatrix} -3 \\ -1 \end{pmatrix}, \begin{pmatrix} -3 \\ -2 \end{pmatrix}, \begin{pmatrix} -1 \\ -2 \end{pmatrix}$

4. $\begin{pmatrix} 1 \\ -1 \end{pmatrix}, \begin{pmatrix} 3 \\ -1 \end{pmatrix}, \begin{pmatrix} 3 \\ -2 \end{pmatrix}, \begin{pmatrix} 1 \\ -2 \end{pmatrix}$

5. $\begin{pmatrix} -1 \\ 1 \end{pmatrix}, \begin{pmatrix} -3 \\ 1 \end{pmatrix}, \begin{pmatrix} -3 \\ 2 \end{pmatrix}, \begin{pmatrix} -1 \\ 2 \end{pmatrix}$

6. $\begin{pmatrix} -1 \\ -1 \end{pmatrix}, \begin{pmatrix} -1 \\ -3 \end{pmatrix}, \begin{pmatrix} -2 \\ -3 \end{pmatrix}, \begin{pmatrix} -2 \\ -1 \end{pmatrix}$

7. $\begin{pmatrix} 2 \\ 2 \end{pmatrix}, \begin{pmatrix} 6 \\ 2 \end{pmatrix}, \begin{pmatrix} 6 \\ 4 \end{pmatrix}, \begin{pmatrix} 2 \\ 4 \end{pmatrix}$

8. $\begin{pmatrix} 4 \\ 4 \end{pmatrix}, \begin{pmatrix} 10 \\ 6 \end{pmatrix}, \begin{pmatrix} 11 \\ 9 \end{pmatrix}, \begin{pmatrix} 5 \\ 7 \end{pmatrix}$

9. $\begin{pmatrix} 3 \\ 1 \end{pmatrix}, \begin{pmatrix} 5 \\ 1 \end{pmatrix}, \begin{pmatrix} 7 \\ 2 \end{pmatrix}, \begin{pmatrix} 5 \\ 2 \end{pmatrix}$

10. $\begin{pmatrix} 1 \\ 1 \end{pmatrix}, \begin{pmatrix} 3 \\ 1 \end{pmatrix}, \begin{pmatrix} 3 \\ 2 \end{pmatrix}, \begin{pmatrix} 1 \\ 2 \end{pmatrix}$

11. $\begin{pmatrix} 1 \\ -2 \end{pmatrix}, \begin{pmatrix} -1 \\ -3 \end{pmatrix}, \begin{pmatrix} 1 \\ -4 \end{pmatrix}, \begin{pmatrix} 3 \\ -3 \end{pmatrix}$

12. $\begin{pmatrix} -1 \\ 2 \end{pmatrix}, \begin{pmatrix} 1 \\ 3 \end{pmatrix}, \begin{pmatrix} -1 \\ 4 \end{pmatrix}, \begin{pmatrix} -3 \\ 3 \end{pmatrix}$

13. $\begin{pmatrix} -2 \\ -1 \end{pmatrix}, \begin{pmatrix} -3 \\ 1 \end{pmatrix}, \begin{pmatrix} -4 \\ -1 \end{pmatrix}, \begin{pmatrix} -3 \\ -3 \end{pmatrix}$

14. $\begin{pmatrix} 2 \\ -1 \end{pmatrix}, \begin{pmatrix} 3 \\ 1 \end{pmatrix}, \begin{pmatrix} 4 \\ -1 \end{pmatrix}, \begin{pmatrix} 3 \\ -3 \end{pmatrix}$

15. $\begin{pmatrix} -2 \\ 1 \end{pmatrix}, \begin{pmatrix} -3 \\ -1 \end{pmatrix}, \begin{pmatrix} -4 \\ 1 \end{pmatrix}, \begin{pmatrix} -3 \\ 3 \end{pmatrix}$

16. $\begin{pmatrix} -1 \\ -2 \end{pmatrix}, \begin{pmatrix} 1 \\ -3 \end{pmatrix}, \begin{pmatrix} -1 \\ -4 \end{pmatrix}, \begin{pmatrix} -3 \\ -3 \end{pmatrix}$

17. $\begin{pmatrix} 4 \\ 2 \end{pmatrix}, \begin{pmatrix} 6 \\ -2 \end{pmatrix}, \begin{pmatrix} 8 \\ 2 \end{pmatrix}, \begin{pmatrix} 6 \\ 6 \end{pmatrix}$

18. $\begin{pmatrix} 7 \\ 5 \end{pmatrix}, \begin{pmatrix} 8 \\ 0 \end{pmatrix}, \begin{pmatrix} 13 \\ 7 \end{pmatrix}, \begin{pmatrix} 12 \\ 12 \end{pmatrix}$

19. $\begin{pmatrix} 4 \\ 1 \end{pmatrix}, \begin{pmatrix} 1 \\ -1 \end{pmatrix}, \begin{pmatrix} 6 \\ 1 \end{pmatrix}, \begin{pmatrix} 9 \\ 3 \end{pmatrix}$

20. $\begin{pmatrix} 2 \\ 1 \end{pmatrix}, \begin{pmatrix} 3 \\ -1 \end{pmatrix}, \begin{pmatrix} 4 \\ 1 \end{pmatrix}, \begin{pmatrix} 3 \\ 3 \end{pmatrix}$

Exercise 27d (p. 166)

1. $\begin{pmatrix} 9 \\ 2 \end{pmatrix}, \begin{pmatrix} 17 \\ 3 \end{pmatrix}, \begin{pmatrix} -5 \\ -2 \end{pmatrix}, \begin{pmatrix} 1 & -4 \\ 0 & 1 \end{pmatrix}$

2. $\begin{pmatrix} 7 \\ 5 \end{pmatrix}, \begin{pmatrix} 14 \\ 18 \end{pmatrix}, \begin{pmatrix} -3 \\ 7 \end{pmatrix}, -\frac{1}{8}\begin{pmatrix} 1 & -3 \\ -3 & 1 \end{pmatrix}$

3. $\begin{pmatrix} 15 \\ 29 \end{pmatrix}, \begin{pmatrix} 26 \\ 54 \end{pmatrix}, \begin{pmatrix} -11 \\ -17 \end{pmatrix}$

4. $\begin{pmatrix} 7 \\ 21 \end{pmatrix}, \begin{pmatrix} 14 \\ 42 \end{pmatrix}, \begin{pmatrix} -3 \\ -9 \end{pmatrix}$, No

5. $\begin{pmatrix} 6 \\ 12 \end{pmatrix}, \begin{pmatrix} 30 \\ 18 \end{pmatrix}, \begin{pmatrix} 18 \\ -12 \end{pmatrix}, \frac{1}{6}\begin{pmatrix} 1 & 0 \\ 0 & 1 \end{pmatrix}$

6. $\begin{pmatrix} 54 \\ 12 \end{pmatrix}, \begin{pmatrix} 102 \\ 18 \end{pmatrix}, \begin{pmatrix} -30 \\ -12 \end{pmatrix}$

7. $\begin{pmatrix} -2 \\ -1 \end{pmatrix}, \begin{pmatrix} -3 \\ -5 \end{pmatrix}, \begin{pmatrix} 2 \\ -3 \end{pmatrix}$

8. $\begin{pmatrix} 2 \\ 1 \end{pmatrix}, \begin{pmatrix} 3 \\ 5 \end{pmatrix}, \begin{pmatrix} -2 \\ 3 \end{pmatrix}$

9. $\begin{pmatrix} 6 \\ -3 \end{pmatrix}, \begin{pmatrix} 9 \\ -15 \end{pmatrix}, \begin{pmatrix} -6 \\ -9 \end{pmatrix}$

10. $\begin{pmatrix} 2 \\ 1 \end{pmatrix}, \begin{pmatrix} 3 \\ 5 \end{pmatrix}, \begin{pmatrix} -2 \\ 3 \end{pmatrix}$

11. $\begin{pmatrix} 10 \\ 5 \end{pmatrix}, \begin{pmatrix} 15 \\ 25 \end{pmatrix}, \begin{pmatrix} -10 \\ 15 \end{pmatrix}$

12. $\begin{pmatrix} 5 \\ 2 \end{pmatrix}, \begin{pmatrix} 4 \\ 3 \end{pmatrix}, \begin{pmatrix} -9 \\ -2 \end{pmatrix}$

13. $\begin{pmatrix} 4 \\ 2 \end{pmatrix}, \begin{pmatrix} 8 \\ 1 \end{pmatrix}, \begin{pmatrix} 6 \\ 6 \end{pmatrix}$

14. $\begin{pmatrix} 2 \\ -9 \end{pmatrix}, \begin{pmatrix} 3 \\ -17 \end{pmatrix}, \begin{pmatrix} -2 \\ 5 \end{pmatrix}$

15. $\begin{pmatrix} -2 \\ -11 \end{pmatrix}, \begin{pmatrix} -3 \\ -20 \end{pmatrix}, \begin{pmatrix} 2 \\ 7 \end{pmatrix}$

16. $\begin{pmatrix} -1 \\ 4 \end{pmatrix}, \begin{pmatrix} 11 \\ 7 \end{pmatrix}, \begin{pmatrix} 5 \\ -8 \end{pmatrix}$

17. $\begin{pmatrix} -2 \\ 1 \end{pmatrix}, \begin{pmatrix} -1 \\ -3 \end{pmatrix}, \begin{pmatrix} -6 \\ -1 \end{pmatrix}$

18. $\begin{pmatrix} 1 \\ 2 \end{pmatrix}, \begin{pmatrix} -3 \\ 1 \end{pmatrix}, \begin{pmatrix} -1 \\ 6 \end{pmatrix}$

19. $\begin{pmatrix} -14 \\ -10 \end{pmatrix}, \begin{pmatrix} -28 \\ -36 \end{pmatrix}, \begin{pmatrix} 6 \\ -14 \end{pmatrix}$

20. $\begin{pmatrix} 5 \\ 2 \end{pmatrix}, \begin{pmatrix} 32 \\ 5 \end{pmatrix}, \begin{pmatrix} -49 \\ -10 \end{pmatrix}$

Exercise 28 (p. 169)

1. £136·29	**2.** £56·31	**3.** £936·09	**4.** £594·00
5. £87·25	**6.** £300·91	**7.** £30·63	**8.** £56·29
9. £1·81	**10.** £65·94	**11.** £69·36	**12.** £302·43
13. £347·33	**14.** £26·44	**15.** £3 423·36	**16.** £2 390·77
17. £215·13	**18.** £755	**19.** £5 458·55	**20.** £5 685·38

Exercise 29a (p. 172)

1. £393·60, £56·25, £159·00, £234·75, £33·30
2. 50, 400, 72, 432, 480

3. £35, 8%; £12·50, $6\frac{2}{3}$%; £5·25, $3\frac{1}{3}$%; £3·15, $6\frac{1}{4}$%; £64·80, $7\frac{1}{2}$%

4. £41·25   **5.** £273   **6.** 5%

7. $15\frac{3}{4}$%   **8.** 108p   **9.** $78\frac{1}{2}$p

10. 1 152   **11.** 700, £100·50   **12.** 225

13. Equal   **14.** 2 400, £1 728, 6·60%

15. $7\frac{6}{7}$%

Exercise 29b (p. 176)

1. £240, £262·50, £307·20, £350, £340·20

2. £12, £17·50, £19·20, £21, £18·90

3. 5%, $6\frac{2}{3}$%, $6\frac{1}{4}$%, 6%, $5\frac{5}{9}$%

4. £750, £416·67, £388·89, £284·09, £520·83

5. £18·75, £12·50, £23·33, £11·36, £23·44

6. 3·91%, 4·17%, 5·56%, 4·55%, 4·69%

7. £1 970   **8.** 93   **9.** £46·08   **10.** 5%

11. £22·22   **12.** 80   **13.** $5\frac{1}{2}$%   **14.** £858

15. 72

Exercise 30a (p. 179)

1. 4, 2   **2.** 3, −5   **3.** −3, −4   **4.** 1, 2

5. −3, 4   **6.** −2, −5   **7.** 5, 2   **8.** −7, −2

9. $2\frac{1}{2}$, 3   **10.** −2, $1\frac{1}{4}$ **11.** 3, 0   **12.** −5, 1

13. −2, $1\frac{1}{2}$ **14.** 0, −2   **15.** $2\frac{1}{2}$, $-3\frac{1}{2}$

Exercise 30b (p. 182)

1. 4, 5   **2.** 2, 3   **3.** 2, −5   **4.** 8, −12

5. −2, 4   **6.** 1, 2   **7.** $-1\frac{1}{2}$, 2   **8.** −2, −2

9. $\frac{1}{3}$, $\frac{1}{4}$ **10.** 3, 1   **11.** −3, −2   **12.** −3, −2

13. $1\frac{1}{2}$, $-\frac{2}{3}$ **14.** $-\frac{3}{4}$, $-\frac{2}{3}$ **15.** 1, 1

Exercise 30c (p. 185)

1. (0, 5), (4, −3)   **2.** (3, 5), $(-1\frac{1}{4}, -12)$

3. (1, 2)   **4.** (3, −5), $(-2\frac{1}{2}, 6)$

5. (−2, 6), (4, −3)   **6.** (1, −2), $(-\frac{1}{7}, 1\frac{3}{7})$

7. (−4, 3)   **8.** (4, −1)

9. $(-1, -1), (1\frac{8}{11}, -\frac{1}{11})$ **10.** $(5, 6), (2, 15)$
11. $(2, 4)$ **12.** $(-2, -1), (2\frac{1}{2}, \frac{4}{5})$
13. $(4, 1), (-8, -3)$ **14.** $(1, 2), (-2\frac{3}{7}, -\frac{2}{7})$
15. $(3, -1\frac{1}{2}), (-1, 4\frac{1}{2})$ **16.** $(2, 1), (-1\frac{1}{3}, -1\frac{1}{2})$
17. $(1\frac{1}{5}, -1), (-1\frac{2}{15}, \frac{2}{3})$ **18.** $(2, -1), (-1\frac{1}{2}, 6)$
19. $(3, -3), (\frac{3}{4}, 1\frac{1}{2})$ **20.** $(4, -1)$

Exercise 31a (p. 186)

1. $\geqslant 1$ **2.** < 4 **3.** $\not> 2$
4. < 4 **5.** $\geqslant -4$ **6.** $\geqslant 2$
7. < 11 **8.** $\not< -10$ **9.** $\geqslant 4$

Exercise 31c (p. 189)

2. 37 (10 l, 27 s); 10 l, 27 s *or* 11 l, 25 s; $23\frac{1}{2}$p
3. 13 toffees, 10 chocs; 3p
4. 34 s, 13 r; £3·58; 32 s, 14 r
5. 14A, 9B; 12A, 11B
6. 20; 16 l, 38 s; 20 l, 30 s and 18 l, 35 s

Exercise 31d (p. 191)

1. $x < 0$ *or* $x > 3$ **2.** $x > 0$ *or* $x < -3$ **3.** $0 < x \leqslant 5$
4. $\{x: -3 < x < 0\}$ **5.** $0 < x \leqslant \frac{1}{5}$ **6.** $\{x: 0 < x < \frac{1}{6}\}$
7. $-4 \leqslant x < 0$ **8.** $\{x: x > 0\} \cup \{x: x < -1\frac{1}{2}\}$
9. $x > 0$ *or* $x \leqslant -30$

Exercise 31e (p. 192)

1. $x < 4$ *or* $x > 6$ **2.** $\{x: 4 < x < 6\}$ **3.** $-1 < x < 2$
4. $\{x: x < -1\} \cup \{x: x > 2\}$ **5.** $x \leqslant -5$ *or* $x \geqslant 5$
6. $\{x: -8 < x < 8\}$
7. $\{x: x \leqslant -4\} \cup \{x: x \geqslant 5\}$ **8.** $-1 < x < 1\frac{1}{2}$
9. $-1\frac{1}{2} \leqslant x \leqslant 0$
10. $0 < x < 2$ *or* $x < -4$

Exercise 31f (p. 194)

1. (3, 3), (3, 4), (4, 2), (4, 3), (4, 4), (4, 5)
2. (2, 7), (2, 8)
3. (1, 2), (1, 3), (2, 1)
4. (5, 4), (5, 5), (5, 6), (6, 5)
5. (3, 14), (3, 15), (3, 16), (3, 17)
6. (1, 3), (2, 2), (2, 3)
7. (11, 2), (11, 3), (12, 2), (12, 3), (13, 2)
8. (2, 5), (2, 6), (2, 7), (3, 5), (3, 6), (3, 7)

Exercise 32a (p. 195)

1. 0·913 5	2. −0·406 7	3. −2·246 0	4. 0·309 0
5. 0·984 8	6. −0·121 9	7. −0·874 6	8. −0·158 4
9. −9·51	10. −0·629 3	11. 0·522 5	12. −0·179 9
13. −0·990 7	14. −1·076 1	15. 0·996 0	16. 0·684 3
17. −0·212 7	18. −6·497(5)	19. −0·929 5	20. −0·288 9

Exercise 32b (p. 197)

1. 13°	2. 167°	3. 64°
4. 116°	5. 14°, 166°	6. 129°
7. 99°	8. 62°, 118°	9. 132°
10. 167°	11. 53° 40′	12. 35° 15′, 144° 45′
13. 35° 8′	14. 79° 42′, 100° 18′	15. 114° 27′
16. 119° 23′	17. 3° 45′, 176° 15′	18. 40° 38′, 139° 22′
19. 94° 15′	20. 166° 3′	

Exercise 33 (p. 200)

1. $\frac{12}{13}, \frac{5}{12}$
2. $\frac{7}{25}, \frac{7}{24}$
3. $\frac{21}{29}, \frac{20}{29}$
4. $\frac{40}{41}, \frac{40}{9}$
5. $\frac{37}{35}, \frac{35}{12}$
6. 0·625, 0·781
7. 0·507, 0·862
8. 0·958, 3·35
9. 0·866, 0·577
10. 0·436, 2·06

11. $\sqrt{1 - s^2}, \dfrac{s}{\sqrt{1 - s^2}}$

12. $\dfrac{\sqrt{x^2 - 1}}{x}, \dfrac{1}{\sqrt{x^2 - 1}}$

13. 0·484 8   **14.** 1·192 4
15. 1·345 6   **16.** 0·454 0
17. 0·674 5

Exercise 34 (p. 202)

1. (i) 48·4   (ii) 121   (iii) 114·4   (iv) 2 704   (v) 14 240
2. (i) £11·83   (ii) £13·89   (iii) £6·93   (iv) £24·24   (v) £147·93
3. up by 3p   **4.** $17\frac{1}{2}$p   **5.** 33 521
6. 56p   **7.** £8·74   **8.** £1·55
9. £64·26   **10.** £6·74   **11.** American, by 6p
12. 242·3 esc   **13.** Lost £5·40   **14.** $261
15. £31·32

Exercise 35a (p. 207)

1. 13·1 cm   **2.** 20·4 cm   **3.** 10° 4′   **4.** 16° 25′
5. A = 45° 17′, C = 82° 43′, c = 20·5 cm
6. A = 44° 24′, B = 63° 36′, b = 8·19 cm
7. A = 22° 49′, C = 34° 11′, c = 7·10 cm
8. 7·17 km   **9.** 346° 12′, 10·4 km   **10.** 47° 19′ *or* 132° 41′
11. 2·40 km, 2 100 m   **12.** 8·8 m   **13.** 607 m
14. $14\frac{1}{2}$ knots (14·55)   **15.** 10·9 cm

Exercise 35b (p. 209)

1. AB = 14·0 cm, A = 60° 36′, C = 77° 24′
    AB = 4·58 cm, A = 119° 24′, C = 18° 36′

2. CA = 1 640 m, A = 76° 15′, B = 52° 45′
    CA = 878 m, A = 103° 45′, B = 25° 15′

3. BC = 6·13 km, A = 56° 18′, C = 77° 42′
    BC = 3·87 km, A = 31° 42′, C = 102° 18′

4. AB = 24·8 cm, B = 51° 58′, C = 56° 2′

5. CA = 8·71 cm, B = 111° 18′, C = 46° 42′
    CA = 3·90 cm, B = 24° 42′, C = 133° 18′

6. 244° 27', 5·49 km *or* 205° 33', 11·5 km
7. 38° 6', 84 s
8. 1 630 m, 58° 49' *or* 178 m, 58° 49'
9. 161° 30' *or* 242° 30'
10. 29·8 sea miles *or* 10·4 sea miles

Exercise 36a (p. 212)

1. 4·36 cm	**2.** 1·98 cm	**3.** 4·42 m
4. 61·8 cm	**5.** 14·5 cm	**6.** 105 cm

Exercise 36b (p. 213)

	A	B	C		A	B	C
1.	44° 25',	57° 7',	78° 28'	**2.**	38° 13',	60° ,	81° 47'
3.	22° 20',	27° 7',	130° 33'	**4.**	25° 12',	48° 11',	106° 36'
5.	53° 3',	87° 13',	39° 44'	**6.**	112° 24',	38° 3',	29° 33'

Exercise 36c (p. 214)

1. $\frac{2}{7}$; 7 cm   **3.** 10·34 cm, 5·31 cm
4. $\frac{5}{21}$; 8·06 cm   **5.** 75° 51', 104° 9'; 11·7 cm

6. (i) $a = 7·54$ m, $B = 52° 34'$, $C = 41° 26'$
    (ii) $c = 10·47$ cm, $A = 47° 32'$, $B = 27° 28'$
    (iii) $b = 9·49$ cm, $C = 61° 10'$, $A = 33° 36'$

7. 8·90 cm, 107° 42'   **8.** 23·1 sea miles, 260° 51'
9. No. 2 by 55 seconds   **10.** 46·5 km, S 65° 37' W

Exercise 37a (p. 217)

1. £11·16	**2.** 18	**3.** 48 days
4. 16 days	**5.** £15·30	**6.** £232
7. 2 h 34 min	**8.** 65 km h^{-1}	**9.** £3·24
10. £9·43	**11.** 10$\frac{1}{2}$ litres	**12.** 31
13. 182 km	**14.** 84	**15.** £1·65 per m

Exercise 37b (p. 221)

1. $\frac{1}{2}$ **2.** $\frac{8}{9}$ **3.** 2
4. $1:3$ **5.** $2:5$ **6.** $3:5$
7. $8:12:15$ **8.** $10:12:9$ **9.** $7:4$
10. $2:1$ **11.** $2:1$ or $3:2$ **12.** $2:1$ or $4:3$
13. $9:4$ **14.** $17\frac{1}{2}\%$ **15.** $y - x:x$
16. $m - n:m$ **17.** $20:23$
18. Decreased in the ratio $n:m$ **19.** Increased in the ratio $k:h$
20. £$\frac{bc}{a}$ **21.** $\frac{du}{v}$ **22.** $22u:21v$
23. $27:8$ **24.** $c^2h:d^2k$ **25.** $k:h$
26. $n^2:m^2$ **27.** $5:2$ **28.** $10:3$
29. $13:12$ **30.** $16:11$

Exercise 38a (p. 226)

1. 8·4 cm, 5·6 cm   **2.** 2·8 m, 0·9 m
3. $\triangle$YOQ, 10·5 cm, 13·5 cm   **4.** 3·5 m, 5·6 m
5. 2·5 m   **6.** 22·6 m
7. 31·5 m   **8.** $\triangle$OBA, 25 cm, 11·4 cm
9. 79·8 cm   **10.** 111 cm

Exercise 38c (p. 233)

1. $1\frac{1}{2}$, 6   **2.** 12, 6   **3.** 4, 8, 12
4. 6, 9, 19   **5.** 2, 10, 3   **6.** $4\frac{1}{2}$, 6
7. 2, 6   **8.** 5, 6, 8   **9.** 2·9 m
10. 36·25 m   **11.** 1 cm   **12.** 5 cm
20. 9 cm, $3:5$

Exercise 38d (p. 237)

1. $3:8$, $9:64$, $9:55$ **2.** $1:6:9$
3. $1:1$ **4.** $4:8:1$
5. $9:24:16:32$ **6.** $25:81$, $16:25$
7. $5:2$ **9.** $9:16:15:1$, $3:1:3$
10. $2:9$

16. $\begin{pmatrix} 6 \\ 3 \end{pmatrix}, \begin{pmatrix} 18 \\ -9 \end{pmatrix}, \begin{pmatrix} 24 \\ -3 \end{pmatrix}, 9:1$

17. $\begin{pmatrix} 5 & 0 \\ 0 & 5 \end{pmatrix}, 25$

18. $\begin{pmatrix} -4 \\ 2 \end{pmatrix}, \begin{pmatrix} \frac{1}{2} \\ -4 \end{pmatrix}, \begin{pmatrix} 3\frac{1}{2} \\ 3\frac{1}{2} \end{pmatrix}, 9:4$

19. $\begin{pmatrix} 2 \\ \frac{1}{2} \end{pmatrix}, \begin{pmatrix} 0 \\ -1 \end{pmatrix}, \begin{pmatrix} 1\frac{1}{2} \\ 3 \end{pmatrix}$

20. $\begin{pmatrix} -3 \\ 5 \end{pmatrix}, \begin{pmatrix} 3 \\ 23 \end{pmatrix}, \begin{pmatrix} 15 \\ -10 \end{pmatrix}$

Exercise 39a (p. 241)

1. (i) One to one   (ii) many to one   (iii) one to many
    (iv) many to many   (v) many to one   (vi) one to many
    (vii) many to many   (viii) many to many   (ix) many to one
    (x) one to many

2. (i) 0   (ii) -1 (iii) 0
    (iv) 15   (v) 35   (vi) $y^2 - 2y$
    (vii) $x^2 - 4x + 3$ (viii) $9x^2 - 6x$
    (ix) $x^2 + 2hx - 2x + h^2 - 2h$

3. (i) 3   (ii) 9   (iii) $\frac{1}{3}$ (iv) 1   (v) 81   (vi) $\frac{1}{27}$
4. (i) -3 (ii) -6 (iii) 0   (iv) 0   (v) -3
5. (i) 2   (ii) $6x - 3h$ (iii) $-3x^2 + 3xh - h^2$

      (iv) $\dfrac{1}{x(x - h)}$ (v) $3 + 2x - h$

Exercise 39b (p. 243)

1. (i) 3   (ii) 9   (iii) 15
2. (i) -1 (ii) 23   (iii) -7
3. (i) -13 (ii) 11   (iii) 89
4. (i) 37   (ii) 7   (iii) 12
5. (i) -209 (ii) 1   (iii) 1

Exercise 39c (p. 244)

1. $(x + 1)(x + 4)(x - 5)$
2. $(x + 1)^2(x - 2)$
3. $(x - 2)(x + 4)(x - 7)$
4. $(x - 3)(2x - 1)(3x + 2)$
5. $(a + 2)^2(2a - 3)$
6. $(b + 2)^2(3b - 5)$
7. $(b + 5)(b - 7)(2b + 1)$
8. $(y - 2)(2y - 1)(3y + 2)$
9. $(p + 2)(p - 4)(2p - 5)$
10. $(q + 2)(2q - 1)(2q - 3)$
11. $(x - 1)(x - 3)(2x - 1)^2$
12. $(x + 1)(x + 3)(2x - 1)(2x - 3)$
13. $(x - 3)(x + 5)(2x + 1)(3x - 4)$
14. $(x + 1)(x - 2)(3x - 7)(2x + 5)$
15. $(x + 2)(2x + 1)(2x - 3)^2$

Exercise 39d (p. 246)

1. $-18, (2x - 1)(3x - 4)$
2. 2, 19
3. $2, 4, x^2 + 2$
4. $3, 10, 3x - 5$
5. $5, (2x + 5)(3x - 1)$
6. $6, 11, -19$
7. $2x - 5$
8. $(5x - 2)(5x - 13)$

Exercise 40 (p. 257)

1. $15 \cdot 9$ km h^{-1}, 077°
2. $7 \cdot 62$ km h^{-1}, 108°
3. $25 \cdot 1$ km h^{-1}, $291\frac{1}{2}$°
4. $1 \cdot 07$ km h^{-1}, $4 \cdot 14$ km h^{-1}, 21 s
5. 075°, $6 \cdot 1$ min
6. $75\frac{1}{2}$° to the bank, straight across
7. $0 \cdot 632$ m s^{-2}, $18\frac{1}{2}$° to the original direction
8. 23° to $6 \cdot 3$ N direction
9. $6 \cdot 36$ N
10. $9 \cdot 85$ m s^{-2}, 15° 18' to original direction
11. 896 km h^{-1}, 191°
12. 693 km h^{-1}, 111°
13. 930 km h^{-1}, 297°
14. 113 km h^{-1}, from 317°
15. $76 \cdot 8$ km h^{-1}, from 008°
16. $74 \cdot 2$ km h^{-1}, from 289°
17. 936 km h^{-1}, 316°
18. 992 km h^{-1}, 062°
19. 1 230 km h^{-1}, 224°
20. 028°
21. 236°
22. 004°

Exercise 41a (p. 262)

1. $\frac{1}{2}, \frac{5}{12}$
2. $\frac{16}{81}, \frac{40}{81}$
3. $\frac{1}{16}, \frac{7}{16}, \frac{25}{169}$

4. $\frac{1}{16}, \frac{3}{8}, \frac{15}{16}$ **5.** $\frac{7}{10}, \frac{44}{45}$ **6.** $\frac{624}{625}, \frac{256}{625}$

7. $\frac{2}{3}, \frac{503}{504}$ **8.** $\frac{5}{108}$ **9.** $\frac{4}{25}, \frac{148}{225}$

10. $\frac{27}{125}, \frac{36}{125}$ **11.** $\frac{9}{10\,000}, \frac{291}{5\,000}$ **12.** $\frac{4}{25}, \frac{3}{25}$

13. $\frac{33}{200}$ **14.** $\frac{24}{125}$ **15.** $\frac{7}{250}, \frac{3}{250}, 0$

Exercise 41b (p. 266)

1. $\frac{2}{17}, \frac{15}{17}$ **2.** $\frac{13}{51}, \frac{13}{102}$ **3.** $\frac{1}{4}, \frac{15}{16}$

4. $\frac{21}{55}, \frac{27}{220}$ **5.** $\frac{9}{32}$ **6.** $\frac{4}{19}, \frac{29}{57}$

7. $\frac{28}{57}, \frac{8}{95}, 1$ **8.** $\frac{10}{143}, \frac{160}{1\,001}$ **9.** $\frac{7}{68}, \frac{27}{136}$

10. $\frac{11}{522}$

Exercise 42a (p. 268)

1. 22 cm^2 **2.** 45 cm^2 **3.** 54 cm^2

4. $14 \cdot 3 \text{ cm}^2$ **5.** $28 \cdot 9 \text{ cm}^2$ **6.** $19 \cdot 8 \text{ cm}^2$

7. 7   **8.** 5   **9.** 6

10. 10   **11.** 12   **12.** 4·1

13. 30·2   **14.** 58·3   **15.** 43·0

16. 35·9   **17.** 42·2   **18.** 30·9

Exercise 42b (p. 271)

1. $11 \cdot 8 \text{ cm}^2$ **2.** $26 \cdot 5 \text{ cm}^2$ **3.** 156 cm^2

4. $5 \cdot 35 \text{ cm}^2$ **5.** $9 \cdot 96 \text{ cm}^2$ **6.** $27 \cdot 78 \text{ cm}^2$

7. $86 \cdot 1 \text{ cm}^2$ **8.** $16 \cdot 3 \text{ m}^2$ **9.** 948 mm^2

10. 172 m^2

Exercise 42c (p. 275)

1. $17 \cdot 3 \text{ cm}^2$ **2.** $47 \cdot 3 \text{ cm}^2$ **3.** $10 \cdot 2 \text{ cm}^2$

4. 248 cm^2 **5.** $16 \cdot 8 \text{ cm}^2$ **6.** $53 \cdot 7 \text{ cm}^2$

7. $33 \cdot 7 \text{ cm}^2$ **8.** $35 \cdot 1 \text{ cm}^2$ **9.** $24 \cdot 4 \text{ cm}^2$

10. $8 \cdot 19 \text{ cm}^2$ **11.** $11 \cdot 1 \text{ m}^2$ **12.** $1 \cdot 28$ ha

13. 951 cm^2 **14.** $19 \cdot 3 \text{ m}^2$ **15.** 123 cm^2

16. 179 cm^2 **17.** $1\,770 \text{ mm}^2, 90\,\%$ **18.** 812 cm^2

19. $15 \cdot 6 \text{ cm}^3$ **20.** $23 \cdot 9 \text{ m}^2$

Exercise 43a (p. 277)

1. $y = 20x, x = 1\frac{3}{4}$ **2.** $A = 6, M = 17\frac{1}{2}$
3. $P = 10\frac{1}{2}, Q = 16$ **4.** $D = 135, V = 5.25$
5. £1 = 7·4 fl; 55·5 fl, £6·08
6. $M = 9.1 \, d \, or \, d = 0.11 \, M$; $M = 155, d = 8.8$
7. $y = 0.35x; x = 34.3, y = 4.2$
8. $S = 11.3 \, V; S = 243, V = 28.3$

Exercise 43b (p. 280)

1. $P = \frac{3}{4}Q^2; P = 75, Q = 5$ **2.** $xy = 30; x = 2\frac{1}{2}, y = 1\frac{1}{2}$
3. $M = \frac{5}{8}R^3; M = 625, R = 1.6$ **4.** $\sqrt{Y} = \frac{2}{3}Z; Y = 100, Z = 6$
5. (i) $+21\%$ (ii) -19% **6.** $+20\%$
7. $+33.1\%$ **8.** -48.8%
9. 0·8   **10.** (i) 3·80 g   (ii) 13·8 mm

Exercise 43c (p. 283)

1. $A = 30, B = 7\frac{1}{2}; -1\%$ **2.** $P = 13\frac{1}{2}, R = 5$
3. $x = 4\frac{1}{2} + \frac{1}{2}y; x = 10$ **4.** $x = 115.2$

5. $x = 51$ **6.** $x \propto z^2$ **7.** $x \propto \dfrac{1}{z^2}$

8. $x \propto y^5$ **9.** $+45.2\%$ **10.** -1.53%
11. 31·4 cm   **12.** 766 N   **13.** 84 min
14. 1 500 cal   **15.** 55·5 m

Exercise 44 (p. 286)

1. 8 cm   **2.** 9 cm
3. 3·6 cm, 6·4 cm   **4.** 10 mm, 26° 34′, 125 mm²
7. $2, 2\sqrt{2}, \sqrt{2}, \sqrt{2}, \sqrt{2}$ **8.** 3·50 cm, 2·87 cm, 6·10 cm, 4·10 cm
10. 4·47   **11.** 5·48
15. 7·56 m²   **16.** 22·1 cm, 1·88 cm

Exercise 45 (p. 289)

1. 1·6 cm, 2·4 cm   **3.** 12 cm   **4.** 12 cm, 8 cm, 40 cm
7. 120 cm   **8.** 35·69 cm   **9.** 12 cm
10. 5 : 1   **12.** 3·75 cm   **13.** $590\frac{5}{8}$ cm²

Exercise 46 (p. 293)

1. (i) $0.628\,4^c$ (ii) $0.739\,9^c$ (iii) 1.514^c (iv) 3.983^c
2. (i) $103°\,6'$ (ii) $45°\,31'$ (iii) $183°\,57'$ (iv) $101°\,46'$
3. (i) $45°$ (ii) $72°$ (iii) $100°$ (iv) $202\frac{1}{2}°$
4. (i) $\frac{4}{9}\pi$ (ii) $\frac{3}{10}\pi$ (iii) $\frac{3}{4}\pi$ (iv) $\frac{11}{12}\pi$
5. (i) $\frac{5}{7}\pi$ (ii) $\frac{3}{8}\pi$ (iii) $\frac{1}{8}\pi$ (iv) $\frac{1}{3}\pi$
6. (i) $\frac{1}{12}\pi$ (ii) $\frac{11}{18}\pi$ (iii) $\frac{41}{90}\pi$ (iv) $\frac{17}{60}\pi$
7. $9°\,10'$ 8. $30\,\text{cm}^2$ 9. $81°$
10. $8.38\,\text{cm}$, $8.51\,\text{cm}^2$ 11. $157\,\text{rad s}^{-1}$
12. $566\,\text{rad s}^{-1}$, $56.6\,\text{m s}^{-1}$ 13. $80\,\text{rad s}^{-1}$, 764 rpm
14. $92.7\,\text{cm}$ 15. $212.6\,\text{cm}$ 16. $90.5\,\text{m}$
17. $41.7\,\text{m}$ 18. $1\,067\,\text{m}$ 19. $145\,\text{cm}$
20. $148\,\text{cm}$ 21. $1.70\,\text{m}^3$

Exercise 47a (p. 298)

1. $44.2\,\text{cm}$ 2. $2\,000\,\text{km}$ 3. $7\,110\,\text{km}$
4. $7\,670\,\text{km}$ 5. $11\,300\,\text{km}$ 6. $17°\,28'\,\text{S}$
7. $15\,900\,\text{km}$, $2\,610\,\text{km}$ 8. $5\,590\,\text{km}$ 9. $36\,700\,\text{km}$
10. $57°\,19'\,\text{N}$ *or* S   11. $135\,\text{km}$ 12. $14\,300\,\text{km}$

Exercise 47b (p. 301)

1. $2°\,5'$ 2. $2\,520$ n miles   3. $13°$ 4. $8°\,46'\,\text{S}$
5. (i) 6 h 18 min   (ii) 4h 20 min   (iii) 6 min 32 s
   (iv) 8 h 25 min
6. (i) 12.19, 318 km   (ii) 11.17, 728 km   (iii) 16.41, 5 940 km
   (iv) 07.59, 6 170 km   7. 36 min
8. (i) 3 h 57 min   (ii) 3 550 n miles   (iii) 6 580 km
9. (i) 2 130 n miles   (ii) 3 940 km
10. (i) 3 260 km   (ii) 3 160 km
11. (i) 7 970 km   (ii) 7 660 km
12. (i) 04.53   (ii) 3 670 n miles   (iii) 6 800 km
    (iv) 6 800 km (6 803)

Exercise 48a (p. 306)

1. $41°\,49'$, $22°\,38'$ 2. $11\,\text{cm}$, $39°\,31'$, $49°\,24'$

3. 54° 44′

4. 14° 29′, 8° 59′

5. 30°, 35° 16′

6. 63° 26′, 66° 35′

7. 6° 54′, 17° 38′

8. 4·5 m, 51° 4′

9. 46° 41′

10. 7 m, 58° 59′, 63° 26′, 71° 34′

11. 53° 8′, 57°

12. 28° 4′, 44° 54′, 31° 58′

13. 22° 9′

14. 33° 4′, $6\frac{6}{11}$ cm

15. 54° 44′, 70° 32′

Exercise 48b (p. 310)

1. 418 m

2. 71·8 m

3. 1 520 m

4. 367 m

5. 387 m

6. 191 m

7. (i) 47° 52′, 58° 55′, 73° 13′ (ii) 54° 34′, 39° 8′, 86° 18′
(iii) 35° 46′, 93° 37′, 50° 37′

8. 75° 38′, 60° 3′, 44° 19′

9. 1 382 m

10. 3·72 km

11. 83·3 m

12. 2 780 m

13. 10 800 m

14. 14° 29′

15. 5·61 m

Exercise 49a (p. 315)

1. $\frac{1}{4}$

2. -2

3. $\frac{5}{9}$

4. $\frac{1}{4}$

5. $-\frac{4}{5}$

6. $\frac{5}{3}$

7. $-\frac{7}{3}$

8. $-\frac{1}{3}$

9. 2

10. 2

11. -3

12. -3

13. 2

14. $\frac{3}{2}$

15. $-\frac{4}{3}$

16. $-\frac{2}{5}$

17. 3

18. 3

19. $\frac{1}{2}$

20. -2

21. $-\frac{2}{3}$

22. $\frac{3}{4}$

23. $-\frac{2}{3}$

24. $-\frac{3}{5}$

25. $\frac{7}{2}$

Exercise 49b (p. 317)

1. $-6, -3, 5$

2. $2, \frac{2}{3}, -\frac{4}{3}$

3. $7, 1, -9$

4. $5, 1, -3$

5. $4, 3, -5$

6. $-2, 1, 3$

7. $-6, -2, 4$

8. $0, -\frac{1}{2}, -1, -\frac{9}{10}$

Exercise 50 (p. 320)

1. 1 770 m, 0·25 m s^{-2}

2. 78·5 units

3. (i) 3, 1, -3 (ii) 20·8 units

4. (i) 144 cm (ii) 33·3 cm s^{-1} (iii) 8 cm s^{-2}

5. 1 050 m^2, 1·46 × 10^6 l s^{-1}

6. 727 m, 0·6 m s^{-2}

7. 10·75 units, −0·67   **8.** 7·81 cm, 1·35 cm s^{-2}
9. 1 570 m; 0·2 m s^{-2}, −0·2 m s^{-2}
10. 10·6 units; 0·5, −1

Exercise 51a (p. 324)

1. $4x^3$ **2.** $7x^6$ **3.** $15x^2$ **4.** $18x^5$

5. $-\dfrac{4}{x^5}$ **6.** $-\dfrac{8}{x^3}$ **7.** $-\dfrac{6}{x^2}$ **8.** $\dfrac{6}{x^4}$

9. $-\dfrac{2}{5x^3}$ **10.** $\dfrac{1}{x^4}$ **11.** 3   **12.** $6x^2$

13. $4x^3 + 10x$ **14.** $2x + \dfrac{1}{x^2}$ **15.** $2 - \dfrac{2}{x^3}$

16. $5x^4 - 20x^3$ **17.** $6x - 4$ **18.** $2x + \dfrac{2}{x^3}$

19. $3x^2 + 2x + 1$ **20.** $9x^2 + 4x + 1$ **21.** $8x^3 - 10x$

22. $-\dfrac{3}{x^4} - \dfrac{4}{x^3} + \dfrac{3}{x^2}$ **23.** $-\dfrac{12}{x^7} + \dfrac{20}{x^5} + \dfrac{6}{x^3}$

24. $35x^6 + 15x^4 - 6x^2 - 4$ **25.** $-\dfrac{2}{x^4} - \dfrac{3}{x^3} - \dfrac{5}{4x^2}$

Exercise 51b (p. 326)

1. 8, 4, 0, −2, −6   **2.** 23, 8, −1, −4, −1, 8, 23
3. 14, 6, −2, −10, −18   **4.** (2, 5)
5. $(1\frac{1}{2}, -1\frac{1}{4})$ **6.** $-\frac{1}{6}, -\frac{3}{8}, -\frac{3}{2}, -6, -\frac{2}{3}$
7. (−1, 4)   **8.** (2, 5)
9. (0, −3)   **10.** −6, −4, 0, 2, 6
11. (3, −24), (−1, 8)   **12.** (1, 4), (2, −6)
13. $-\frac{1}{8}, -\frac{1}{2}, -8, -8, -2, -\frac{2}{9}$ **14.** $(-1, 2), (-\frac{1}{3}, -1\frac{1}{9})$
15. (3, 0), (−3, 0), (−2, 0), 30, 6, −5

Exercise 51c (p. 330)

1. $7 \, \text{m s}^{-1}, 11 \, \text{m s}^{-1}$
2. $3 \, \text{m s}^{-2}, 5 \, \text{m s}^{-2}$
3. $22 \, \text{cm s}^{-1}, 6 \, \text{cm s}^{-2}$
4. $3 \, \text{cm s}^{-2}$
5. $2 \, \text{m s}^{-1}$
6. $3 \, \text{cm s}^{-1}, -3 \, \text{cm s}^{-1}, -2 \, \text{cm s}^{-2}$, after $3\frac{1}{2}$ s
7. $6 \, \text{m s}^{-2}, 2 \, \text{m s}^{-2}$
8. $21 \, \text{cm}; 2 \, \text{s}; 11 \, \text{cm s}^{-1}, -12 \, \text{cm s}^{-2}$
9. $2 \, \text{s}$ or $4 \, \text{s}; 3\text{s}; 9 \, \text{cm s}^{-1}, 12 \, \text{cm s}^{-2}$
10. $20 \, \text{cm s}^{-1}, -8 \, \text{cm s}^{-2}, 2\frac{1}{2} \, \text{s}, 4 \, \text{cm s}^{-1}, 16 \, \text{cm}, 25 \, \text{cm}, 5 \, \text{s}$

Exercise 52a (p. 335)

1. 2, min., 1
2. -3, max., 14
3. 2, max., 4
4. $-2\frac{1}{2}$, min., $-6\frac{1}{4}$
5. 0, min., 0; 1, max., 1
6. 2, min., -15; -2, max., 17
7. $\frac{1}{4}$, min., $2\frac{3}{4}$
8. $-1\frac{1}{2}$, max., $7\frac{3}{4}$
9. 1, min., -12; -2, max., 15
10. -2, pt. of infl., -3
11. 0, pt. of infl., 2
12. 2, max., 21; -1, min., -6
13. 1, pt. of infl., 1
14. 2, max., 48; -3, min., -77
15. -1, min., 0; $-2\frac{1}{3}$, max., $1\frac{5}{27}$

Exercise 52b (p. 338)

1. 25
2. 40
3. $800 \, \text{m}^2$
4. 32
5. $144 \, \text{cm}^3$
6. $12 \, \text{m}^2$
7. $343 \, \text{cm}^3$
8. $1\,960 \, \text{m}$
9. $48\pi \, \text{cm}^2$
10. $\frac{16}{27} \, \text{m}^3$
11. $\frac{64}{27\pi} \, \text{m}^3$
12. $8\,788 \, \text{cm}^3$
13. $972 \, \text{cm}^2$
14. $\frac{60}{\pi + 4} \, \text{m}$
15. $\frac{4}{3\sqrt{3}}\pi a^3 \, \text{cm}^3$

Exercise 53a (p. 341)

1. $x^4 + c$
2. $\frac{x^3}{9} + c$
3. $-\frac{1}{x} + c$
4. $\frac{1}{8x^4} + c$
5. $8x + c$
6. $2x^2 - 5x + c$

7. $x^2 + x + c$

8. $2x^3 + \dfrac{x^2}{2} - 2x + c$

9. $\dfrac{x^4}{2} - x^3 - \dfrac{3x^2}{2} + 2x + c$

10. $\dfrac{3x^5}{5} + \dfrac{2x^3}{3} - 5x + c$

11. $\dfrac{x^2}{2} - \dfrac{2}{x} + c$

12. $\dfrac{3x^4}{4} + \dfrac{1}{6x^2} + c$

13. $\dfrac{x^8}{8} - \dfrac{x^6}{3} + \dfrac{5x^4}{4} + c$

14. $-\dfrac{1}{x} + \dfrac{1}{x^2} - \dfrac{1}{x^3} + c$

15. $-\dfrac{2}{3x^3} - \dfrac{3}{2x^2} + \dfrac{4}{x} + c$

Exercise 53b (p. 344)

1. $y = x^2 - x + 2$

2. $v = 2u^3 - 2u^2 - 3u - 5$

3. $y = 2x^2 - 5x + 4$

4. $y = 4x + 3$

5. $x = 28t - 2t^2, 14\,\text{s}$

6. $v = \dfrac{t^2}{2} + 2t + 3, 9\,\text{cm s}^{-1}$

7. $y = x^3 - 2x^2 - 5x + 2$

8. 48 m

9. $y = 3 + 7x - 2x^2 - 2x^3$

10. $x = -2$ or 4

11. $h = 78.4t - 4.9t^2, 313.6\,\text{m}$

12. $v = 4 + 8t - \dfrac{3t^2}{2}$

13. $y = \dfrac{x^3}{3} - x^2 - \dfrac{3}{x} - 3$

14. 4 m, $3\frac{1}{3}$ m, $10\frac{2}{3}$ m

15. $v = 117.6 - 9.8t, h = 117.6t - 4.9t^2, 686\,\text{m}, 686\,\text{m}$

Exercise 53c (p. 346)

1. 18   **2.** 21   **3.** 8   **4.** $2\frac{1}{2}$

5. 91   **6.** $\frac{7}{24}$ **7.** -2 **8.** $\frac{2}{3}$

9. $4\frac{1}{6}$ **10.** 20   **11.** $70\frac{1}{2}$ **12.** 126

Exercise 53d (p. 349)

1. 39	**2.** 6	**3.** 123	**4.** $24\frac{2}{3}$
5. $2\frac{2}{3}$	**6.** $20\frac{5}{6}$	**7.** 15	**8.** $12\frac{2}{3}$
9. $85\frac{1}{3}$	**10.** $21\frac{3}{4}$	**11.** $40\frac{1}{2}$	**12.** $21\frac{1}{3}$

Exercise 53e (p. 352)

1. 30π	**2.** 18π	**3.** $\dfrac{8\pi}{5}$	**4.** 24π
5. $\dfrac{54\pi}{7}$	**6.** $\dfrac{32\pi}{3}$	**7.** $\dfrac{52\pi}{3}$	**8.** $\dfrac{16\pi}{15}$
9. $\dfrac{94\pi}{3}$	**10.** $\dfrac{838\pi}{15}$		

Revision examples

I

1. (a) 2·85 km (b) 2·95 km **2.** (i) 1·80 (ii) 39
3. 20 cm (i) $\frac{2}{3}$ (ii) 42 cm **4.** 0·8r

5. (b) $x = \sqrt{\dfrac{a - by}{3y}}$ (c) $x - 2$; $2x - 3, 3x + 1$

6. (i) $v = 4t - t^2 + 5$, $x = 2t^2 - \frac{1}{3}t^3 + 5t$ (ii) 5 s, $33\frac{1}{3}$ m
  (iii) -7 m s^{-1}, -8 m s^{-2} Towards O; increasing
7. (i) 4 (ii) $\frac{3}{8}$ (iii) $\frac{2}{9}$ **8.** 49, 15; 56
9. (i) 4·41, 1·59 (ii) 1·71, 4·78
10. (a) $\frac{256}{625}$ (b) $\frac{1}{40}$ (c) $\frac{6}{125}$

II

1. (i) 30 mm³, 1 000 (ii) £3 200
2. (i) 3 (ii) $AX^2 + BX + C$
3. (a) 2·85, $-0·35$ (b) max. at $(0, 1)$; min. at $(2, -3)$
  (c) 19 sq. units
4. (i) 66° 26′ N or S (ii) 22° 40′ S, 60° 20′ E
5. (i) 27 m (ii) 90 km h⁻¹, 68 km h⁻¹
6. (i) $-3, 5$ (ii) $9\frac{1}{3}$ sq. units (iii) 10 sq. units
7. $2x + 3y \geqslant 30, 4x + y \geqslant 20, 4x + 3y \geqslant 30, x = 3, y = 8$; 50p
8. $(3, 6, 2), (1, 2, 2), (6, 12, 6)$; 3 m; $n = -2$
9. $(1, 1), (0, 2), (-1, 1), \sqrt{2}, \sqrt{2}$; 45°, 90°;

$$Q = \begin{pmatrix} 0 & 1 \\ 1 & 0 \end{pmatrix}; R = \begin{pmatrix} 1 & 1 \\ 1 & -1 \end{pmatrix}; (1, 1), (2, 0), (1, -1);$$

$$R^{-1} = \begin{pmatrix} \frac{1}{2} & \frac{1}{2} \\ \frac{1}{2} & -\frac{1}{2} \end{pmatrix}; (1, 1)$$

10. 4 320 gallons, 2·08 h, m = 720, $1·48 < t < 5·12$

III

1. (a) $x - 2, 2x^2 - 3x + 3$
   (b) (i) $\frac{1}{3}$ (ii) $(-2, 4)$ (iii) $(3, 4)$ (iv) $36° 52'$ (v) $(15, 0)$
2. (a) 9·33 cm (b) 9·98 cm (c) $69° 15'$ (d) 24·15 cm^2
3. (i) 45 cm (ii) 500 cm^2 (iii) 0·08 litres
4. 3, 9, $y = 9x - 15$; max. at $(-1, 3)$, min. at $(1, -1)$, $(0, 1)$
5. $T = \dfrac{2\pi r}{v}$, $r = 42\,100$ km
6. (i) $046° 28'$ (ii) 32·1 m (iii) 88·6 m
7. 12 ordinary, 10 superior; £86
8. 15
9. $R = \begin{pmatrix} 3 & 5 \\ 2 & 4 \end{pmatrix}$; $S = \begin{pmatrix} 8 & 10 \\ -1 & -1 \end{pmatrix}$; $P^{-1} = \begin{pmatrix} 4 & -5 \\ -3 & 4 \end{pmatrix}$;

   $Q^{-1} = \begin{pmatrix} \frac{1}{2} & 0 \\ \frac{1}{2} & 1 \end{pmatrix}$; $P^{-1}Q^{-1} = S^{-1}$; $x = -9, y = 7$
10. 13 m, 3·1 m s^{-1}

IV

1. $(3, -1), (-3, 2)$
2. 675 m^3; 4 580 litres
3. (i) $a = 3, b = 1$ (ii) $4\frac{1}{2}$ sq. units
4.   1   2   3
   C 54·4 A 51·2 B 48·4
   C 54·0 B 44·0 A 43·8
6. 20 cm, 46·0 cm, 61·8 cm
7. (i) F; $x < -1$ also (ii) T (iii) F; $x < 0$ and $x > 1$ also
   (iv) F; $(x - 1)^2 \geqslant 0$ (v) T (vi) F; $-1 \leqslant \cos x < 1$
   (vii) T
8. $x + y \geqslant 100$, $x \leqslant 50$, $5x + 3y \leqslant 450$; 40 easy, 72 upright
9. (i) $\frac{1}{4}$ (ii) $\frac{1}{5}$ (iii) $\frac{2}{5}$ (iv) $\frac{3}{20}$ (v) $\frac{11}{20}$ (vi) $\frac{8}{25}$
10. (i) -2 to -1, 0 to 1 (iii) 3·2; too small

V

1. $1\frac{1}{2}$ cm; 70·7 cm^3
2. (i) 14·4 cm (ii) 17·7 cm (iii) 35° 18′
3. (i) 9, 4, $-9\frac{1}{2}$ (iii) $a = c$ for all values of b
4. (i) $\frac{1}{4}\mathbf{a} + \frac{1}{3}\mathbf{b}$ (ii) $\frac{1}{3}\mathbf{b} - \frac{3}{4}\mathbf{a}$; $\frac{4}{3}, \frac{4}{9}, \frac{3}{1}, \frac{4}{5}$
5. (i) 94·1 km; 2.44 p.m. (ii) 4.30 p.m.; 69·2 km h^{-1}
6. (i) 1 025 h (ii) 270 h (iii) 46%
7. (a) 120° (b) 2·36 m^2 (c) 1·38 m^2 (d) 6 770 kg
8. Anti-clockwise rotation of 36·9° about 0; $\begin{pmatrix} 0 & -1 \\ 1 & 0 \end{pmatrix}$;

   anti-clockwise rotation of 90° about 0; anti-clockwise rotation of 53·1° about 0.
9. (a) 270 (b) 430
10. 180° rotation about $y = -1$.

VI

1. (a) $(2, -1), (3·6, 3·8)$ (b) $x - 2$; $2x^2 - 3x - 3$ (c) 11
2. 1·41, 7, $y = \dfrac{x(p^3 - 1)}{p^3 + 1}$; 10, 0, 0, 36; $(x - 2)(x - 3)(x + 4)$

3. (i) 10 cm (ii) 17 cm (iii) 32·5 cm
4. 1·3, $-2·1$, 1·8
5. (iii) 11·9 cm
6. (a) 4, $y = 4x - 12$ (b) max. at $(0, 13)$, min. at $(4, -19)$
   (c) 4:5
7. (a) 180° (b) 20π cm (c) 40π cm (d) 0·8 m s^{-1}
8. (i) by 750 n ml; 37° 30′ N, 20° E

9. (i) $\begin{pmatrix} 0 & 0 \\ 0 & 0 \end{pmatrix}$ (ii) $\begin{pmatrix} kx \\ ky \end{pmatrix}$; $0 \leqslant x, 0 \leqslant y, x + y \leqslant k$

10. (i) 34·8 (ii) 3·85 (iii) 15%

VII

1. (i) $7 \cdot 14 \, \text{m}^2$ (ii) $94 \cdot 3 \, \text{m}^2$ (iii) £206
2. (a) $1 \cdot 5 \times 10^{21}$ (b) $3 \cdot 2 \times 10^7$ (c) $9 \cdot 5 \times 10^6$
4. $x = 10$, $y = 25$
5. (i) $1 \cdot 68 \, \text{cm}$, $4 \cdot 56 \, \text{cm}$ (ii) $43 \cdot 3 \, \text{cm}^3$ (iii) $3 \, \text{cm}$
6. (a) $4\frac{1}{2} \, \text{s}$ (b) $16 \, \text{m}$ (c) $3 \, \text{s}$ (d) $27 \, \text{m s}^{-1}$ (e) $13\frac{1}{2} \, \text{m s}^{-2}$
7. $\frac{64}{15}\pi \, \text{cm}^3$, $46\frac{2}{3} \%$
8. 15, 51
9. (i) $1 \cdot 73 \, \text{m s}^{-2}$ (ii) $92 \, \text{m}$
10. (i) $\frac{1}{6}$, $\frac{11}{15}$ (ii) $\frac{2}{87}$ (iii) $\frac{1}{10}$

VIII

1. $24\pi \, \text{cm}^2$
2. (i) 76 (ii) $3 \cdot 17$
4. $x + y \leqslant 80$, $3x + 2y \leqslant 210$; £97·50
5. (i) $\frac{5}{12}$ (ii) $\frac{3}{16}$, $\frac{29}{48}$
6. £73·70   (a) £3 750 000   (b) £2 062 500; 53p
7. Doubled linearly and reflected in x-axis; $\begin{pmatrix} 2 & 0 \\ 0 & -2 \end{pmatrix} \begin{pmatrix} x \\ y \end{pmatrix}$
8. (i) $99 \, \text{s}$ (ii) $120 \, \text{s}$, $75 \, \text{s}$ (iii) 17%
9. $\frac{2}{3}\boldsymbol{p} + \frac{1}{3}\boldsymbol{q}$; $\frac{1}{2}\boldsymbol{q}$, $2\boldsymbol{p}$; $2:1$
10. $a = 0 \cdot 028$, $b = -0 \cdot 3$; $s = 10 \cdot 9$

IX

1. $\{1, 2, 8, 9, 10\}$, $\{1, 3, 5\}$, $\{1, 2\}$, $\{1, 2, 3, 5\}$
3. (i) 8, $\dfrac{1}{3x^2}$ (ii) 5×10^3 (iii) 4 (iv) 4

4. $R = \begin{pmatrix} -1 & 0 \\ 0 & -1 \end{pmatrix}$, $S = \begin{pmatrix} 1 & 0 \\ 0 & 1 \end{pmatrix}$, $P = $ reflection in $y = x$,

$Q = $ reflection in $y = -x$, $R = $ rotation of $180°$ about O,

$S = $ identity, $PT = \begin{pmatrix} 1 & 0 \\ 0 & -1 \end{pmatrix}$, $TP = \begin{pmatrix} -1 & 0 \\ 0 & 1 \end{pmatrix}$,

$T = $ anti-clockwise quarter turn about O, $PT = $ reflection in x-axis, $TP = $ reflection in y-axis

5. (a) $-2\frac{1}{2}$ (b) (i) $38° 40'$ (ii) $73° 44'$
6. (i) $\frac{1}{25}$ (ii) $\frac{1}{4\,800}$ (iii) $\frac{61}{125}$
7. (a) 27 cm^2, 9 cm^2 (b) $5°$, 19.9 m, 10.4 m
8. $40°$; $2\,716 \text{ km}$
9. 73 g, 12 g, 83 g
10. 1.43

X

1. (a) £1 500   (b) £77·16
2. (i) $(6 - x)$ cm; 10 cm, 14 cm   (ii) (a) 8 times   (b) 9 times
3. $\frac{1}{2}b$, $\frac{1}{2}(a + b)$, $\frac{3}{4}a + \frac{1}{4}b$
4. 516 m, 17.2 m s^{-1}
5. $y = 2ax - 4a^2$; $(2a, 0)$; $(0, -4a^2)$; $x + 2ay = 2a$; $(0, 1)$
6. $18°$
7. (i) $12 - x - y$; $x = 3$, $y = 6$
8. $-k$; k^2, $2k^2$, $2k$
9. $(0, 0)$, $(2, 0)$, $(3, 2)$; $(0, 0)$, $(6, 0)$, $(9, 6)$;

$T_1 = $ shear; $T_2 = $ enlargement centre O, factor 3; $\begin{pmatrix} 3 & 3 \\ 0 & 3 \end{pmatrix}$

10. (i) 4   (ii) 4·4   (iii) $\frac{1}{5}$